The Manual of Weight-training

The Manual of Weight-training

Edited by
George Kirkley
and John Goodbody

Stanley Paul
London Melbourne Auckland Johannesburg

Stanley Paul & Co. Ltd

An imprint of Century Hutchinson Ltd
62–65 Chandos Place, London WC2N 4NW

Century Hutchinson Australia (Pty) Ltd
PO Box 496, 16–22 Church Street, Hawthorn, Melbourne,
Victoria 3122

Century Hutchinson (NZ) Ltd
32–34 View Road, PO Box 40–086, Glenfield,
Auckland 10

Century Hutchinson (SA) Pty Ltd
PO Box 337, Bergvlei 2012, South Africa

First published 1967
Reprinted 1968, 1971
Revised edition 1973
Reprinted 1975
Revised edition 1978
Reprinted 1982, 1983, 1985
Revised edition 1986

© George Kirkley and John Goodbody
1967, 1973, 1978, 1986

Set in Linotron Sabon by Input Typesetting, London

Printed and bound in Great Britain by
Butler and Tanner Ltd, Frome, Somerset

British Library Cataloguing in Publication Data
The Manual of weight-training.—Rev. ed.
1. Weight lifting
I. Kirkley, George   II. Goodbody, John
796.4′1   GV546.5

ISBN 0 09 164340 6 (hardback)
       0 09 164341 4 (paperback)

Contents

Acknowledgements   6
Preface   7

SECTION ONE

1 Introduction to Weight-training: *John Goodbody*   10
2 Weight-training for Women: *Vivian Grisogono*   27
3 Weight-training with Machines: *Howard Davies*   32
4 Descriptions of Weight-training and Other Exercises:
  The Editors   50
5 Manual Handling at Work and Play: *George Hickling*   89
6 Bodybuilding for Beginners: *George Greenwood*   92
7 Championship Bodybuilding: *Chris Lund*   101

SECTION TWO

8 Weight-training for Athletics: *Ron Pickering*   112
9 Weight-training for Swimming: *Brian Crompton*   127
10 Weight-training for Wrestling: *Jack Ingle*   130
11 Weight-training for Football: *Bill Watson*   135
12 Weight-training for Rowing and Sculling: *Jim Railton*   140
13 Weight-training for Judo: *Syd Hoare*   146
14 Weight-training for Rugby: *John Taylor*   149

SECTION THREE

15 A Brief History of Weightlifting: *George Kirkley*   154
16 Olympic Weightlifting for Beginners: *George Kirkley*   164
17 The Technique of Olympic Weightlifting: *Al Murray*   180
18 Modern Methods in Coaching: *David Webster*   188
19 A New Concept in Olympic Weightlifting: *John Lear*   193
20 Powerlifting for Beginners: *George Kirkley*   206
21 World Class Powerlifting: *John Goodbody*   213

Appendix I   World Weightlifting Championships
    and Olympic Games Results 1960–1985   217
Appendix II   World Powerlifting Championships
    Results 1971–1985   233
Appendix III   Major Bodybuilding Championships
    Results 1960 – 1985   243
Appendix IV   Conversion Table – Kilos to Pounds   245

Acknowledgements

The authors would like to thank Paul Anthony and Samantha Bennett for acting as models, and Powersport for the use of their facilities. Thanks, too, to Dominique Shead at Stanley Paul for her painstaking editing.

For the use of copyright photographs, the authors and publishers would like to thank Colorsport, All-Sport, Chris Lund, *Guardian*, Sporting Pictures (UK) Ltd, Judo Photos Unlimited and, in particular, Derek Evans for all his excellent photographs in chapter 4 and the colour section.

Preface

It is a source of satisfaction to the editors that, since the original edition of this book in 1967, weight-training has become one of the most widely practised physical activities in Britain. The immense growth in the number of gymnasiums, catering for those interested in improving their physique, has come about partly because of the popularity of exercising with machines. And this new edition reflects the trend with a special section devoted to using Powersport apparatus.

The interest in competitive bodybuilding has never been greater – the Austrian, Arnold Schwarzenegger, has, without question, become the most celebrated male physique in history whilst women's bodybuilding is now well established. Powerlifting has been running its own world championships since 1971, and Olympic weightlifting remains an attraction at events like Olympic and Commonwealth Games.

In sport, too, weight-training has become so accepted that it seems incredible the prejudices that once surrounded its use ever existed. One of the outstanding reasons for the improvement in sporting performances in the past thirty years has been the increasing use of weight-training. Certain sports clearly benefit more from this training than others, but there is still a gap in some sports to be filled by people qualified in the science of weight-training.

Weight-training needs to be adapted to the particular activity, and the needs of all sports are different. Thus a footballer will need to practise a totally different type of training from that of a shot-putter. In certain cases, especially in the heavy throwing events in athletics, the weight-training will be similar to the type that actual competitive weightlifters use. This book will guide you how to adapt weight-training to your particular needs. The reader is advised not only to examine the sections of this book specially relevant to his/her requirements, but also to look at the other chapters, many of which will give fresh insight into weight-training. The chapters offer a variety of opinions from different eras, so outlining a tradition of teaching.

Amid our pleasure at the growth in the use of weights, we must lament that this has sometimes been accompanied by the use of drugs. We must reiterate what we (and many of the authors) have stated elsewhere – our total opposition to drug-taking to enhance performances. When the first edition of this book was being published the use of drugs was just becoming commonplace in certain sports. In 1968 Louis Martin, Britain's finest-ever Olympic weightlifter, lost the Olympic title to a Finn, Kaarlo Kangasniemi. Today Kangasniemi is an invalid, his health, as he admits, ruined by taking drugs to win a gold medal.

What is depressing is that nearly twenty years later the problem of drug taking has escalated rather than diminished. Despite all the efforts of bodies like the International Olympic Committee and the Sports Council here in Britain, drug taking has increased. We cannot stress strongly enough that, apart from the proven side-effects, drug taking is cheating. It is not only cheating one's opponents, but also oneself. The satisfaction which can be gained from lifting heavier and heavier weights, from improving one's physique or one's sporting performance, is spoilt if this is aided by the illegal use of drugs.

GEORGE KIRKLEY
JOHN GOODBODY

SECTION ONE

1
Introduction to Weight-training
John Goodbody

John Goodbody, who was educated at Westminster School, Trinity College, Cambridge University and Birkbeck College, London University, works as the Sports News Correspondent for *The Times*. He began weight-training at the age of sixteen in a former chapel next to Westminster Abbey, with Gordon Waller, later to become part of the successful pop singing duo 'Peter and Gordon' as his first training partner. He broke two national junior records and later concentrated on judo, being a light-heavyweight member of the British squad in 1970. He now largely practises long-distance swimming and running – including completing the London Marathon in 3 hours 24 minutes – but still uses weights regularly. John entered Fleet Street at eighteen, and took both his degrees while continuing his journalistic career. He has worked in every continent, covering forty seven sports at international level including five Olympic Games and several world weightlifting championships. Between 1978 and 1982 he lived in Paris as a foreign correspondent for UPI. He has had seven books published.

The benefits from weight-training depend on intelligent, hard work. Whatever schedules are attempted and whatever facilities and coaches are available, these are relatively unimportant compared with the dedication of the individual and the consuming determination to train regularly. Bodybuilders have coined an expression 'stickability', the refusal to give up. In modern sport this has become more valuable than ever before as increasing numbers of people devote themselves to excellence.

There must certainly be careful examination of training schedules, preferably with qualified coaches or instructors, to determine that the exercises, sets and repetitions are suitable for the required activity. But this must be followed by the determination to carry out those schedules despite social distractions and tiredness. The late Percy Cerutty, coach to the unbeaten Australian miler Herb Elliott and also an advocate of weight-training, once wrote with striking directness: 'It is the weak who give up. It is the strong who train on. It is the champion of the future who will be found training on.'

A delight of weight-training is that one can measure improvement exactly. Improvement can be seen with every repetition, every set, every exercise. This is one reason why a valuable adjunct is a training diary so that the individual can note the results. It is particularly satisfying to look back over the months (and years) to see the improvement.

Not everyone has the same innate ability to improve at the same rate. The heaviest people have the capacity to lift the heaviest weights, which is why the sports of weightlifting and powerlifting each have ten bodyweight categories. Furthermore, people of all sizes can be divided into three body types. This is known as somatotyping. The three types are ectomorph (thin), endomorph (fat) and mesomorph (muscular). But very few people are completely one type. Usually they are a blend of the three, with one prominent. There is a complicated system of analysis, expertly explained by Professor Tanner in 'The Physique of the Olympic Athlete' after his research at the 1960 Olympic Games, which details the make-up of the individual and shows what physical properties each of the competitors possesses.

A natural mesomorph is likely to improve his physique and strength through weight-training more quickly than an ectomorph, who will have to struggle to overcome a slender build, or the endomorph, who is fighting against overweight. Yet with conscientious, sensible training these two latter types will still be able to overcome many of their physical disadvantages.

Whatever the standard of a weight-trainer, there will always be the problem of the 'plateau'. Frequently a person will find improvement stops and he will have to wait for several weeks, or even months, to progress. Then quite suddenly and unexpectedly the improvement will come. Progress, after the initial months, is rarely steady. A period of stagnation will be followed by what is termed a 'break through'. Then there is another period of consolidation. Sometimes a change of schedule helps, but often one just has to wait and continue training. The closer one is to one's physical limits the longer the wait for a 'break through'.

In this chapter are detailed several general features of weight-training that should be examined before the reader turns to the specialised chapters later in the book.

Where to train

Although training at home has certain advantages such as convenience and no restriction on hours, these are outweighed by the facilities of gymnasiums where there is often plenty of equipment, instruction and also training partners. Ideally, perhaps, the keen individual should go regularly to a gym but still have weights at home for the odd, extra session that he can fit into his life. Vasily Alexeev, the Soviet Union's 1972 and 1976 Olympic super-heavyweight champion, often used to have workouts at home when the mood took him – sometimes after midnight. When inflation is taken into account, buying your own weights is much cheaper comparatively than twenty five years ago, and a set will last for ever. Yet most of the serious work must be done in a gymnasium. Be careful when selecting a gym that you go to the right kind. Some specialise in weight-training for sport (particularly sports centres), some for serious bodybuilding, some for competitive lifting, but most are for general workouts and will cater for several needs. Do not commit yourself to a large membership fee until you are certain that the gymnasium is the most suitable one for you. By far its most important feature should be the right atmosphere – friendly but hard-working.

Training partners

Not only are training partners useful as 'spotters', helping one as a safety precaution with heavy lifts, they are also invaluable for advice and inspiration. As far as possible train with people of the same ability so that you are always forced to try to do your best. Equally important is that they should be enthusiastic – never cutting short a workout and frequently suggesting another exercise, another repetition and so goading you into emulating them. As in so many physical activities, training partners play an enormous part in the ultimate success of the individual.

What time of day to train

Most people find that intensive exercise is best practised when the body has been awake for several hours. Professor A. N. Vorobyev, in his book *A Textbook of Weightlifting*, collates the experience of weightlifters in the Soviet Union and states: 'Immediately after sleep or night work there occurs a fall in strength of 20 to 30 per cent in comparison with the day time.' He says that strength attains its maximum three to five hours after waking. However, it is not always possible to train at an ideal time. Many people may find that their body becomes used to training in the early evening, and therefore they produce their best performance then.

Bill Pearl, a famous Mr Universe winner, begins exercising at 5 a.m. and many bodybuilders have early morning sessions. It is far more important that the sessions are fitted in around one's work and social activities rather than that they should be postponed because the timing is not ideal. Yet one consideration is not to train immediately after a heavy meal. No one can be expected to be at their best in such circumstances.

Frequency of training

This will depend entirely on the object of the weight-trainer. Most people aiming at general fitness or preparing for a sport will exercise a maximum of three times a week. For athletes and sportsmen their weight sessions have to be fitted round their specialised training. Many will use weights more out-of-season than in-season (see the section later in this chapter on 'strength retention'). Three sessions a week is really the minimum out-of-season for a committed weight-trainer. For many years it was believed that individual muscles needed forty eight hours' recuperation from heavy training to allow them to grow. It was thought, therefore, that three to four workouts a week was the maximum not just desirable but possible. More than that was regarded as a complete waste of time because the body simply would not recover.

Bodybuilders circumvented this by using the split routine. They trained six days a week, but certain parts were exercised three days a week (Mondays, Wednesdays and Fridays) and the remaining parts on the other days. In this way every muscle got forty eight hours' recovery. Although daily workouts had become commonplace by the 1960s, weightlifters and bodybuilders remained complacent that the stress on the individual muscles was so much greater in their activities that it was retrogressive to train more frequently. The Bulgarian weightlifters, who first popularised daily and then several workouts a day in the early 1970s, revolutionised the sport.

Judy Vernon, 1974 Commonwealth Games 100m hurdles champion, used weights regularly during her competitive career

Nowadays weight-lifters frequently train every day. However, bodybuilders have generally still maintained the original practice. They have never had to confront the implications of this discovery, partly because their concentration on hypertrophy requires so many sets for individual body parts that it remains more suitable to continue to split their exercises in any one week and train six days a week, exercising different body parts on alternate days.

Rest periods between sets

This varies according to the ambitions of the weight-trainer. In circuit-training, when a major object of the exercise is to put stress on muscular endurance or even stamina, the pause between sets can be as brief as it takes an individual to move from one piece of apparatus to another. Howard Davies explains schedules in this manner in Chapter 3 'Weight-training with Machines'. Similarly, many bodybuilders do not pause in such routines as super sets and tri-sets. This is outlined in Chapter 7, 'Championship Bodybuilding'. For heavy lifting, particularly involving massive exercises like Squats, the rest period is longer and may also be determined by the number of lifters using the same equipment. Professor Vorobyev has gauged that the majority of lifters rest between two and five minutes. If it should exceed eight minutes then the lifter will be forced to warm up again.

Safety rules

One of the delights of weight-training is that it is comparatively safe. Accidents usually happen only when basic rules are ignored. These include:

1. When lifting free weights (barbells and dumbbells) make certain that the collars are securely fastened.
2. When using machines ensure that the selector pin is firmly in the weight stack and the pins in the power racks are not bent. With the machines check the attachment and that ropes are not frayed.
3. When using heavy weights get people to 'spot' for you – lifting the barbell for you to start the exercise and helping to return it to the stands.
4. When 'spotting' for a training partner do not let your attention be distracted. Watch your partner and act immediately if he gets into difficulties. 'Spotters' should keep their hands just under the barbell – but without touching it – on exercises like the Press on Bench (flat and inclined) and the Squat.
5. When using stands for Squats always begin the exercise by backing out of the apparatus. This is because when the lifter is tired at the end of the set it is valuable for him to see the stands in front of him so that he knows exactly where to return the barbell.
6. If training alone, ensure there is a margin of safety in all your exercises. Do not attempt maximum lifts unless you are certain you

have an 'escape route' should you get into difficulties. For instance, on the Press on Bench, if you cannot raise the barbell off your chest you may be able to cheat it up by arching your back and raising your hips off the bench. But find this out beforehand – not when you are in the middle of an exercise. One major advantage of machines is that you can use maximum weights with safety.

Clothing

What you wear depends on the weather and the type of training you are doing. Basically you should wear what feels comfortable. A tracksuit is ideal if you are cold, but most gyms are kept warm and a T-shirt and tracksuit trousers are suitable. But keep a top handy to stop getting cold between lifts. Training shoes are best for the feet unless you are a competitive lifter or raising really heavy weights, when a pair of leather boots with tarsal straps and non-slip soles is essential. Boots aid proper balance on heavy lifts.

Many serious lifters also use a belt made of good quality leather. To conform with international regulations this should not exceed a width of 10 cm. A belt supports the whole of the trunk, and in exercises like Squats helps maintain an acceptable posture. One possible disadvantage is that the weight-trainer finds a belt indispensable. In athletics, nowadays, one often sees throwers wearing lifting belts to give them confidence. They have become so used to using them in heavy weight-training that they even need them for throwing.

Smoking and alcohol

Tobacco does not aid one to increase strength. Indeed, there is clear evidence that it is a handicap. One cigarette reduces the haemoglobin by about 8 per cent, and since haemoglobin carries the oxygen in the blood and because oxygen is necessary for physical performance smoking will clearly affect athletic excellence. In the long-term the link between lung cancer and cigarette smoking has been well established.

Alcohol is a little different. Drinking certainly slows down the removal of lactic acid – the fatigue product caused by exercise. But it has value for purposes of relaxation and, in moderation, probably does little harm.

Injuries

Injuries are the bane of sport. But if the safety rules mentioned above are observed and warming up carefully carried out, then injuries should be rare. Weight-training is not a hazardous activity, and frequently one can practise it for several years without missing any session through injury. Stiffness often occurs, particularly if training has been intensive or a new exercise employed, but this disappears quickly. Hot showers and embrocation ointments are sometimes useful, and massage by some qualified practitioner is valuable. When stiffness occurs to the lower back it is often as a result of faulty lifting. Many trainers are meticulous when they raise the barbell using the legs, looking up and keeping the back flat. They are less careful when they lower the weight from the chest to the ground, partly because the exercise has caused physical tiredness. I am convinced that a large number of injuries to the lower back come in lowering rather than lifting the weight. In exercises like Power Cleans or Power Snatches it is probably as well if you lower the barbell from the chest to the thighs as a precaution before returning it to the ground.

Severe injuries should be examined by a doctor. Usually a GP is not qualified in sports injuries, so try to get a referral to a specialist or seek out a specialist, osteopath or physiotherapist yourself. There are many highly qualified in sports medicine, but you sometimes have to work hard to get to see them.

The one exercise that is particularly controversial is the Squat or Deep Knees Bend. In the early 1960s Dr Karl Klein of the University of Texas published research in which he concluded that full Squats loosened the knee joints and therefore the exercise was harmful. He tested 128 competitive weightlifters who had done full Squats against 386 college students, who had undergone no such experience, and found a high percentage of the weightlifters had unstable collateral and anterior cruciate ligaments. In *The Strongest Shall Survive*, a book on training for American Football, the USA international weightlifter and coach, Bill Starr, who was one of those tested, questioned Dr Klein's findings. He said that the research was not conducted under rigid testing procedure and also that it was not so much Squats that caused the damage but violent movements which all competitive weightlifters perform – like heavy Squat Cleans and Squat Snatches, when the lifter drops sharply into a deep position. In effect, Starr argued, the wrong exercise had been given the 'villain's role'. Starr also cited the work of Earle Meyers in *Research Quarterly* (42:4, 1971), in 'Effect of selected exercise variable on ligament stability and flexibility of the knee'. This concluded that full Squats, when performed correctly, were actually beneficial to the knee joint as they built up the muscles, tendons and ligaments that surround the knee. Certainly it is an area of concern and interest, not least to those competitive weightlifters (including the author) whose careers have ended because of damaged ligaments.

Weight-training for the disabled

Although weight-training had been used for many years for rehabilitation for the injured, it is only comparatively recently that it has been considered suitable for the disabled to compete in weightlifting. Fortunately, the efforts of such bodies as the British Paraplegic Sports Society Ltd and the British Sports Association for the Disabled at Stoke Mandeville, have shown that the disabled can compete with distinction. The BSAD recognises weightlifting as a sport for paralysed people in wheelchairs whether they have an injury or disease of the spinal cord, including poliomyelitis. The International Stoke Mandeville Games Committee recognises only the paraplegic Press on Bench for international and national competition, but world and continental records are also accepted on the Pull Over and Press on Back and the Lateral Raise Lying.

Diet and nutrition

More has been written on these subjects than any other aspects of health, but research has concentrated on the needs and desires of ordinary people and not on active competitors whose requirements are clearly different. There is a particular shortage of work in analysing the diets of people who practise weight-training for sport and competitive lifting. People, who are interested in using weight-training either for general fitness or losing weight, should assess their needs from the multitude of books on the market. People practising bodybuilding will find chapters appropriate for their needs in both 'Bodybuilding for Beginners' and 'Championship Bodybuilding' later in the book.

Much of the interest in diet for serious trainers centres on how much more they need to consume in proteins and vitamins than ordinary people, given that both need a balanced diet of good, wholesome food with an emphasis on natural products. In his book *Modern Weightlifting and Powerlifting*, George Popplewell, a former British light-heavyweight champion and splendidly informed coach, quotes the Soviet A. E. Falameev as recommending the following daily vitamin doses for a lifter in hard training: C, 50 mg; B1, 2 to 10 mg; B6, 3 to 4 mg; B12, 10 mg; PP, 15 to 30 mg; A, up to 5 mg; E, up to 10 mg. Professor Vorobyev estimated that for each kilo of bodyweight the lifter requires 2.4 to 2.5 grammes of protein, although a lifter weighing more than 80 kg does not increase his requirement proportionately. In his daily diet Vorobyev states that a weightlifter should include not less than 300 to 400 grammes of meat, preferably lean, and advocates the value of liver since it has 'exceptional nutritional value'.

The consumption of quantities of food and milk by some super-heavyweights may be completely useless since adequate amounts of vitamins and proteins are exceeded. But it does ensure that the individual's bodyweight is maintained, and more easily than eating even greater amounts of food of lower calorific value.

Some books on bodybuilding will advocate food supplements, but these are sometimes written by those people with a vested interest since they are linked to the manufacturers of these products. Just whether supplements are indeed valuable is impossible to decide without careful examination of the individual's diet and training. Many serious trainers take the attitude that since a moderate intake of supplements is certainly not harmful they should continue taking them on the basis that they *might* be doing good. Without more research it is impossible to verify the value of supplements.

Strength retention

This usually applies to sportsmen and women, who are concerned during their competition season to concentrate on their events but want to maintain their strength levels. This subject is explored in the chapters on weight-training for the individual sports, but some general remarks are appropriate.

It is clearly pointless to stop weight-training completely during the competition season after all the hard work has been done in the off season. Instead, the schedule should be shortened and/or the number of sessions diminished. Even one session a week will help arrest the decline in strength. In 1966 the German physiologist Professor T. Hettinger used plaster casts to immobilise limbs and found an average loss of 15.1 per cent of the initial strength. Training once every three weeks reduced by 40 to 50 per cent the speed of the reduction of strength. Trained muscles lost their strength faster than untrained ones. Although many sportsmen will, of course, be offsetting any reduction in strength through competing and training in their particular activity, nevertheless the evidence is well-documented that even one or two weight-training sessions a week will allow them to retain more of their hard-earned strength than they would do otherwise.

Most bodybuilders and competitive lifters will train all the year round in different phases. Yet many people who use weights do have mild withdrawal symptoms when they are on holiday or are forced to travel and cannot, for one reason or another, lift weights. A reasonable substitute is a chest expander, which is portable, cheap and long-lasting. Although the range of movements is limited, a moderate workout can be had when combined with free-standing exercises like Abdominal Curl (sit-ups) and Press-Ups or the Canadian 5 BX plan.

Breathing

Each exercise has its own breathing pattern which is soon learnt naturally. Generally speaking, one inhales during the least arduous part of the exercises, usually immediately prior to the effort, and exhales as one finishes the hardest part. This also helps to keep a rhythm going. In all exercises one should breathe on every repetition, but in some of the most severe movements one may be forced to take a few breaths between repetitions. This is commonplace in exercises of massive movements like Squats. It sometimes helps the lifter to expel air aggressively – this gives a psychological boost as the repetition is completed. Between sets and exercises one should breathe normally.

Warming up

Warming up is frequently skipped by sportsmen and women, sometimes with dire consequences. It is an important feature of a training session or competition in any sport, and no one can be expected to perform their best without fully preparing the body for the intensive work to come. With adequate warming up there is far less chance of injury since the muscles become more elastic, so reducing the risk of sprains and tears. The higher temperatures also improve contraction and reflex times of the muscles. Ever since 1943, when Juttle studied the influence of warmth and cold on muscles and discovered that warming up increases muscular activity by no less than 19 per cent, there has been concrete evidence of its benefit.

The more severe the work or competition and the colder the weather, the more extensive should be the warm-up. The analogy with starting a car in the winter is a valid one. Warming up serves the following purposes: (1) to prepare the person mentally for the effort to come; (2) to raise the pulse and respiratory rate; (3) to raise the body temperature; (4) to increase the mobility of the joints.

For weight-training there are four important stages of warming up.
1.   Jogging (if necessary on the spot), skipping or even cycling for a minimum of three minutes.

2.   Stretching exercises, done smoothly without speed or jerks. Two to four repetitions of each exercise should be done with the position held for approximately ten to twenty seconds. A typical routine – one taught to qualified instructors of Powersport apparatus – is as follows:

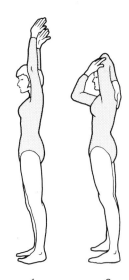

1   2

1. Windmill: circle the arms backwards alternately, pushing the hands away and bring the upper arm close to the ear. Then repeat with both circling together

2. Back scratcher stretch: with one arm reach down towards the space between the shoulder blades, the other hand being placed over the elbow joint to push slowly down the back bone to the point of tension. Repeat with other arm

3. The twister: standing feet astride, raise both elbows sideways to 90° and interlace the fingers. Keeping feet firmly anchored, rotate the trunk with elbows assisting the range of tension – first one side, then the other.

4. Side stretch: stand feet astride. Keeping the shoulders pulled well back, reach as far down the side of one leg as possible while raising the opposite arm and holding it close to the ear. Repeat each side

5. Straddle stretch: with feet astride as wide as possible, bend knees and place both hands flat on floor. Making sure that the hands do not lift, slowly try to straighten the knees as you rock the weight of the body backwards. If you succeed in straightening the knees, further stretch can be obtained by bending at the elbows

6. Thigh stretch: stand with support from wall or chair-back. Bend one knee raising the foot behind, grasp the foot with the free hand and pull it upwards and backwards. Keep trunk upright throughout. Repeat each leg

7. Hamstring stretch: crouch, placing finger tips on floor, knees together. Keeping the weight of the body over the finger tips, slowly raise the hips and attempt to straighten the knees. For further stretch, press chin to chest as you do the movement

8. Heelcord stretch: stand in forward lunge position with wall support. Raise toes of leading foot, with knee bent, on to a book or platform two inches high. Increase the degree of forward lunge until point of tension is reached. Repeat each leg

3. Two suitable exercises to accustom the body to using the weights are the High Pull-up and Power Snatch (both listed in Chapter 4, Descriptions of Weight-training and Other Exercises). These movements activate both the upper and lower limbs, but for people of less than a year's experience of training the High Pull-up is simpler. The Power Snatch is an excellent movement and can be used as a strong, dynamic exercise in its own right. Many serious trainers like to begin their session with several sets of Power Snatches. But, for warm-up purposes, the weights for both exercises should be kept light with the repetitions at least ten.

4. Perhaps the most important warm-up of all occurs in the first set of each exercise when the weight is deliberately kept light so as to get the blood flowing to the particular muscles used for that exercise but before it comes under maximum stress. Indeed, one of the purposes of increasing the weights in each set of a particular exercise – a practice that will be examined in greater detail later in the book – is that it allows a gradual warm-up for the heaviest weights. Even the most experienced lifter will do this. For instance, at the 1981 World Weightlifting Championships in Lille the editors saw the Soviet Union's super-heavyweight champion Anatoly Pisarenko begin his warming up on the Clean and Jerk with 60 kg although he had already competed on the Snatch. But he needed a thorough warm-up for a slightly different movement. Later he cleaned and jerked over 250 kg in the actual event. It is an example for anyone using weights.

Warming down

If many weight-trainers do not bother to warm up before a workout even fewer warm down. It need last less than ten minutes, but is a valuable method of gradually allowing the body and mind to recover its normal state. The first thing to be said about warming down is that the body must be kept warm. Tracksuits with hoods and sweat tops should be used as the trainee jogs, skips or cycles gently and does a few stretching exercises similar to those used in warming up. Warming down helps dissipate the lactic acid which has accumulated in the muscles and causes stiffness. Since the body is thoroughly warm it is the time that it is most receptive to stretching movements. Warming down aids recovery and pleasantly rounds off the session.

BASIC TERMINOLOGY OF WEIGHT-TRAINING

Repetitions. Often known as 'reps'. These are the number of times an exercise is repeated in a set before stopping.

Sets. A group of repetitions in a single exercise is known as a set.

Straight Sets. This is the most widespread system of training. It consists of a number of sets. Between each set the trainee pauses, usually between thirty seconds and five minutes (see 'Rest Periods' earlier in the chapter) before doing subsequent sets. The number of sets varies with the exercise, the load and the trainee's ambitions. If say five sets of six repetitions were performed this is written in abbreviated form as 5 × 6.

Super Sets or Alternate Sets. Here two sets of two different exercises are performed before there is a rest. The two exercises are then repeated one after another before another pause. The same sequence continues until the number of sets is completed. Originally super sets were only used by alternating one exercise for one part of the limb and then another for its antagonist. For example, the Two Hands Curl, which activates the biceps, would be followed by an exercise for the triceps. But recently bodybuilders have used super sets for the same muscle – i.e., two different types of biceps exercise. Each system has the advantage that the blood is kept in the same region of the body. Super sets are widely used by bodybuilders as part of 'flushing'.

Tri-sets. The same system as super sets except three sets of three different exercises are used before the pause.

Flushing methods. This is another body-building term and involves a successive number of exercises for the same body part. Often this practice will include super sets or tri-sets. It helps bodybuilders pump up their muscles by concentrating a greater volume of blood in one part of the body than would be the case if successive exercises for different parts of the body were carried out. Weight-lifters and people weight-training for sport do not use these methods as it prevents them from developing their full potential in strength.

Cheating. Although this term is widely used, it is really a misnomer and is more accurately described as assisted inner-range work (see 'Range of Movement' in 'Basic Kinesiology' later in this chapter). 'Cheating' allows a heavier weight to be employed by the use of a slight assistance movement, so as to overcome the resistance of the additional weight but increasing the resistance on the most difficult range of the exercise. Examples are leaning back on the Two Hands Curl and the bouncing of the barbell and raising the hips in Press on Bench. But is important that the trainee must feel the resistance to the end of the movement. If too much assistance is given, then the purpose is lost.

Tonnage. This is the total weight lifted in a session and is established by multiplying the average weights lifted by the total number of repetitions.

Strength and power. Strength is the ability of a muscle (or muscle group) during contraction to exert force against resistance through maximal effort. This should not be confused with power, which is the result of force and velocity according to the formula 'Power equals Force times Velocity'. The term Power-lifting – the international competition on Press on Bench, Squat and Dead Lift – is really inappropriate since velocity or speed of movement plays very little part in the activity and it is almost entirely a measurement of force

(strength). Olympic lifting and, to a much greater extent, many sports have a greater need of power. The less the resistance the more velocity (or speed) is important. Through weight-training, sports competitors try to improve their force so that their power will increase.

Muscular endurance. The ability to do a large number of repetitions of a given exercise – for example, hundreds of Sit-ups, Press-ups or Squats without any weight. Muscular endurance should not be confused with aerobic endurance, seen in such events as long-distance swimming, running and cycling, where strength has a less significant role to play. Muscular endurance is useful for many sports and is best developed through doing high repetitions of an exercise and through circuit training.

Isometric training. There was a vogue for isometric training in the 1960s and, although it is less popular now, there is still ample evidence that it can increase strength. It has been found that if maximal contraction is extended for at least five seconds then the muscle is strengthened statically. An example of isometric training is clasping one's hands together and using maximum force to try to pull them apart. As we will see in the subsequent section 'Basic Kinesiology' a muscle can be contracted statically against the fixed resistance. There have been several attempts to analyse its value for acquiring strength as compared with isotonic work like lifting weights. The work of Professor T. Hettinger and Dr. E. A. Muller in 1953 claimed that an increase of 5 per cent a week was possible. But Hettinger later modified these claims. Professor Vorobyev in *A Textbook of Weightlifting* collates experience in the Soviet Union and says that the increase in strength of muscles will be the same whether isometric or isotonic exercises are used. But he adds the vital qualification that isometric strength is not so readily transferred to dynamic strength, which is better acquired through exercising on weights or machines.

The great advantages of isometric work are that it can be carried out in a very short period of time and without equipment, and therefore can easily be fitted in as extra sessions. Yet among the disadvantages are:

1. There is low motivation because the activity is not accurately measured and this impedes maximum effort, although special apparatus is available for certain movements.
2. Isometrics have far less effect on muscular endurance and hypertrophy (muscular development) than isotonic work.
3. For someone with any type of heart disorder isometrics can be dangerous since maximum force has to be used to get benefit.
4. The strength acquired is less easily transferable to other activities than from isotonic work.

BASIC KINESIOLOGY (SCIENCE OF BODY MOVEMENT)

It is not our intention to cover this subject in detail because there are plenty of academic books available on a subject of distinct relevance to weight-training. Weight-trainers and particularly coaches are urged to spend time studying anatomy, physiology and kinesiology since they form the scientific background of strength-gaining. The following section is a brief introduction to the subject with the hope that readers will be encouraged to study more deeply.

Levers

A lever is a rigid bar which moves round a given point – the fulcrum. In the human body the long bones are levers and a fulcrum is a joint, such as the knee or shoulder joint. This is acted upon at two separate points. The first is the resistance – barbells, dumbbells, the weight of the individual's body or the resistance from pulley equipment or springs. The second is the force (effort), which is exerted to overcome the resistance. The amount of force

needed depends upon the force of resistance and the relative distances from fulcrum to the point of muscular effort. In all cases the Law of Moments (turning force) applies. Under this law the turning moment equals force applied times distance from fulcrum. It follows that the greater the distance from the joint (i.e. the longer the arms or the legs, as relevant), then for a given effort the more effective the result. Depending upon the positions of fulcrum (F), the point of application of force or muscular tension (P), and the point where the weight resistance acts (W) there are three possible classes of lever.

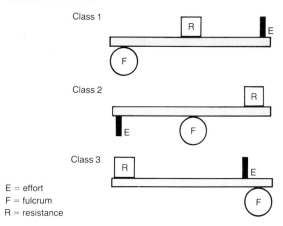

E = effort
F = fulcrum
R = resistance

In the first-class lever, the fulcrum (joint) lies between the effort and the resistance, as in a set of scales. The movement of the skull is an example of this kind of lever. When the head is raised the face is the resistance, moving up on the axis as a fulcrum while the muscles of the back produce the effort.

In the second-class lever the resistance always lies between the fulcrum (joint) and the effort (muscle). Two simple examples of this are raising the body on tiptoe or pushing/pulling a wheelbarrow.

The third class of lever is one which particularly concerns the weight-trainer. Here, the muscular effort is between the weight and the joint. This provides the least efficient mechanical situation. The flexing of the forearm in a Two Hands Curl is a perfect example. The difference between second- and third-class levers can be demonstrated by the amount of weight that can be raised in a Two Hands Curl compared with a Heels Raise.

Understanding levers is important because they have relevance to analysing sporting performances. In Abdominal Curls (sit-ups) the upper body is the weight. The power comes from the stomach, and the thigh muscles and the hip joints are the fulcrum. Person 'A', with a light torso and long legs, will often have little difficulty in completing many repetitions because the lever is more favourable than for Person 'B', with a heavy torso and short legs. However, if the action is turned round and Leg Raises are used for strengthening the abdominal muscles then Person 'B' may have less difficulty than Person A. This is because the length of levers (the legs) and the weight (the load) put Person A at a disadvantage in Leg Raises, whereas they were advantageous in orthodox Abdominal Curls.

Moreover, the length of levers is vital for certain sports. This explains, for instance, the slightly different physical properties of shot-putting compared with weightlifting, although they share certain common characteristics. Shot-putters want long levers to propel the weight for as long as possible whereas weight-lifters prefer to have short levers because they are more advantageous mechanically. Top-class shot-putters tend to be taller and have longer arms than super-heavyweight lifters.

Muscular movements

There are three types of muscular tissues: cardiac, smooth and skeletal. All have a different structure and function.

Cardiac muscle tissue is found exclusively in the heart and allows it to beat spontaneously.

Smooth muscle or visceral muscle tissue has long, spindle-shaped fibres and is found in various internal organs like the digestive, urinary and reproductive system.

Skeletal or voluntary system produces movements to the skeleton and joints.

It is the third group which concerns us and the muscles here have four types of contraction. The first three are dynamic movements:

1. *Isotonic or concentric.* Here the muscle shortens with varying tension while lifting a constant load. A simple example is the Two Hands Curl, when the biceps shortens as the weight is curled into the shoulders round the fulcrum of the elbow joint.
2. *Eccentric contraction.* Here the muscle lengthens under tension. The term lengthening should be used with caution because the muscle is actually returning to its normal length. If we take the Two Hands Curl again, the weight is gradually lowered, assisted by the downward pull of gravity until the barbell once more arrives at the starting point on the thighs. The muscles move eccentrically to lower the bar.
3. *Isokinetic contraction.* The tension developed by the muscle while shortening is maximal over the full range and applied at a constant speed. The resistance varies according to the leverage being applied. Isokinetic contraction is used in the new kinds of apparatus (see Chapter 3, 'Weight-training with Machines').
4. *Isometric (or static) contraction.* Here the muscle develops tension while holding a fixed position and so does not change length. In the Two Hands Curl if the barbell is checked halfway through the movement, the muscles are moving statically to defy the pull of gravity and, through the tension generated, are put under stress and so become stronger.

All muscles can also work in four interchangeable, mechanical ways. These are: prime movers or agonists; opposers or antagonists; fixators or stabilizers; synergists or neutralisers.

1. *Prime Movers (agonists).* When muscles are the prime movers they are the principal muscles in the movement. When the barbell is raised in the Top Hands Curl the biceps and brachialis act as the prime movers.

2. *Opposers (antagonists).* When muscles act as the antagonists, they lengthen to allow the shortening to take place of that muscle which is acting as the prime mover. The antagonist is on the other side of the joint. In the Two Hands Curl, when the biceps is the prime mover, the triceps is the antagonist.

3. *Fixators (stabilisers).* Muscles are fixators when they work statically to stabilise a joint in one position so that the movement by a prime mover can take place. For instance, in Press on Bench, the latissimus dorsi act as fixators while the arms and shoulders move the weight.

4. *Synergists (neutralisers).* This term is used for several purposes, but here it implies the basic principle of checking unnecessary movement. A muscle can cross more than one joint, and when it does so it can move at every joint it crosses. This is not always desirable and therefore synergic muscle action provides the necessary check.

Range of movement

Muscles can move from full extension of joint to full flexion. This is called the full range of movement and applies if the joint is completely healthy. The range of movement is commonly divided into three parts. Once again we will use the Two Hands Curl as an example with the movement of the biceps.

1. *Inner range.* This is the last third of the movement, when the muscle is working at its shortest length. In the Curl this is when the barbell approaches the chest.

2. *Middle range.* This is the middle third — when the muscle is neither at its shortest nor longest length. Often the middle third is the range which causes most difficulty because the leverage is unfavourable.

3. *Outer range.* This is the first third — when the biceps begins the movement and the muscle is at its greatest length.

Understanding the range of movement of a muscle is important for such actions as 'cheating' or assisted inner-range work.

THE SCIENTIFIC BASIS OF WEIGHT-TRAINING

Weight-training is based on a principle of progressive overload. To raise the level of strength, stamina or size, the body must be subjected to increased resistance through heavier weights, more repetitions or longer or more frequent training sessions. The lesson from the Greek legend of Milo of Croton still has some validity. Milo carried a calf daily and as it grew so did his strength. He was still able to carry it when it was a four-year-old bull because his body had adapted to the greater demands being placed on it.

During the 1960s an American radio station tried to substantiate the feat. A seventeen-year-old boy, weighing 65 kg, started a daily routine of lifting a calf, which on the first day weighed 34 kg. This continued for 201 days and the boy had to give up the effort when the calf had gained 130 kg. The boy's bodyweight increased by only 1.5 kg.[1] It was an interesting experiment, even if the boy had eventually to give up, because his rate of training did not match the daily weight gain of the animal and/ or because the boy's ultimate strength limit was below that of the bull's bodyweight.[2]

Yet the principle remains. To increase strength or size the body must be asked to perform tasks which it previously has not achieved.[3] If the resistance remains the same, there will be no improvement. The legend of Milo teaches the modern weight-trainer other lessons. Training must be increased steadily. It must be regular and it must be specific. Milo never strained himself because the animal's bodyweight increased only slightly each day and therefore his own body was able to adapt to it gradually.

One of the great advantages of weight-training, whether with free weights or machines, is that it is exact. Every time you exercise you know how much resistance you are employing. Therefore, there should be less excuse to strain your body. Yet even experienced weight-trainers strain tendons or muscles. This particularly occurs after a period of inactivity when the weight-trainer uses a resistance close to that before his lay-off — with disastrous results. The author remembers handling 180 kg in his final session on Squats before a three-week holiday in 1964, only to strain his hip adductors on his first set after his return, although the weight was only 100 kg. The weight-trainer cannot be too careful.

The importance of specificity must also be stressed. Milo was able to lift the bull because he trained to do it. Methods of training have been subjected to research in recent years as the desire for improvement has escalated. What strongly emerges is that training must be geared to the particular sport or activity in which the weight-trainer is interested. The frequency of sessions and the kinds of sessions are discussed in subsequent chapters. Most have evolved partly from active experience and partly from scientific research.

Much of the work originates from the 1940s. Thomas L. Delorme and A. L. Watkins were concerned primarily with physiotherapy for patients recovering from injuries or accidents.[4] Their research centred on the most efficient way of gaining strength, and they applied the practice commonplace in weightlifting to their patients. This consisted of three sets of ten repetitions in the individual exercises. But Delorme and Watkins systematised a method of increasing the weight of each set with the final set demanding maximum efforts.[5] So if the maximum number of repetitions (RM) was, say, 60 kg they proposed the following routine: 1×10 (30 kg), 1×10 (45 kg), 1×10 [60 kg]. This was later refined into the pyramid system which is used extensively today, in which the weights increase as the number of repetitions decrease.

Simultaneously, other research in the United

States found that, contrary to previous beliefs, weight-training did not make sportsmen slow. In the 1950s increasing numbers of Americans, particularly in track and field athletics and American football, began using weights, whilst in Britain, Al Murray, then National Weightlifting Coach and a contributor to this book, had worked with several national coaches like Walter, now Sir Walter, Winterbottom, Geoff Dyson (athletics) and Bert Kinnear (swimming) in establishing weight-training programmes for sportsmen.

The participation, for the first time, of the Soviet Union at the 1952 Olympic Games gave further impetus to both weightlifting and weight-training. The competition between the United States and the Soviet Union meant new training methods were used as the rivalry increased, whilst in the 1950s Olympic weightlifting was dominated by the struggles between the two countries.

The first challenge to the theories of Delorme and Watkins came with the belief of Zinovieff that to increase strength most effectively it was important to reach as heavy a weight as possible early in the sets on any particular exercise — otherwise the muscles became tired before they were being asked to work against maximum resistance. Zinovieff reversed the procedure by starting (after a brief warm-up) with the heaviest weight first and progressively decreasing the load, a system known as the Oxford Technique.[7] Independent research claimed it was 55 per cent more effective than Delorme's methods.[8]

Discussion escalated in the 1950s and 1960s with the work of Richard Berger and R. T. Withers, who conducted a series of tests on American students.[9] Both found that for increasing sheer strength, as opposed to hypertrophy (muscular bodyweight) or muscular endurance, that between three and nine repetitions of each set were most effective. This, they recognised, was in direct contrast to the experience of top-class weightlifters, who were increasingly using fewer repetitions and more sets. This was largely because weightlifters had the experience to concentrate their strength into very low repetitions (one to three), and so got the benefit from the heavy weights in a way that ordinary students were unable to do. Berger himself recognised that the weightlifter must exercise with weights as close to those he is obliged to use in competition.

The trend in the 1980s for weightlifters is clearly towards using weights as close to those attempted in competition – i.e., maximum. One of the leading Soviet Union coaches, Professor A. N. Vorobyev, is quite clear on this point, stating that to use weights of at least 90 per cent of the maximum weight is 10 per cent more effective than a programme of 80 per cent of maximum weights, and 40 per cent more effective than a schedule of 70 per cent of maximum weights.[10] Vorobyev goes on to stress that for hypertrophy training five to six repetitions were most effective – a practice which bodybuilders had been using for years. Top-class bodybuilders are not as strong as international powerlifters and Olympic weightlifters largely for this reason – they do not use weights close to their limit and so do not fully develop their strength because they are more concerned with the symmetry of their physique. The comparatively light (65 to 80 per cent of maximum) weights they use allow bodybuilders to 'pump up' the muscles to induce hypertrophy.

Readers who wish to develop their potential for a sport, or are concerned with using weights for physical fitness, will be told in later chapters how to apply these findings to their sports. For instance, a shot-putter is interested in increasing not only his strength but also in developing his physique, because under the laws of physics the total momentum of two interacting bodies is always maintained. Now momentum equals mass times velocity so that the heavier the shot-putter the greater the velocity a given effort will impart to the shot and the further the distance covered. As Geoff Dyson, the former National Coach, once said: 'You cannot fire a cannon from a canoe.'

Therefore a shot-putter will mix the low repetitions employed by a weightlifter/power-lifter with slightly higher repetitions to ensure hypertrophy so that both needs (strength and mass) are satisfied. Unlike all competitive lifters (except super-heavyweights) a shot-putter does not have to worry about keeping within a particular bodyweight. There are very few international shot-putters who weigh less than 110 kg. However, although many shot-putters have been outstanding lifters, the long levers of arms and legs needed to propel the 7.27 kg shot over as long a range as possible are not ideally suited to weightlifting, where short levers are useful. The contrary, of course, also applies for short levers and shot-putting. The use of weight-training for a shot-putter is largely to help the athlete push the ball faster – and so further. If the shot were much heavier, strength would become an even greater factor than it is. On the other hand, if the shot were much lighter (say only two kilos) then speed would be at a premium.

Many competitors use weights to help develop their explosive speed such as in sprinting. An outstanding example of this is Allan Wells, the 1980 Olympic 100-metre champion. Yet they must be careful because there is clearly an upper limit after which further increase in strength will have no significant effect upon the improvement in speed of movement. The Law of Diminishing Returns will apply and will depend on individual characteristics – such as the bodyweight of the competitor. He may also have to be careful that through weight-training he does not increase his bodyweight excessively, otherwise it will be counter-productive in his ambition to run faster. The benefits of weight-training for speed have been well-documented.[11] But it is important that the overall schedule is constructed with these points in mind.

Similarly, weight-training for the development of muscular endurance and also stamina have to be carefully programmed. The ability to lift a heavy weight once does not necessarily mean that an individual can complete many repetitions with a light weight. For instance, although a leading super-heavyweight lifter may be able to handle 300 kg in the Squat, he might have far greater difficulty than say a leading middle-distance runner if he had to do 200 repetition Squats without any weight resistance at all. Dr W. M. Sazorski has pointed out that maximum strength ceases to be a critical factor if the strength requirement is less than 30 per cent of the maximum.[12] On the other hand, neither does the ability to complete more repetitions of an exercise necessarily mean an increase in maximum strength. Muller has reported a study in which hand cranking for sustained periods at a load of about 40 per cent of the maximum improved cranking endurance, while sheer strength dropped at the same time.[13]

For weight-training to benefit muscular endurance the repetitions must be high (often more than fifteen), the weights correspondingly light, the rest periods short and the exercises involving major muscle groups. For stamina some sort of circuit training is essential because otherwise the demand on the cardiovascular system will be slight or even non-existent. In a recent test on a group of untrained middle-aged male volunteers, no improvement was found in maximum oxygen uptake although the upper body strength increased by an average of 50 per cent and lower body strength by 33 per cent. This was largely because the exercise undertaken was not sufficiently sustained to ensure endurance benefited.[14]

Circuit training certainly has several advantages because it can make a simultaneous contribution to many different physical properties, although it will not develop any of them to their complete potential. For instance, strength can never be fully developed because the sustained nature of the exercise precludes the use of weights above 80 per cent of the maximum. Yet many competitors, who specialise in events demanding a high level of stamina, prefer to use orthodox weight-training to circuit training. They prefer to increase their stamina in their specific sport by using weight-training simply to raise their levels of strength. For instance, many middle- and long-distance runners use weights to improve the arms, and legs, drive needed for acceleration at the end of the race. They cannot obtain this type of resistance through actual running.

What is important is that the individual should carefully analyse his or her own training programme to make certain that the kind of exercise, the number of repetitions and the severity of the activity are appropriate to the weight-trainer's needs. The reason that weight-training is so popular as a means of exercise is because it is so versatile, able to be adapted to so many requirements.

REFERENCES

1. Peter V. Karpovitch, *Physiology of Muscular Activity*, Philadelphia, 1965. Page 26.
2. L. E. Morehouse and A. T. Miller, *Physiology of Exercise*, St Louis, 1976. Page 254.
3. L. E. Morehouse and P. J. Rasch, *Scientific Basis of Athletic Training*, Philadelphia, 1958. Page 120.
4. T. L. Delorme and A. L. Watkins, *Progressive Resistance Exercise*, New York, 1951 and T. L. Delorme 'Resistance Exercise', *Archives of Physical Medicine*, 27, 607–30. October 1946.
5. Op. cit. Delorme and Watkins. Pages 7 and 24.
6. Edward Chui, 'The effect of weight-training on athletic power', *Research Quarterly*, 21:188–202, October 1950; W. S. Korpas and P. V. Karpovitch, 'The effect of weightlifting on the speed of muscular contractions', *Research Quarterly*, 22:145–148, May 1951; Edward Capen, 'The effect of systematic weight-training on power, strength and endurance', *Research Quarterly*, 21:83–93, May 1950.
7. A. N. Zinovieff, 'Heavy Resistance Exercise, the Oxford Technique', *British Journal of Physical Medicine*, 14:129, June 1951.
8. R. O. McMorris and E. C. Elkins, 'A study of production and evaluation of muscular hypertrophy', *Archives of Physical Medicine*, 35, 420–26, August 1954.
9. Richard Berger, 'Effect of varied weight-training programmes of strength', *Research Quarterly*, 41:1, March 1970.
10. A. N. Vorobyev, *A Textbook of Weightlifting*, International Weightlifting Federation, 1978.
11. L. E. Smith and L. D. Whitley, 'Influence of three different training programmes on strength and speed of limb movement', *Research Quarterly*, 31:132–142, 1966; Edward Chui, 'Effects of isometric and dynamic weight-training on strength and speed of movement', *Research Quarterly*, 35: 246–267, 1964.
12. Dr W. M. Sazorski, '*Die Korperlichen Eigerschaften des Sportslers in Teorie und praxis von Korperkultur*', 17, 1968, cited in *Strength Training for Athletics*, Frank Dick, Carl Johnson and Wilf Paish, British Amateur Athletic Board publication, 1978.
13. E. A. Muller, 'Influence of Training and of Inactivity on Muscular Strength', *Archives of Physical Medicine*, 41, 449, 1970.
14. B. F. Burley et al., *Medicine and Science in Sports and Exercises*, 15, 483.

2
Weight-training for Women
Vivian Grisogono

Vivian Grisogono, MA (Oxon), MCSP, is a chartered physiotherapist with wide experience of fitness training. She set up a full-time Injuries Unit at the Crystal Palace Sports Centre in 1978 and was a physiotherapist to the World Student Games in 1977, at the Commonwealth Games in 1978 and at the 1980 Winter and Summer Olympic Games. She is currently honorary physiotherapist to the Women's Squash Rackets Association. Vivian founded the charity, 'Fitness and Rehabilitation Centres Ltd', to operate physiotherapy units with gymnasium facilities. She is currently running gym-fitness operations at a GP surgery in West London and she is Honorary Lecturer to the London Hospital Diploma Course in sports medicine.

Weight-training, weightlifting and powerlifting were traditionally male activities. When women took up these sports they inevitably followed the male example rather than creating parallel versions of the disciplines tailored to the female body. There has not been a female version of the superman created from the puny weakling humiliated by having sand kicked in his face. Nor has the famous bullworker been given a feminine-named counterpart. Arguably, women will never catch up with men in terms of muscle strength or power, so they could not strive to compete on equal terms with men – unless they are very close to the male side of the sexual divide, or they increase their 'masculinity' by taking hormonal drugs.

Yet women may want to prove their muscular fitness in competition, so powerlifting and bodybuilding have provided frameworks in which women can compete against each other. In powerlifting, the competitive structure is the same as in men's competitions: maximum lifts in three types of movement, and the highest achiever in each weight category wins the prize. Competitive bodybuilding highlights the dilemma of women in what was essentially a male sport. Judges and competitors often seem to disagree on whether the accolade should be awarded for toned, defined musculature combined with suppleness (such as a ballerina or gymnast might have) or for masculine-style bulk with evident potential power.

The beef-cake type of female bodybuilder often instils a dread of any kind of weight-training in women outside the sport. Many women believe that weight-training automatically and immediately changes the normally accepted female form. On entering a weight-training gym, their first reaction is usually 'I don't want to develop big, ugly muscles'. What they fail to realise is the enormous amount of time and effort required for a woman to change her muscle contours even marginally. Serious female bodybuilders virtually have to devote their whole life-style to their sport, spending endless hours training in the gym and analysing meticulously the quantity and type of every mouthful of food they eat.

The alternative female bodybuilder, who aims at toned, defined muscles without overwhelming bulk, demonstrates the benefits of weight-training which should not repel the female outsider. Even though many women would not choose to display their bodies in the extrovert context of bodybuilding competitions, most women taking up physical exercise would share the general aims of this type of bodybuilder. These aims are: body fitness and health; minimum fat; good muscle tone; good joint flexibility; and good body posture and alignment. These add up to the overall aim of a body which a woman can be confident in and proud of. Weight-training for its own sake can achieve these aims, when it is done in a properly controlled, disciplined way. Weight-training is therefore as good a choice of activity for the woman seeking fitness as aerobics, cycling or badminton. It is a better choice than many forms of exercise because it is done in graduated progression, so that the participant is always improving, rather than just maintaining fitness.

Weight-training can also form an important part of a more varied programme of physical exercise. It can be combined with other types of fitness training like aerobics, dance exercise, Yoga or any other sports. It can be important background training for a sport done on a serious competitive level. Weight-training can provide three important elements when it is done in conjunction with other activities. First, it can be used to strengthen muscles specific to the main sport, so it provides directly appropriate training. Second, it can be used to strengthen muscles not specifically involved in the sport, with the aim of giving body balance and preventing uneven stresses. Third, it can offer a measure of injury prevention, partly through creating body balance, partly through defined protective exercises, and partly through strengthening muscles so that they work efficiently and are less vulnerable to fatigue and stress. These elements are particularly important for the woman using weight-training as a background to competitive sport, but they are also a very useful counterbalance for the woman involved in recreational fitness classes or games.

Some years ago, weight-training simply meant training using free weights, barbells and dumbbells. More recently, the invention of sophisticated fixed-weights systems like Powersport has increased the use of the term. These systems have definite advantages over free weights. They greatly increase the safety of weight-training, mainly because the weights are held supported, and away from the user. They provide specific movements, each station defining its use, and providing a set starting position which usually fixes the user so that only the working muscles can perform the movement. They generally provide a systematic workout for all the major muscle groups of the body, giving a good balance of work for the trunk, arms and legs. They are easier to use, technically, than free weights and they eliminate the dangers of poor handling of the weights in between exercises, for instance when the weights are being stacked away.

It is often said that a roomful of fixed-weight equipment is especially daunting to women. However, it can equally be argued that the brightly coloured upholstery and tidiness make the seats and benches more inviting to the female than the stark wood, bare floors and confusion of steel which usually meet the eye in the older type of free-weight gymnasium. It is certainly true that most women are pleasantly surprised to find that they can achieve the required movements in a fixed-weights system at their first try, in contrast to the slow process of learning each free-weight training technique through patient handling of the unloaded barbell before the real work of weight-training can begin.

The other aspect of weight-training which should be congenial to female trainers is the use of light resistance loading, like strap-on weights, which are easy to use, and add an extra dimension to movements which might have become too easy. Weight-training does not only mean using disc weights with barbells, or weights machines, but it also includes any type of resisted, loading exercise, including exercises against springs and those using the body's load, such as Press-ups and Sit-ups.

There are various principles governing weight-training schedules, depending on the aims of the person and the type of benefit required. One essential principle is that of graduated progression: the workload must be gradually increasing if there is to be an effective training result. Equally, for safety's sake, the workload must take into account such factors as fatigue, injury or illness, so that the person training is not pushed dangerously, for the sake of progression, when there is good reason to lay off for a while.

When a programme is made up, the following decisions have to be made: (1) which exercises are to be performed, (2) how much loading should be used, (3) how many repetitions of each exercise, (4) how many sets, (5) how often should the sessions take place, and (6) how long the overall programme should last.

Counterbalancing the desire for improvement should be the awareness that boredom makes a programme counterproductive. The sessions should not be so frequent, or the programme so long, that the person loses the motivation to try hard and increase the work done. If the weight-training is being combined with other activities, it should be programmed not to interfere: it is no use trying to play a brilliant tennis game immediately after a rigorous training session.

For general toning purposes it is probably safest and most efficient to use muscle endurance or strength work, using light weights and repeating the exercise movements many times in a set. The De Lorme principle of ten-repetition sets (outlined in the section 'The Scientific Basis of Weight-training' in chapter 1) can be used, or the repetitions may number fifteen, twenty or thirty, providing the weight is light enough for the exercise to be done properly throughout the set. Providing there is an increase in the work done session by session, whether on the number of repetitions, speed of repetitions, number of sets or number of exercises, the muscle-toning effect will take place. In order to gain flexibility while improving muscle strength, the exercise chosen should work the muscles through their full range, and the weights should be light enough to prevent any shortening of the range through muscle fatigue. Full-range exercises are particularly valuable, because they not only provide body suppleness but also strengthen the ligaments round the working joints. Most of the fixed-weights systems build in the principle of full-range work by starting each movement in a pre-stretched position.

If fat reduction is one of the aims of the schedule, an efficient way of achieving it is to incorporate aerobic training with the weight-training element. Safe exercises must be chosen, which can be incorporated into a circuit, which is performed moderately, but not too fast. The circuit of exercises can either be done in a continuous pattern, allowing no rest between exercises, and lasting for at least twenty minutes, or it can be done on an interval basis, allowing a 'rest phase' for moving between exercises and changing weights or adjusting seats. On the basis of an interval of twenty seconds of work to ten seconds' 'rest' the schedule should last for thirty minutes, giving twenty minutes of work.

When starting a circuit-training schedule, the participant should do very little whilst she gets used to the movements of the exercises and the concepts of training in this way. There should be a gradual increase up to the training level, when the pulse rate should be lifted at the end of the circuit. The pulse count aimed at varies according to the age and fitness of the participant, and it can vary from about 110 beats in an older, unfit person up to 180 or higher in a younger, fit person. The circuit should allow for increase through more weight loading, greater speed of movement in the exercises, or more exercises. On this basis, women can gain significant fat loss from just two circuit-training sessions a week for six weeks. This combines with improved muscle tone and cardiovascular fitness to provide an extremely economical method of gaining overall fitness.

Some suggested exercises and areas to work on for a general weight-training programme, or as a circuit, are (for description of exercises see Chapter 4):

1. Heels Raise, 2. Leg Press (weight pressed through balls of feet), 3. Abductor Exercise, 4. Dorsal Raise (trunk extension), 5. Abdominal Curl, 6. Leg Extension, 7. Leg Curl, 8. Lateral Raise Lying, 9. Press on Bench, 10. Two Hands Curl, 11. Lat Machine Pull Down, 12. Roller Bar Winding.

Many women look for specific exercises for toning up noticeably flabby or weak areas on their bodies, usually round the hips and stomach, where female fat deposits are greatest. Protective exercises are an important background to fitness training, and toning up obviously unfit areas can be part of an overall protection programme. Female feet often suffer through ill-advised fashion shoes; calves are vulnerable to tightness and strain under the influence of circulation changes caused by the hormonal cycle or the Pill; knees can suffer through localised weakness, or bad stresses relating to stiff ankles or hips; the lower back and hips can suffer because of poor stomach or back muscle tone; and shoulders and neck can tighten through stress or poor posture.

A simple protective programme could consist of doing the following range of exercises ten times, morning and evening, or in brief intervals during each day:

1. *Feet*. Press your toes flat into the floor, not letting them curl, hold for count of three, then relax (barefoot or in shoes).
2. *Calves*. Stand with the balls of your feet on the edge of a step, with heels over the edge. Let your heels drop down to stretch your calves, then rise up onto your toes, hold for two, then repeat.
3. *Knees*. Sit on the floor with legs straight out in front. Press your legs straight, tightening the thigh muscles and pulling your feet back towards you at the ankles so that your heels lift off the floor. Hold for three, then relax.
4. *Hips*. Lie on one side. Lift upper leg up sideways, take it slightly backwards then slowly lower (ten times each side).
5. *Trunk*. Lie on your back with the knees bent, feet flat on the floor. Lift your head

and shoulders gently forwards to reach your hands towards the knees. If this is easy, put your hands behind your head and sit up to touch your elbows to your knees. Try to do this with your feet free rather than fixed or held.

6. *Seat and Back*. Lie on your stomach. Lift both legs backwards just a little way, part them, bring them together, then slowly lower.
7. *Upper Back and Shoulders*. Lie on your stomach with your hands by the sides. Lift your head and shoulders back a little way, pressing your shoulder blades together, then slowly lower.
8. *Neck*. Sitting or standing, gently lift your shoulders up and circle them backwards, keeping your arms by the sides.
9. *Shoulders*. Standing, swing your arms up and backwards to describe large circles in the air.
10. *Elbows*. Standing with your arms held straight out sideways, rhythmically bend and straighten your elbows to touch the shoulders, then stretch your hands away from you.

Women share the same injury risks as men from doing sport of any kind, but there are certain ways in which they are more vulnerable to some kinds of injury. Immediately before a period, or at the start of it, the body's ligaments tend to relax a little, especially in the back. At this stage, even slight stresses can cause back strains, and it is important to avoid back stretches like toe touching, and to be very careful with exercises involving shearing over the pelvic joints, like lifts using the split technique, or leg lunges.

Pregnancy is an important feature in a female's life. It is generally accepted that a fit woman is likely to have fewer problems during and after childbirth than the unfit. But very high levels of fitness can create problems, most notably if the stomach muscles are too tight. Possibly a schedule which balances stomach strengthening with stretching before pregnancy might be advisable.

During pregnancy it is absolutely essential to avoid any sudden or great increases in abdominal pressure: this means that any kind of heavy weight-training or hard trunk exercises are out, especially during the vulnerable earliest stages. Women react very differently to the stresses of pregnancy. When it comes to doing exercises the woman should first be guided by her doctor and second by how she feels at any stage.

Weight-training has an important part to play in a fitness programme for women. It can constitute the whole programme, or it can be combined with other types of exercise. Weight-training is therefore very adaptable. For the woman who wants to 'pump iron', powerful, heavy weight-training is a must for her. For the woman who wants a fitter, firmer, leaner and more pliable body, weight-training can achieve these benefits, safely and efficiently, in as little time as two weekly forty-minute sessions for six weeks. The important guidelines are to assess what you really want out of a fitness schedule; how you can fit training into your life-style; and where you have to go to be properly taught and supervised in a programme tailored to your individual needs. In this way, any woman can get the most out of weight-training with minimal sacrifice of time and effort.

Weight-training with Machines
Howard Davies

Howard Davies, BSc, DLC (PE), is Technical Director of Powersport International and has been associated with Multigyms since they were first produced in the UK in 1972. He studied Economics at Swansea University, and it was there that his interest in athletics and weight-training developed. He completed a Post Graduate Diploma in PE at Loughborough Colleges in 1967 and taught PE at Duffryn Comprehensive and St Julian's High School, Newport, Gwent. Howard competed in the 400 metres for Great Britain in the 1968 Mexico Olympic Games and also for Wales in the 1966 and 1970 Commonwealth Games in Jamaica and Edinburgh, as well as other international events, including the Europa Cup and the World Student Games. His time of 20.8 seconds for 200 metres still stands as a Welsh native record. Since joining Powersport, Howard has devoted a lot of time to the development of new strength-training machines, including Powercams, and also lectures on strength and fitness training, having examined most modern training methods both in the UK and USA. He is currently producing a wide range of fitness-training charts on the use of training machines.

When Multigyms were first produced in 1972 one could scarcely realise how popular they were to become. They were first regarded with suspicion by weightlifters and weight-trainers as a rival to traditional barbell and dumbbell training. But there are now more than 4000 machines in locations such as: Crystal Palace National Sports Centre; the Army School of Physical Training at Aldershot and all major Army camps; the whole of the London Fire Brigade; all Royal Navy ships in the Falklands Task Force; Manchester United Football Club; the Gleneagles Hotel; the Welsh and Scottish Rugby Union HQ, plus hundreds of sports centres, YMCAs, universities, colleges, schools, youth and community centres, hospitals, prisons, sports clubs, Royal Navy ships, as well as the fashionable new health and fitness clubs. Indeed, the Multigym has dramatically increased the numbers of people involved in weight-training and opened up the sport of weightlifting to a much broader audience.

The Multigym owes much to the sound mechanical principles on which it was based, but if there are three key words to sum up its secret of success they would be: SAFETY, SIMPLICITY, CONVENIENCE.

Safety. As the weights are situated within a fixed frame and travel on separate guide bars, the risk of injury to the user is minimised.

This is best illustrated by a comparison between a Press on Bench using a barbell and one using a machine. The user can adopt a safe starting position without having to support the weight. He/she can then place all the effort into the concentric phase of the lift (i.e., pushing the barbell up) without fear of losing balance or of the weights slipping off the barbell. Compare this action with the barbell Press on Bench, where the weight has to be supported by the user, then lowered to the chest (eccentric phase) before trying to push the weight back up. With a barbell, the person has moved from the strongest position mechanically to a weak position without knowing whether he/she has the ability to push the weight back up. Since most weight-trainers exercise to 'momentary muscular failure' – the principle of overload (explained later in the chapter) – there is an inherent danger unless you have skilled, strong training partners.

With the Multigym, the weight can be released or dropped at any stage and it will return to the starting position without risk of injury. Thus, the person training can perform a more effective, intensive exercise programme safely without training partners.

Simplicity. Most of the stations are self-explanatory and put the user into the correct exercising position with the minimum amount of adjustment. The amount of skill required to perform certain exercises, such as the seated Leg Press, is minimal and, if compared to a free-weight exercise such as the Squat, it is extremely simple to teach, allowing the user to build up strength and confidence before progressing to more advanced exercises. One does not have to support weights on the back, a movement requiring great skill/strength and coordination, or squatting onto low benches where the effect of the weights on the spinal column can be likened to that of a pile-driver on the vertebrae.

Convenience. Few people who train nowadays have unlimited amounts of time, and so the exercise programmes to be successful must be instantaneous – but never forget to warm up properly. The Multigym allows immediate access to a wide variety of exercise without waiting for a barbell to be free; second, to load the barbell, find the collars and the spanner; third, find help to load the barbell onto the stands and, finally, to wait for a partner to complete his exercise before being able to 'spot' for you.

With the Multigym, changing from the heaviest to the lightest weight takes only a matter of seconds, and you can move to the next exercise with the minimum of setting up or delay. In addition, the versatility of many of the stations, once you have mastered the basic exercises, will allow you to select an alternative to the exercise you want to perform using similar muscle groups, if the room is crowded and your original exercise station is being used.

No wonder people being introduced to the sport for the first time look for the Multigym training room rather than free weights, partly because the apparatus is a tidy and welcoming alternative to a pile of weights. Nothing is more intimidating for a new club member, especially a woman, entering the training room for the first time, and being faced with a committed bunch of trainers who tend to regard the room as sacrosanct, and with looks implying that woe betide the person who strips 400 lb off the squat stands in order to lift the barbell off the rack.

It would appear from my comments so far that Multigyms offer the only training option and that I am anti-barbells and dumbbells. Nothing could be further from the truth. As an ex-athlete, who firmly believes in weights as a preparation for sporting activity, the use of barbells and dumbbells is very important in a well-developed training programme. And to prove it, here are a few areas where free weights are preferable.

Disadvantages of Multigyms

1. While in one way performing an exercise on a Multigym through a fixed arc of movement is advantageous when learning an exercise, the ability to use other muscle groups as stabilisers or fixators is very important in all types of sporting activity. Sportsmen and women, in particular, should look to balancing their weight-training programmes between machines and free-weight programmes as each method will work the muscles in different ways.

2. The removal of the need to balance the barbell in an exercise when training on a machine often leads to false confidence when transferring to free weights. Always take care to adjust your weight loads to the type of training you are performing.

3. Multigyms work generally through a single plane of movement. The construction of some joints, particularly the shoulder joint

(ball and socket) allows a far greater range of movement than most machines can create. In this area in particular, the use of dumbbells to perform complex multi-directional movements is recommended for full development of the surrounding musculature.

4. It is also important for people not to get stereotyped in their form of training, and the use of alternative methods to make programmes more interesting and varied is as important as allowing adequate rest between training sessions or taking a break from training every few months.

5. Multigyms have limited use for competitive Olympic and powerlifters.

THE MECHANICS OF MULTIGYMS

Most training machines rely on two different principles to provide the resistance.

Figure 1: Bench press lever arm as a second class lever

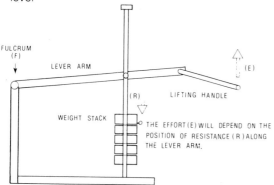

1. *Levers.* In exercises such as the Press on Bench, Shoulder Press, seated Leg Press and Calf Raise, the mechanical principle used is a second-class lever.

Here the resistance (weight stack) lies between the fulcrum (pivot bar) and the effort (lifting handle). This provides a mechanical advantage which, unless the machine is calibrated to allow for this, the weight-stack resistance and the effort required to lift it are substantially different. By fixing the weight stack at the mid-point of the lever arm the effective resistance is halved.

The Multigym manufacturers allow for this by calibrating the weight stack to the resistance required at the point of lifting. But other manufacturers do not. So be sure to re-test all maximum lifts when transferring from machines to free weights.

2. *Simple pulley.* Other exercise stations, such as the High Lat Pulley, Low Pulley or Rowing Station, Leg Extension, Hack Squat and others use a rope-and-pulley system to change the direction of the lift. In most cases it is a simple pulley system using a direct lift, which means the resistance remains constant throughout.

Figure 2: The biceps curl: the amount of work performed in lifting a 20 kg barbell. Work output measured in Newton Metres:

10° 0.05m 20 kg	30° 0.15m 20 kg	90° 0.35m 20 kg	150° 0.15m 20 kg
1.00 NM	3.00 NM	7.00 NM	3.00 NM

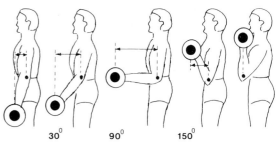

The greatest amount of work required to lift the bar is when the elbow is at 90° where the bar is furthest away from the body, thus placing the greatest stress on the muscles. This is often known as the 'sticking point', and with a traditional barbell exercise it is only this point where the muscles are maximally overloaded. In all other parts of the exercise the person is working with a sub-maximal load.

NEW DEVELOPMENTS OF MACHINERY

Barbells generally only provide constant resistance in a straight line. Since most joint movements are rotational, and because the body's leverage is changing constantly throughout rotational movement, barbells cannot be effective in maintaining a heavy resistance throughout the full range of muscle movement (see Figure 2).

Maximum tension on the muscle is developed at only one point – at 90° – often called the sticking point.

It was to overcome these problems that most new developments in machinery were introduced. These included Automatic Variable Resistance or 'AVR' (see Figures 3a and 3b) and introduction of a cam (see Figure 4) instead of a pulley, which altered the leverage throughout the range of movement. The cam principle was developed by Arthur Jones of Nautilus in the United States in the late 1960s and early 1970s and, although it has become fashionable amongst the most exclusive health clubs, like all other forms of resistance training it has both advantages and shortcomings.

Variable resistance training generally has proved to be effective in producing strength gains when working at a high intensity, and resistance with reasonably low repetitions, but it is not as effective in general resistance work for improving all-round fitness and muscle tone, and therefore not so suitable for beginners or inexperienced users.

As each machine is specific to a single joint action using one group of muscles, it has its limitations in the bodybuilding field where small variations in a pattern of movement, which are possible with dumbbells, would require a much wider range of machines than are currently produced to achieve the same result. It is for this reason that dumbbells should be used alongside the Powercam or a Nautilus machine to achieve a complete body workout.

AUTOMATIC VARIABLE RESISTANCE (AVR)

This system involves changing the leverage during a movement to produce a more effective resistance at the same time as the muscle and joint leverage alters in the body to allow greater muscular force to be used.

The changes in resistance are based on the sum of the two forces acting on the lifting lever.

Figure 3: Principle of Automatic Variable Resistance (AVR)

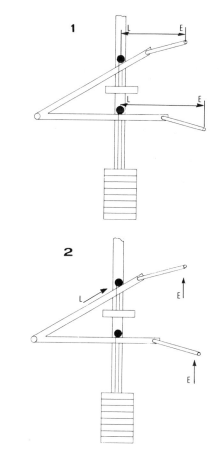

(1) As the lever moves upwards the distance between the effort (E) and the load (L) decreases, so increasing the effective effort required.

(2) As the load (L) moves the lever arm so the effort (E) increases, i.e., the greater the angle of incline the more effort is required to move the load (L).

THE OPERATION OF A CAM MACHINE

An eccentric-shaped cam is used to replace a pulley. This allows the distance from the axis of rotation to the position where the cable leaves the cam to change throughout the range of movement. This varies the resistance according to the ability of the muscle group to develop tension in that particular exercise.

Having examined the mechanics of the machinery, we must now look at how best we can put the machines to use.

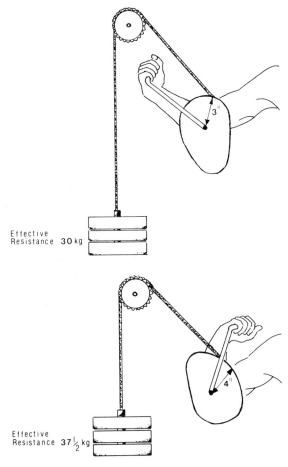

Effective Resistance 30 kg

Effective Resistance 37½ kg

Figure 4: Variable resistance – the operation of a cam

Objectives of strength training

When people go to a gym each person usually has some idea of what he or she wants to achieve. It is the duty of the instructor to identify these needs and set a programme accordingly.

I have tried to identify the most common

objectives and then to define how the programme can be modified to suit these requirements. The most common requests are for programmes which will improve strength, speed, stamina or endurance, size, or alternatively to tone up the system generally and lose weight.

Those who want to achieve the last of these objectives, i.e., weight loss, are those likely to be the most disappointed unless guided correctly. Weight-training will not normally achieve significant weight reduction unless it is accompanied by a dietary programme or a sensible approach to eating. This is because weight-training will improve muscle tone and, depending on how it is performed, some increase in muscle mass. Since muscle weighs more than fat any small reduction in body fat could well be offset by an increase in LBW (lean body weight). It is therefore important in any weight-reduction programmes not to use actual bodyweight as the measure of success but to use skinfold calipers and relate improvements to those in lean body weight or reduction to body fat.

It is also true to say that most weight-training is anaerobic, which is a system that does not use body fat as an energy source unless it is extensive and prolonged. Aerobic activities, such as static cycling, treadmill running, rope-skipping, rebound jogging, rowing and others, need to be interspersed with low-intensity light resistance weight-training, and maintained for twenty to thirty minutes to burn off some of the fat stores and improve aerobic capacity (a programme of exercise for general body conditioning is appended to the end of the chapter under super-circuit weight-training).

With regard to the other objectives, they are somewhat easier to define in terms of a programme and can be broken down into the following headings which we shall call the 'Key Training Variables'. Once again sample programmes are shown for each of the different forms of training at the end of the chapter.

Weight-training with Machines

Key training variables

Number of exercises
Exercises per muscle group
Weight load or resistance
Number of sets of each exercise
Rest between sets

Number of repetitions
Speed of exercise
Number of sessions per week
Rest between sessions

Variables	Toning		Stamina	Speed	Strength	Size
	General fitness/ conditioning	Local or specific endurance training	Circuit weight-training	Athletic power for sport	Specific strength development	Body-building
No. of exercises	10–12	10–20	8–16 per circuit Min. rest between exercises	12–15 to cover both general & specific muscle groups	8–16 aim for a balanced programme	15–20
Exercises per muscle group	1	2–4	Preferably no two prime-movers exercised consecutively	1–2 not simultaneous	1 not simultaneous	2–4 pre-exhaustion super-sets tri-sets giant-sets negative sets
Weight load % of 1RM % of 5RM % of 10RM	N/A N/A 50–80%	*This will vary with the type of system used, e.g. simple sets/pyramid sets* 20–30% 30–40% 40–50%	25–40% 40–50% 50–70%	75% 90% 100%	80–100% 90–100% N/A	70–80% 70–80% 70–80%
No. of reps	10–12	30–40	12–15 or 20–30 secs	6–8	1–6 to failure on last set	8–12 to exhaustion
No. of sets	1–2	3–6	2–3	1–3 depending on intensity	1–3	3–6 per exercise
Rest between sets	Approx. 1 min	No more than 1–2 mins	2–3 mins max. none between exercises	2–3 mins max.	3 min. max.	1 min. max. 2–3 mins between exercises
Speed of exercise	Medium tempo well controlled	Fairly fast even tempo	Medium tempo. Average 2 sec. per rep.	Fast concentric. Slower eccentric	Controlled 1½–2 secs concentric 3–4 secs eccentric	2–4 secs concentric 4–6 secs eccentric
Exercise sessions per week	2–3	3–4	3–4	2–3	3	4–6 split routines
Rest between sessions	36–48 hrs	24 hr min.	24–48 hrs	Min. 36–48 hrs	36–48 hrs	24 hr.

Figure 5: Key training variables

It can be seen from the accompanying chart (Figure 5) that different objectives require different techniques. Here are few general rules to help:

Muscle toning and general conditioning

If someone simply wants to tone up, it is not necessary to work with a high resistance, or at high intensity for long periods. Muscle tone can be improved and maintained with a regular (say twice per week) sub-maximal programme which does not require lifting heavy weights.

The person can begin a programme by using isometrics, callisthenics, or even just stretching routines for a couple of weeks before starting on the Multigym. The chapter 'Bodybuilding for Beginners' will help.

When people first progress on to Multigyms one of the most difficult questions to answer is 'What weight do I use?'

Most exercise programmes state that you should first find your one repetition maximum (the amount of weight you can lift just once). But for the novice there is a good chance that trying to establish this will cause injury which will prevent the training programme from continuing.

With the Multigym there are two methods of establishing the one repetition maximum without risk.

(a) *Trial-and-error method.* First, try the lowest weight and progress by one weight increments until you find your maximum. But I suggest that you do not try for a one repetition maximum but instead work on a 10RM (ten repetitions maximum – the most weight you can lift ten times). Then 60 to 80 per cent of this becomes the actual weight you lift in your initial programme. However, determining this can lead to fatigue and muscle soreness in those who have not trained before. A good alternative is:

(b) *The isometric method.* Select a weight which is far too heavy for the person to lift and place the trainee in the position to start the exercise. Ask the person simply to push or pull against the weight, at the same time breathing normally or exhaling through the mouth. Repeat this process, but reduce the

weight load each time until you see some slight movement as the effort is made. As soon as you see this slightly visible movement tell the person to stop and return the weight to the starting position. Make a note of the weight and assume that this is the one repetition maximum. Reduce the resistance by half and check that ten repetitions can be performed comfortably. This becomes the weight resistance in the programme.

This technique should be repeated for all exercises that are to be performed. For beginners take these tests over a number of sessions.

A programme can be based on the basic core exercise programme outlined later in this chapter. This provides good overall body conditioning based on one-to-two sets of the twelve exercises shown with ten repetitions of each exercise performed.

Strength-training programme

It must be remembered that machines such as the Multigym and Universal Gym, and others, were designed as strength-training machines, but it was never intended that they satisfy the demands of each and every person performing weight-training. Many competitive and 'heavy event' athletes, particularly throwers, would find insufficient weight-load to satisfy their requirements. On some stations, especially the Leg Press, which was designed to introduce leg work and ultimately Squats with a high degree of safety, many men will find that they have the ability to progress above the maximum weight load of the machine.

In this case do not attempt to load more weight on the machine than it was designed to hold. This would ultimately cause the machine to break with possible injury to the individual. People who have progressed to this stage should look towards free weights or other machines which are more specific to strength work, namely Powercams and Nautilus machines.

Muscular strength is defined as the ability of a muscle to exert maximum muscular force against a resistance. It has been demonstrated as a result of extensive research that muscular strength is best developed by observing a number of important principles in training.

1. *Overload* Muscles must be 'overloaded' to develop muscular strength. This means working at a high intensity and with a heavy resistance – usually only one to three sets of an exercise are performed with a low number of repetitions.

For one-set programmes No more than 1 × 10 to 12 repetitions
For two-set programmes No more than 2 × 6 to 8 repetitions
For three-set programmes No more than 3 × 6 repetitions

In each case the final set must be performed to failure.

Using a Multigym in a strength-training programme it is easy to rest the weight at the starting position between repetitions. Do not allow this to happen other than momentarily. Keep the tension on the muscle at all times – so use the 'touch and go' technique with graduated weight stacks. Do not bounce the weights as you risk injury and damage to the machines.

2. *Progressive resistance* Since an overloaded muscle gains strength during the course of a weight-training programme, the initial overload (resistance) will soon be inadequate.

As a rule of thumb, I suggest that Multigym users limit this increase to 5 per cent maximum per week. This allows the joint and musculature, including tendons, ligaments and connective tissue, to be conditioned gradually, thus minimising the risk of chronic injuries.

3. *Sequence* The arrangement of exercises in a strength-training programme is important and consideration should be given to this when designing a gym. (a) Larger muscle groups should be exercised before smaller ones – i.e. legs/chest/back/abdomen. Training fresh enables heavier weight loads to be used – e.g.,

do not leave the Press on Bench or Squat to the end of a training programme. (b) For strength training and sports training no two exercises should be performed in succession using the same muscle group as prime movers. This does not apply to bodybuilding (see separate chapters on bodybuilding or competitive lifting).

4. *Muscle balance.* Strength training should be designed to produce strength development in all major muscle groups, but for specific activities the muscles on both sides of a joint should be worked. If the muscles on one side of a joint are worked – e.g. biceps, elbow flexors, then the opposing muscle groups should also be exercised – e.g., triceps, elbow extensors. If one exercise using an opposing muscle group immediately follows the other, this system is called antagonistic or super sets. The result is a symmetrical and balanced development of the body's musculature resulting in fewer injuries and improved athletic performance.

5. *Specificity.* Weight-training should exercise the muscle groups actually used in the sport or event for which the individual is training, and should simulate as closely as possible the movement patterns and speed associated with it.

6. *Recovery time and maintenance.* Individuals vary in their recovery periods because of physiological differences and metabolism. Therefore, when producing programmes or advising on recovery times, these serve only as guidelines and individual programmes will need to be modified to suit.

There are three aspects of recovery time – (a) between sets of an exercise, (b) between workout, (c) between programmes.

(i) Between sets. Weight-training is almost exclusively an anaerobic activity. Recovery between sets is therefore fairly rapid, but full restoration of muscle phosphagen takes up to three minutes and to repay the alactacid oxygen debt between three and five minutes. Therefore, training for strength should allow for three to five minutes rest between sets, where these are performed at maximum intensity.

(ii) Between workouts. Rest periods also need to allow for restoration of the muscle glycogen (fuel) which can take between twenty-four and forty-eight hours to replace. It is therefore recommended that training is limited to three to four sessions per week on alternate days, except for extremely experienced lifters.

(iii) Between programmes. Training on the same programme for six to eight weeks can lead to boredom. After completion of a programme, say every eighth week, take a break. Do not stop training, but do something completely different for a week before starting your next programme.

Maintenance of strength gains

This is often referred to as the Principle of Regression. Once strength gains have been achieved they can only be maintained by a programme of one or two sessions per week.

7. *Speed of movement* Speed in relation to the human body is the ability to move all or parts of it at high velocities. Many coaches fear that slow, heavy weight-training will reduce the speed of movement in competition. There is little or no evidence to support this. What is more significant is that modern research shows quite the opposite. Slow, *high intensity* (and here is the key) strength training improves speed of muscle contraction.

The answer lies in the structure and function of the muscle fibres. We know of red (slow-twitch) muscle fibres and white (fast-twitch) muscle fibres. Genetics determine what proportion of each our body contains, and it is for this reason that some people with a high percentage of fast-twitch fibres appear to be natural sprinters, whilst others with a high percentage of slow-twitch fibres are more suited to endurance events. However, when we exercise it is the brain which determines

which type and how many of each fibre type are called on to perform the movement. This is called fibre recruitment or graded contractions. The brain is a very orderly instrument and only calls up sufficient fibres for its needs. The red (slow-twitch) fibres are recruited first for slow, *low-intensity* work. The white (fast-twitch) fibres are further sub-divided into two or three more classifications. Again these are recruited in an orderly fashion depending on the force or intensity of muscle contraction required to produce the movement. The last, or fastest, type of these is only brought into play by extremely high-force requirements. Since heavy weights require the greatest force to move them, then to train all types of fibres we need to work at as high an intensity as possible.

High-resistance, high-intensity training produces a consistent loading on the muscles and reduces the ballistic effect produced when lifting lighter weights quickly. In addition, a rapid acceleration or 'deceleration' of the load can enormously increase stress at one point of the movement, leading to injury to muscles or connective tissue and ligaments.

As a general rule the lifting phase (concentric contraction) should take 1½ to 2 seconds, or the lowering (eccentric contraction) should take 3 to 3½ seconds, but these times may vary according to the type of exercise and range of movement performed in that exercise.

8. *Range of movement* Muscles which move a resistance through a full range of movement perform more work than one which only operates through a partial range. In addition, strength gains are achieved over the whole range of movement and, contrary to some opinions, strength training through the full range of movement increases flexibility in the joint. Also remember the principle of muscle balance in relation to range of movement, because if both sides of a joint are not fully exercised over a whole range injury could once again result.

For competitors like athletes and swimmers

it is advisable that the recovery time between exercises be used to perform active and/or passive stretching movements to maintain or improve flexibility in the range of joint or muscle which has been exercised.

9. *Measurement* All training programmes must have a goal to be effective. This helps to maintain interest and motivate people to improve. Measurement is an important tool in promoting this and any programme must set out with a series of measurements which must be re-tested after a suitable period. Examples of a number of different programmes for strength training using machines are shown at the end of this chapter.

Endurance-training programme

Muscular endurance is defined as the ability to continue exercising with a given sub-maximal workload. In practice pure muscular endurance-training programmes are rarely seen. To produce a programme covering the whole body and performing sufficient exercises and repetitions to complete that programme would be an all-day task. Endurance is usually practised as an aerobic training session. However, the advent of training machines has seen a development of one of the most popular forms of endurance training, one which combines endurance of both aerobic and anaerobic capacity, along with general improvement in strength. This is circuit weight-training.

Circuit training, originally developed in Leeds by Morgan and Adamson, has been developed and extended so that there are many variations on the basic theme. However, Multigyms and other training machines proved especially useful in fulfilling many of the different requirements of circuit weight-training as opposed to traditional strength training.

The machinery required almost no setting up, weight resistance could be varied to suit the individual in seconds, various layouts could be produced to suit different types of circuit, and large numbers of people could exercise in a relatively small space in complete safety as no loose weights or barbells were being used.

The primary uses of circuit weight-training are:

(a) A starter conditioning programme for a broader training programme.
(b) A strength-maintenance programme during the season for sports players.
(c) A rehabilitation programme for those unable to run because of injury.
(d) A middle-of-the-road conditioning programme for people attending gyms.
(e) As an alternative session to relieve boredom of a specific strength-training or aerobic fitness routine.
(f) It has also been used for cardiac rehabilitation programmes with a great deal of success.

Principles of circuit weight-training (CWT)

1. CWT usually comprises eight to sixteen exercises performed in a continuous fashion with a minimal rest between exercises. Each exercise is usually performed for fifteen to thirty seconds (or eight to fifteen repetitions) -- at about two seconds per repetition.
2. Each set of exercises (eight to sixteen) represents one circuit. Two to three circuits are performed in a single exercise session.
3. The load/resistance varies according to how fit you are. When starting, choose a resistance which allows you to work for the set time but produces fatigue towards the end of each exercise. As a rough guide: 50 per cent of your 10RM for beginners, 40 to 50 per cent of your 5RM for moderately trained people, 40 to 50 per cent of your 1RM for trained people.

For very fit athletes or for strength-orientated circuits, this load can be increased to about 70 per cent of 1RM.

4. Recovery between exercises varies from ten to twenty seconds (thirty seconds was used on cardiac rehabilitation patients) depending on your standard of fitness and your objectives – shorter on endurance or aerobic circuits, longer on strength circuits. Use this time to move to the next exercise and get in the right position to begin. Recovery between circuits should be no longer than two to three minutes, or if you are working on recovery pulse as soon as the pulse has dropped to 120 beats per minute.

5. Design the circuit so that the exercises alternate between upper and lower body to improve cardio-respiratory effect and prevent blood pooling. Do not allow two exercises to be performed consecutively for the same muscle group, e.g., undergrasp chins and biceps arm curls (both biceps/elbow flexors). This will also help to prevent local muscle fatigue and prevent injury, especially cramp.

6. Try to maintain good muscle balance between opposite sides of a joint movement. So if you are using a Multigym Leg Extension/Leg Curls Bench in a circuit, use the machine to perform Leg Extensions (for quadriceps) on the first circuit and Leg Curls (for hamstrings) on the second circuit.

7. Pulse control. To ensure that people are working at the correct intensity, strict control should be kept on their pulse rates. Figure 6 shows the maximum heart rates for various ages and the target zone in which you should work to improve aerobic condition. Circuit weight-training should be aimed towards producing the higher end of the target zone immediately following completion of the last circuit. Individuals should also check their resting pulse rate weekly to monitor any improvements in fitness.

Figure 6: Average maximum and target zone heart rates

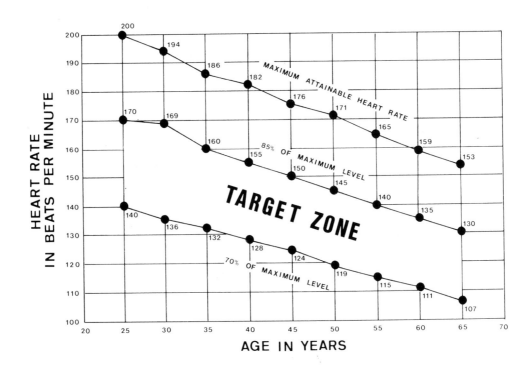

8. All circuit weight-training should include a five-minute pre-stretch and a warm-down of five minutes walking, jogging or cycling plus post stretch.

Types of circuit weight-training (CWT)

The standard form of weight-training has been described in the previous section where weight machines provide the resistance on all exercises. There have been recent developments called super-circuits which have been shown to improve the aerobic capacity more significantly than standard CWT.

The super-circuit uses an anaerobic activity such as jogging on the spot, skipping, static cycling or rebound jumping using a mini-trampette to produce this improved cardio-vascular performance. Aerobic training must be done using large muscle, rhythmic activities which can be sustained over a relatively long period (fifteen to twenty minutes). Standard circuit weight-training tends to employ relatively small muscle groups over shorter periods, which produces considerable gains in anaerobic performance, but less so in aerobic capacity.

The super-circuit becomes a continuous exercise often performed with music, with a weight exercise being interspersed with an aerobic activity which takes the place of the rest period. To maintain continuity of use on the machine, both activities are of the same duration, usually between fifteen to thirty seconds.

Results from various independent tests using super-circuits showed significant improvements in both strength gains and cardio-vascular efficiency over standard weight-training, but insignificant changes in body composition (total bodyweight, lean bodyweight, percentage of body fat).

Strength-training circuits again offer dozens of permutations based on different sports, but one of the most popular is the muscle balance circuit using agonist/antagonist opposing muscle group in sequence. For strength-training circuits the load is increased and the time spent on each exercise reduced. This can vary from five to fifteen seconds, depending on the load, and a rest between exercises of about ten seconds is allowed.

Size training programme

The activity of bodybuilding is gaining rapidly in popularity for both sexes. The use of machines has been an important factor in being able to offer more effective resistance for muscle groups which were not as efficiently trained by free weights.

Among the first of these was the Lat Machines, especially the Seated Lat where the trainee was able to handle more than his or her bodyweight. Other machines, particularly cam machines such as the Pullover, have further increased the effective range on movement on lat exercises.

Machines, which provide alternatives to dumbbell work, are vertical and inclined Pec-Decks which maintained tension on the muscle through the full range of movement to peak contraction and the favourite high and low pulleys which are often produced in a different format for cable cross-over work.

Among the most popular of the Powercam range of variable resistance machines for men is the Preacher Curl, which works the biceps 'the hard way', and for women wishing for all-round thigh development the Hips Abductor/Adductor machines are very effective.

As bodybuilding principles and techniques are covered in other chapters of this book, I suggest that the principles outlined in these chapters are adapted for the type and range of machinery found in the gym you use.

How muscle size (hypertrophy) is developed

It was originally thought that training, especially high-intensity training, produced an increase in muscle fibres (or fibrils) as a result of fibre splitting and regenerating more fibres. Although this is so in the case of rats, no research has yet been able to measure if it also applies to humans. However, it is true that strength training increases the number of Myofibrils (Actin/Myosin Proteins), many hundreds of which go to make up a muscle fibre. Also, the saturation of the muscle with blood – a technique used in bodybuilding known as 'muscle pump' – increased the number of blood vessels within the muscle which, in turn, increased size. This also results in an increase in the amount and strength of tendons and connective tissue running through the muscle.

Strength gains can be achieved without large increases in muscle bulk with the correct training. The main reasons for this are:

1. The brain improves its ability to utilise the muscle contractions more efficiently – often regarded as an improvement in skill.
2. The Myofibrils, although they increase in number, become more densely packed – called contractile element packing. This phenomenon is especially important to sportsmen who want to improve strength without increases in size. It is also prevalent in women who, because of different hormone structure, do not develop size to the same extent as men when achieving equivalent strength gains.

Warm-up and Stretching. The warm-up is an *essential* part of any sporting or physical activity. However, the importance of a complete warm-up is often overlooked. The reasons for warming-up are:

1. It raises body and muscle temperatures, increasing the metabolism of skeletal muscle and increases blood supply and oxygen to the muscles
2. It also increases blood supply to the heart
3. With more nutrients from the increased blood supply, muscles become more elastic, thus reducing the risk of sprains and tears
4. The higher temperatures improve contrac-

tion and reflex times of skeletal muscles
5. It also allows the person to adjust psychologically for the performance ahead.

Warm-up should therefore include three phases:

1. General circulation/blood supply – jogging/static cycling/massage, etc
2. Stretching activities – about eight to ten exercises (see section on warm-up in the chapter 'Introduction to Weight-training'). These may vary or be increased according to the event
3. Formal activity – skill practice to prepare for activity and improve hand/eye coordination.

Warm-down. Likewise it is not advisable to stop suddenly after intense physical activity, particular anaerobic, because of the build-up of lactic acid in muscles which can cause stiffness. This stiffness can be reduced by slowing down the heart rate gradually, allowing the heart and nervous system to dispose of the waste products in the muscles. Therefore, jog/walk plus gentle stretching should be performed for up to five to ten minutes after exercise.

A warm-up/stretch routine for weight-training is included in an earlier chapter in this book. For details of exercises refer to page 16.

WEIGHT-TRAINING FOR WOMEN

There are many women turning to weight-training as an alternative to aerobics, often as a result of poor tuition, leading to injuries in the lower back and calves.

Weight-training will help women to tone up and achieve some of their aims – namely (a) to flatten the stomach; (b) tone up hips and legs; (c) firm-up bust; (d) strengthen arms and shoulders.

Facts and fallacies

1. 'Weight-training will make me muscle-bound'. FALSE.

Women do not develop muscle bulk to the same extent as men because of a lack of testosterone (male hormone). Depending on body type, some women will develop muscle faster than others but, if you work with a light weight and moderate repetitions, muscle tone will be improved without large muscle development.

For women training for sport, using heavy weights will also not lead to great muscular development if the repetitions are kept low (below six). Strength development in women can be achieved by CEP (Contractile Element Packing) where muscle density and strength improves without significant increase in size.

Figure 7: Contractile Element Packing (C.E.P.)

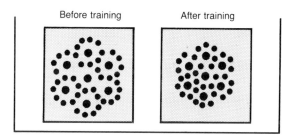

If you feel that size is increasing too fast, stop training that area and use isometrics (static contractions) to maintain muscle tone. Recommence training after a few weeks with light weights.

2. 'By weight-training I will lose fat off my hips and increase the size of my bust'. FALSE.

Body fat is not significantly affected by weight-training. Diet is more important. Not dieting itself, but sensible eating plus an aerobic session such as walking/swimming or cycling, or even jogging. This session must involve the whole body with rhythmic movement for at least twenty minutes. Walking for thirty to forty minutes at a brisk pace is better than jogging three to five minutes, then collapsing, and also involves less wear and tear on the joints. Also, the first place women lose fatty tissue is off their bust, but weights can

tone up the underlying pectoral muscles and improve firmness and shape.

3. 'I cannot re-shape my body – I am the classic pear shape'. FALSE.

You can always improve shape. Create an illusion of a slimmer waist and hips by working the shoulders and chest to create better shape. At the same time flatten your tummy to emphasise this.

There are two machines – the Module 15 High Pulley and the Module 20 Low Pulley – which are especially effective for women's shaping programmes. Each has very light weight increment (2.5 kg or 1.25 kg depending on whether you are working one or both arms and legs together). The Low Pulley machine, with an ankle strap, is one of the best all-round hip machines, allowing the full range of hips flexion/extension/abduction to be performed, whilst the Double High Pulley machine is especially effective for all chest and shoulder girdle movements.

A word of warning to women who are extremely supple. Many women have a far greater range of joint movement than men, especially in the elbow, knee, spine and shoulder. When these women work through a full range of movement to lock out, the joint, as in the case of the elbow and knee, goes past 180° and into hyperextension. At this point the tension is transferred out of the muscle and into the joint, often resulting in painful joints and symptoms such as tennis elbow, etc. If women (particularly slim women) can hyper-extend their joints, instruct them to stop short of full lock out and maintain tension on the muscle. This will prevent further injuries.

BEGINNING AN EXERCISE PROGRAMME USING MACHINES

Choosing the correct exercises

For most people selecting a range of exercises from the choice available in the gym can be quite a nightmare. I have seen many tackling this problem haphazardly, resulting in a poor and often unbalanced exercise programme.

First, we must assume that people want to use a weight-training programme for 'total body conditioning', and therefore attempt to choose a programme which covers most primary muscle groups and major joint movements.

The 'core programme' outlined in Figure 8 is designed around a twelve-station Multigym which provides the necessary range of exercises for this purpose. The variations shown offer alternatives for the same body area which can be used later, or in more advanced training programmes employing other machines from the Multigym, Unigym or Powercam range. These are not all described or pictured in this book but are mentioned to give the person some guidance to future training. Wallcharts and descriptions are available from Powersport.

The order and choice of exercises has also been designed to achieve the principles of correct exercise sequence and muscle balance described previously.

This programme will suit both general conditioning/strength training/circuit-training programmes. See Key Training Variables for Repetitions/sets/resistance levels, etc.

The basic exercises are illustrated in the section on training machines.

MUSCLE TONING AND GENERAL CONDITIONING PROGRAMME (Stage 1)

Based on a twelve-station Multigym or equivalent stations

1. Seated Leg Press
2. Press on Bench
3. Lat Machine Pull Down (behind neck)

Figure 8 Core exercises – basic exercises plus alternatives

	Basic Exercise	Variations		
1. Legs	Seated Leg Press	Squat	Hack Squat	
2. Chest	Press on Bench	Pec-Deck	Straight-arm Pull over	Inclined Press
3. Back	Lat Machine Pull Down	Seated Pulley Rowing	Bent-arm Pull Over Powercam	Bent-over Rowing
4. Front Thigh	Leg Extensions	Seated Leg Press	Hack Squat	Squat
5. Rear Thigh	Leg Curl	Standing Leg Curl	Hips and Back Extensor	
6. Shoulders/Neck	Upright Rowing	Shoulder Press	Powercam Lateral Raise	Shoulder Shrug
7. Abdomen	Bent Knee Sit-up	Knee Raise Hips Flexor	Side Bend	Trunk Twisting
8. Lower Back	Dorsal Raise (back hyper extension)	Hyperextension on Leg Curl Bench	Powercam Back	
9. Lower Legs	Calf Raise	Toe Press (Leg Press)		
10. Front Upper Arm	Biceps Curls	Preacher Curl	Undergrasp Chins	
11. Rear Upper Arm	Triceps Push Down	Triceps Press Powercam	Dips	French Press Low Pulley Machine
12. Forearm	Wrist Roller	Wrist Curls Low Pulley	Wrist Gripper	

4. Leg Extension
5. Leg Curl
6. Upright Rowing (low pulley)
7. Bent Knee Sit-up (flat) or Declined Sit-ups
8. Dorsal Raise (back hyperextension)
9. Calf Raise
10. Biceps Curl (low pulley)
11. Triceps Push Down (lat machine)
12. Wrist Roller

Workload: 10RM or 50 per cent of observed 1RM using isometric technique, described earlier in chapter ('Finding the Right Weight').

Sets: One, or as training progresses, two to three. Two to three sessions per week.

Repetitions: ten to fifteen. Increase by one weight increment when you can perform fifteen repetitions on any one exercise.

Vary the exercises with others for similar muscle groups (see core exercise programme) as the programme advances.

Back hyperextension (Exercise 8). Anyone suffering from a weak back is not recommended to use the Back Hyperextension Machine until they have strengthened the back using basic floor exercises.

CIRCUIT WEIGHT-TRAINING PROGRAMMES (Stage 2)

Once a basic muscle-toning programme has been followed for four to six weeks, circuit weight-training can be introduced and/or alternated with Stage 1.

Based on a thirteen-station Multigym (work clockwise)

1. Shoulder Press
2. Leg Extension/Leg Curl
3. Press on Bench
4. Abdominal Sit-up
5. Jump Dips
6. Seated Leg Press
7. Lat Machine Pull Downs
8. Dorsal Raise (back hyperextension)
9. Seated Rowing/Biceps Curl
10. Hips Flexion

Note: To improve muscle balance, alternate the exercises shown on stations 2 and 9 between circuits 1 and 2

Workload

50 per cent of 10RM	Beginners
40–50 per cent of 5RM	Moderately trained people
40–50 per cent of 1RM	Trained people

For top sportsmen or strength circuits, the load can be increased to 70 per cent of 1RM

Circuits and Reps/Time

Beginners	1–2 circuits	15–20 seconds
Moderately trained	2 circuits	20 seconds
Trained people	2–3 circuits	20–30 seconds

MUSCLE BALANCE CIRCUIT OR STRENGTH CIRCUIT (Stage 3)

Based on fourteen single Unigym stations or combined Unigym/Powercam

1. Press on Bench
2. Seated Lat Pulley
3. Hack Squat
4. Leg Curl
5. Shoulder Press
6. Biceps Curl (low pulley)
7. Abdominal Sit-up
8. Hyperextension
9. Calf Raise
10. Pec-deck
11. Seated Pulley Row (low pulley)
12. Hips Flexor
13. Twister
14. Seated Leg Press

1. Press on Bench
2. Powercam Pull Over
3. Hack Squat
4. Powercam V-Bed Leg Curl
5. Powercam Lateral Raise
6. Powercam Preacher Curl
7. Powercam Triceps Press
8. Powercam Abdominal Machine

9. Powercam Low Back Machine
10. Calf Raise
11. Powercam Inclined Pec-Deck
12. Powercam Rear Deltoid
13. Powercam Hips Adductor
14. Powercam Hips Adductor

Workload – Circuits – Repetitions – Time: As standard circuit.

SUPER CIRCUITS (Stage 4)

Any of the circuits shown previously are capable of being adapted to a more effective aerobic circuit (often referred to as super circuits) by introducing an aerobic activity such as static cycling, skipping, mini-trampoline rebounding, etc., between each weight exercise.

Super circuits – reps/time
Both activities operate for the same length of time, usually between fifteen to thirty seconds.

STRENGTH-TRAINING PROGRAMMES (Stage 5)

The basic programme can follow the exercises shown in the basic core exercise programmes also using variations for different body parts.

1. Strength-training programmes have many variations on these suggested schedules, depending on what you want to achieve.
2. The last set of repetitions should always work to failure.
3. Do not perform more than one to two exercises per muscle group on a strength programme.
4. Do not perform too many repetitions on sets of strength work – instead keep the weight-load high.
5. Ensure full recovery between sets (use rest for stretching).

BODYBUILDING (Stage 6)

This is too complex a subject to be covered in a short chapter, but those starting out for the first time should initially condition themselves on some of the stages outlined earlier. E.g.

Stage 1 – General muscle toning and conditioning (4 to 6 weeks)
Stage 3 – Muscle balance strength-training circuit (4 to 6 weeks)
Stage 5 – Strength-training programmes (4 to 6 weeks)

At the completion of each of the strength-training sets include an extra set of fifteen to twenty repetitions at 50 per cent RM to induce muscle pump. Then start to include two or three exercises per muscle group performed consecutively – e.g., chest: Press on Bench, Pec-Deck, Pull Overs. This will saturate the area with blood, which induces growth. As you increase the number of exercises you will find that your session becomes too long or too exhausting. At that stage starting a split routine will allow you to train on consecutive days but using different body parts. For example, body part one – front legs/back/abdominals/front upper arms/forearms/calves – body part two – rear legs/chest/abdominals/rear upper arms/lower back.

Monday	Tuesday	Wednesday	Thursday
One	Two	Rest	One

Friday	Saturday	Sunday
Two	Rest	One

There are many more advanced techniques such as super-sets/tri-sets/giant sets/negative reps/pre-exhaustion/forced reps/descending sets, which are covered in the chapter 'Championship Bodybuilding'. At this stage seek some further advice and join a club.

References for this chapter are on p. 246.

COMPETITIVE WEIGHTLIFTING (Stage 7)

Again this is covered in later chapters in the book, and the best advice is to seek a club with an approved BAWLA coach, or join one of the many BAWLA weightlifting courses operated around the country.

Seated Leg Press. A good general exercise for the legs and hips. Position – Sit on the seat with your feet on the floor. Adjust the seat along the sliding rail so that your knees are about 4 in clear of the footplate (this ensures that your knees are not too deeply bent when you begin exercising). Place both feet firmly in the centre of the footplate, with no part of the foot outside the footpad area. Keeping your back firmly against the seat back, push your feet away smoothly and under control until your knees are locked out. Return slowly and repeat. Exhale as you press, inhale on return

Press on Bench. An exercise for the chest, front of the shoulder and rear upper arm. Position – Lie flat on the bench, feet shoulder-width apart on the floor. If your feet cannot reach the floor or your back is arched on the bench, bend your knees and place your feet on the bench. This will keep your back flat on the bench during the exercise. The bar should be in line with the sternum (breast bone). Grasp the hand grips with wide overgrasp grip, turn the elbows out (hands directly above the elbows). Press handlebar up and lock out elbows. Lower the bar under control and repeat. Exhale during the lift, inhale on return

Lat Machine Pull Down. An exercise for the large back muscle (lats) plus chest and biceps. Position – Kneel facing the machine so that the lat bar is directly above the tip of the shoulder. Keep the back straight and with arms fully extended grasp the bar in a wide overgrasp grip. Pull the bar down to the back of the neck, ensuring that the elbows have been drawn down to the sides of the body and slightly backwards. Tilt the head forwards slightly during the pull. Exhale on the pull, inhale on the return stroke

Leg Extension. An excellent exercise for the quadriceps (knee extensors). Position – Sit on the machine with your back straight and the knee joint in line with the pivot of the lever arm. Hold the sides of the frame with your hands and lock your feet behind the padded rollers. The rollers should be resting on the front of the lower leg. Extend both legs until the knees are fully locked out, then pull your toes back towards the knees on lock out. Hold briefly, then return under control to the starting position and repeat. Exhale as you push up, inhale on the return

Upright Rowing. An excellent shoulder (deltoid) exercise which also works on the scapulae (via trapezius) and elbow flexors (biceps). Position – Place your feet slightly more than shoulder-width apart, straddling the footpads. Hold the bar with overgrasp (palms down) with hands about 6 in apart. Inhale as you pull the bar up to the chin, at the same time keeping the elbows high and above the bar at all times. Lower the bar slowly whilst exhaling and repeat

Bent-knee Sit-ups. A good exercise to tone up the stomach and trunk. Position – If exercising for the first time, place the board flat on the floor. As you become stronger the board can be raised up the ladder. Lie on the board with your insteps tucked under the foot rollers and with the knees bent. Place your hands loosely by the side of your head, but do not interlock your fingers as this can lead to possible neck injury. Sit up until your elbows touch your knees and concentrate on curling your trunk forwards with your chin on your chest. Hold briefly then return under control and repeat. Exhale as you sit up, inhale on the return

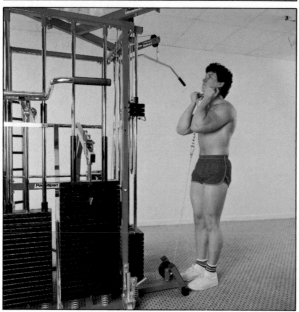
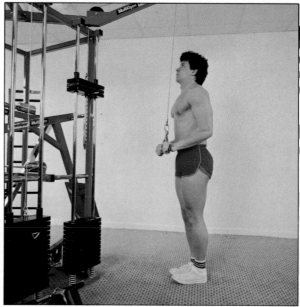

Biceps Curl. Exercises the front upper arms and forearms. Position – This can be performed in a standing or kneeling position, but in either case it is necessary to have a wide base (feet or knees apart) to give stability to the trunk. Also stand or kneel as close to the footpads as possible so that the pull on the cable is near vertical. Hold the handlebar with undergrasp about shoulder-width apart, with arms hanging straight down at your sides. Keeping the upper arms still with elbows tucked in by your sides, curl the bar up to your chest by bending the elbows. Hold the bar at full contraction for a second, lower and repeat. Inhale as you lift the weight, exhale on the return. Do not rock the hips during the movement

Triceps Push/Press Down. This exercise isolates the muscles at the back of the upper arm. Position – Stand facing the machine, holding the bar with a narrow grip, and lock the elbows to the side of the trunk so that only the elbows (not the shoulders) are used in the movement. Push down and extend the forearms fully until the elbows are locked out. Hold for about one second and push down with the hands. Return to the starting position under control and repeat. Exhale on downwards stroke, inhale on return

Calf Raise (*right*). An exercise for the calf muscles (ankle extensors). Position – Stand facing the machine and adjust the height so that shoulder pads touch the tip of the shoulders when standing on the floor. Step onto the toe platform with bent knees and a straight back, taking the weight as you straighten the knees. Keeping the balls of your feet on the toe platform, stretch the heel fully towards the floor whilst keeping your knees straight. Lift up fully on to your toes, hold for a moment, then lower gently and repeat. Exhale as you lift, inhale on the return. For complete calf development vary each set of exercises: (1) feet apart, toes straight; (2) toes touching, heels apart; (3) heels touching, toes apart. Hold these positions during the exercise

Leg Curl (*below*). This exercises the rear thighs (hamstrings). Position – Lie face down on the bench, head towards the machine. Your knees should extend over the end of the bench so that the knee joint is in line with the pivot of the lever arm. Place the heels under the padded rollers, pads towards the top of the Achilles tendon. Grip the bench with your hands and curl the lower leg until the knee is at right angles with the upper thigh. Hold and return to the starting position under control and repeat. Inhale on the lift, exhale on the return

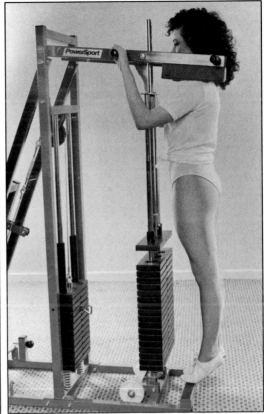

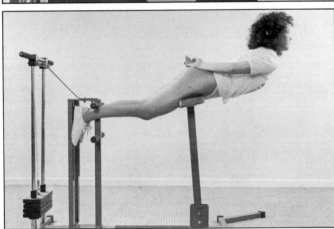

Dorsal Raise (hyperextension) (*above*). Good for strengthening the back and toning up the buttocks. Position – Adjust the pad so that it rests on the top of the thighs and supports the pelvis when in the starting position with your knees straight. Place your heels under the footrest and make sure that the soles of your feet are firmly against the back rail. Keep your legs straight and pads supporting the thighs. Lower your trunk into the starting position. Place your hands on the back of the thighs if you are a beginner, then as you get stronger move them to a position behind your head. Raise your trunk smoothly upwards under control until the trunk and legs are in a straight line. DO NOT over-extend as this may lead to compression of the vertebrae with possible back injury. Hold the finish position for two seconds, then lower gently under control. Exhale as you raise up, inhale on the return

Wrist Roller (*right*). To develop strength in the hands, wrist and forearms. Position – Standing facing the machine, grip the knurled handgrip and by flexing and extending both wrists alternately, roll the weights to the top of the guide bars. Do not let them slide down, but work the wrists on the return stroke. For variation use an undergrasp grip

Unigym Seat Lat Pull Down (*right*). A single free-standing exercise machine for performing lat exercises from a seated position with knee restraints for working with more than bodyweight. The seat and knee pads swivel through 180° to permit pull downs behind the neck to be performed

9 Station Multigym (*below*). The most popular of the range of multi-station exercises with nine stations capable of producing a complete body work-out for arms, trunk and legs, with nine separate exercise stations around the central frame

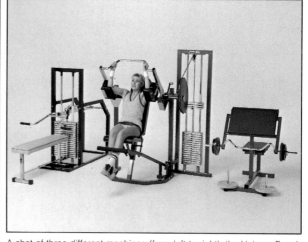

A shot of three different machines (from left to right): the Unigym Bench Press, the Powercam Pullover and the Gladiator Preacher Curl

Multigym Compact Super Five (*left*). A smaller version of the larger machine described above, showing the squat exercise being performed. Using linear bearings on specially hardened guide shafts, the carriage slides vertically allowing a safe method of performing this popular exercise

	Beginner	Intermediate	Advanced
BODY PART	*Example 1*	*Example 2*	*Example 3*
Legs general	Seated Leg Press	Hack Squat	Front Squat
Chest	Press on Bench	Pec-Deck	Straight-arm Pull Over
Back	Lat Machine Pull Down	Seated Pulley Rowing	Bent-arm Pull Over (Powercam)
Front Thighs	Leg Extension	Leg Extension	Leg Extension
Rear Thighs	Leg Curl	V-Bed Leg Curl (Powercam)	Standing Leg Curl
Shoulders/Neck	Upright Rowing	Shoulder Press	Lateral Raise (Powercam)
Abdomen	Bent-knee Sit-ups	Hips Flexor	Abdominal Curl (Powercam)
Lower Back	Dorsal Raise (hyperextension)	Hyperextension on Leg Curl Station	Lower Back (Powercam)
Calves	Calf Raise	Toe Press (Seated Leg Press)	Seated Calf Raise (Leg Extension Machine)
Front Upper Arms	Biceps Curl	Preacher Curl (Powercam)	Undergrasp Chins
Rear Upper Arms	Triceps Push Down (Lat Machine)	Triceps Press (Powercam)	French Press (Low Pulley)
Forearms	Wrist Roller	Wrist Curls (Low Pulley)	Reverse Wrist Curls (Low Pulley)
Inner Thighs	Hips Adductor (Module 20)	Hips Adductor (Powercam)	Hips Adductor (Powercam)
Outer Thighs	Hips Adductor (Module 20)	Hips Adductor (Powercam)	Hips Adductor (Powercam)
METHOD	*10RM Method* 3 sets of 10 reps (10RM load)	*Simple Sets Method* 3 sets of 6 reps (6RM load)	*Pyramid System* 4 sets plus
Set 1	10 reps at 50 per cent – 10RM	Warm-up set at 50 per cent	8 reps – 70 per cent 1 RM
Set 2	10 reps at 75 per cent – 10RM	6 reps at 100 per cent – 6RM	6 reps – 80 per cent 1 RM
Set 3	Rep to maximum at 100 per cent 10RM	6 reps at 100 per cent – 6RM	4 reps – 90 per cent 1RM
Set 4	N/A	6 reps at 100 per cent – 6RM	1 to 2 reps – 100 per cent 1RM
PROGRESSION	When reps on last set reach 15, find new 10RM and re-set loads	Fatigue will mean that you normally fail on 2nd/3rd set. Increase weight when you can perform 3 full sets of 6	Re-test for 1 RM once 3 reps can be achieved at previous best. Reps and sets can vary enormously on a pyramid programme

Descriptions of Weight-training and Other Exercises

George Kirkley and John Goodbody

Descriptions of weight-training and other exercises not described fully in the appropriate chapters (arranged in alphabetical order).

Abdominal curl

Sometimes called the sit-up, or abdominal raise. Start by lying supine on the floor with hands held behind the neck. From this position raise the upper body upwards and then forwards. Exhale during this movement. If it is found difficult to sit up, anchor the feet under a loaded barbell or a strap on a sit-up board. The knees must be bent. Return to starting position, pause to inhale once or twice, then repeat. For added resistance a light barbell can be held behind the neck, or a weight held at the chest. When using a weight it will be found necessary to anchor the feet.

Abdominal curl with trunk twisting

A similar movement, except that when raising the body turn to the right as much as possible from the waist. On the next movement, turn to the left, then repeat in alternate manner throughout the repetitions.

Abdominal knees curl

Start by lying supine on the floor, with arms by the sides. Bend the legs, keeping the heels together, and bring the knees up as near as possible to the face. Pause a second, then return to the starting position. Breathe naturally throughout.

Note: those exercises using machines, which are not described here, can be found at the end of the previous chapter.

Abductor raise

Lie on your side with your trunk and legs both straight. Lift the upper leg upwards. Arch the back slightly so as not to let the leg come forwards. For extra resistance fix a weight to upper ankle.

Alternate dumbbells curl

Stand upright, feet apart about 18 in, holding a dumbbell in each hand in the hang position by the sides, palms facing the front. Curl the right dumbbell to the shoulder keeping the upper arm almost stationary. Lower the dumbbell and at the same time curl the left dumbbell to the shoulder. Continue curling in alternate manner, one arm following the other. Breathe naturally throughout.

Alternate dumbbells press

Stand erect, feet apart about 18 in, holding a dumbbell in each hand at the shoulders with the rods parallel with each other. Start by pressing the right dumbbell to arm's length overhead. Lower back to the shoulder and at the same time start to press upwards with the other arm. Continue the movement by pressing up and down with each arm alternately. Make sure to keep the shoulders level and press the dumbbells directly upwards – not out to the side. Breathe naturally throughout.

Alternate forward raise with dumbbells

Stand erect, feet apart about 18 in, holding a dumbbell in each hand in the hang position by the sides with the rods parallel with the line of the feet, knuckles to the front. Keeping erect, raise the right arm forwards and upwards until it is level with the shoulders, or slightly above. Return to the starting position and at the same time raise the left arm forwards and upwards. Continue the raising in alternate manner. Make sure to keep the arms locked at the elbow throughout. Breathe naturally throughout.

Alternate pull over in back bridge

Assume the wrestler's bridge position – the top of the head resting on the floor (or a cushion for comfort) with the body held clear of the floor and only the feet touching so that the body is supported by only the head and feet. Start with arms held out backwards holding a dumbbell in each hand resting on the floor. The arms should be kept straight and parallel with each other. Keeping it straight, raise the right arm upwards until it is upright with the dumbbell held directly over the head. Return to the starting position and at the same time raise the left arm upwards. Continue the movement in alternate manner, with one arm moving up and the other down. Breathe naturally throughout.

Barbell one hand seesaw movement

Stand with the feet well apart and hold a loaded barbell between the legs, well clear of the floor and facing back to front. Hold it level (parallel with the floor) at the start, then by wrist pressure force the front end of the barbell downwards towards the floor (but without letting it touch) then lever back until the rear end of the barbell nearly touches the floor. Repeat in alternate manner, using only wrist power to produce the seesaw movement. Repeat the movement with the other hand.

Barbell windmill rotating

Hold an empty barbell in the middle in front of the body on straight arms and rotate it in windmill fashion by turning it in an anti-clockwise direction in a circular motion, using each hand alternately, one over the other. Vary the movement by rotating the barbell in a clockwise direction.

Bench jump

Hold a barbell across the back of the shoulders (or, alternately, a dumbbell in each hand) and stand in front of a bench (use a low one for a start). Slightly bend the knees, then immediately jump up on to the bench with both feet together. Stand up and steady for a second or two, then reverse the movement by jumping back to the floor. As an alternative try jumping right over the bench on to the floor at the other side. Turn round, then jump back from that side of the bench.

Bent-over rowing

Grasp a barbell with a fairly wide handgrip, knuckles to the front. Adopt a bent-forwards position with the feet placed apart about 20 in. The upper back should be parallel with the floor and the starting position is with the barbell held at arms' length hanging downwards. Keeping the body still, the knees slightly bent and the back flat, pull the barbell upwards until it touches the upper chest. Hold a second then return to the starting position. During the pulling movement the elbows should be taken out sideways as much as possible. If it is not possible to touch the chest with the barbell, then pull as near as possible to it, but constantly persevere so that eventually the complete movement can be made. Inhale as the pulling action begins.

Bouncing split squat (a variation of leg lunge)

Hold a barbell across the back of the shoulders, standing with feet about 8 in apart. Split the feet quickly into the Snatch position, moving the left foot forwards, the right foot backwards. Hold the position for just a second then reverse the position of the legs by first pushing up a little from the low split position and quickly moving the right foot forwards and the left one backwards. Repeat the movement in alternate manner for the required repetitions. Breathe naturally throughout.

Chair dips with raised legs

Place two chairs facing each other with the fronts of the seats about 20 in apart and another higher chair away from them so that the feet can be rested on the one chair and the hands on the edges of the seats of the two facing ones. The body must be held straight so that from a position with the arms locked the body is lowered until the chest comes as low as possible between the two chairs. The movement is the same as the familiar floor dips (press-ups), except that the chest can be lowered further, thus effecting a longer-range movement. Press back to arms' length and repeat. Inhale as the body is pressed back to the locked arms' position.

Cheat curl

Grasp a barbell with a shoulder-width grip, palms facing the front, and stand erect with the barbell resting across the thighs on locked arms, feet astride about 18 in. Start the movement by leaning forwards slightly, so that the shoulders move forwards about 8 in, then immediately, on a rebound, start to curl the weight to the shoulders by flexing the forearms on the upper arms whilst leaning back to a point where the shoulders are taking back about 8 in from the erect position. Do not bend back too far, otherwise there will be strain on the back, since the trainee will be in a hyperextension position. This 'cheating' movement from the regular erect position enables one to handle much more weight and it is a great favourite with many bodybuilders. Dumbbells can also be used as an alternative.

Chinning the bar

An overhead horizontal bar is best for this movement, but if not available then any strong overhead support that can be grasped will do. Grasp the bar with the hands about shoulder-width apart, palms facing towards the body. Let the body hang freely then pull upwards until the chin goes above the bar. Lower to starting position. An alternative is to pull the body up until the back of the neck touches the bar, with the palms of the hands facing away from the body. This is a harder movement. Inhale as the pull is made.

Dead lift

Stand close to the barbell and take a shoulder-width grip with the knuckles of one hand to the front, the other to the rear. The feet should be placed about 10 in apart, the back kept straight, buttocks fairly low and the shoulders a little forward of the barbell. Using maximum legs' pressure on the floor and keeping the arms straight, stand erect until the barbell rests across the thighs with the shoulders taken back. Inhale at the start of the movement.

Dips on parallel bars

Grasp the two protruding bars. Keeping the elbows close to one's sides lower the body to where the upper arms are at least parallel to the bars. There should be a strict vertical line of movement. Weight can be added to a special harness to increase resistance.

Dips on parallel bars (with reverse grip)

The same movement as above except the hands are reversed with the knuckles facing inwards.

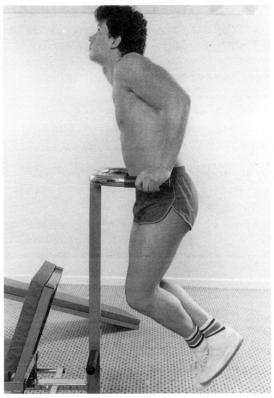

Dips on parallel bars (using chairs)

If parallel bars are not available this movement can be done by using two strong chairs placed about 18 in apart with the backs facing. Rest the body on the bars or chairs by taking a handgrip on each with the body in between. Start with the body erect and the arms locked. If using chairs it will be necessary to bend the knees and bring the feet clear of the floor. Lower the body as far as possible, then press back to the starting position. Progression can be made by fixing discs to the body, using a belt for this purpose. Breathe naturally throughout.

Dumbbell pullovers across bench

This is a favourite exercise of Arnold Schwarzenegger. It works the lats and upper pectorals as well as the serratus, just beneath the armpits. Lie across a bench with only the upper back touching the apparatus and the feet firmly placed on the floor. Grasp a dumbbell above your head and then slowly lower it behind your head. Your arms should be a little bent. When the weight touches the floor pull it back to the starting position. Concentrate on really stretching the rib cage.

Flying movement

This is a similar movement to the Lateral Raise – Lying (bent arms) described on page 64. Many weight-trainers use a variation by crossing the arms above the chest as much as possible to fully contract the pectoral muscles. Breathe naturally throughout.

Flying movement in back bridge

A similar movement, but performed this time whilst holding the wrestler's bridge position, as described earlier.

Flying movement in front bridge

Assume the front bridge position, with the body supported on the forehead and the feet facing downwards. In this position sweep the arms from a position underneath the thighs out sideways as far as possible and then return.

Front bridge with neck rotating

Assume the front bridge position, as described earlier, using a cushion for comfort, and rotate the neck from side to side; also try to make small circular movements. For added resistance hold a dumbbell in each hand and rest in the lower back.

Front squat

A variation of the normal Squat described on page 79, but with the weight resting on top of the shoulders, with the chest held high, instead of at the back. The movement is harder than the normal Squat and consequently not so much weight can be handled. Olympic weight-lifters who use the squat style of lifting find the Front Squat of great value.

Good morning exercise

Stand erect, feet astride about 18 in, holding a barbell behind the shoulders. Keeping the knees bent and the back flat, bend forwards from the waist until the body is parallel with the floor, or even past that position if found easy. In order to preserve balance it will be necessary to take the hips back a little as the bend over is made. Return to starting position. The name of the exercise is derived from the body movement, as if one were bowing and saying good morning. Exhale as the bend over is made.

Hack lift

Hold the bar behind the back at arms length. The feet should be placed apart about 10 in and the heels raised on a block of wood or something similar about 2 in high. Squat as low as possible, leaning forwards slightly to preserve balance. Return to the upright position. Inhale whilst lowering the body. A Hack machine can also be used.

Halting dead lift

Stand close to the barbell, with the feet about 10 in apart. Grasp the barbell with a shoulder-width grip, one hand with the knuckles facing forwards, the other reversed, and using the 'hook' grip. The back should be straight and the shoulders slightly forward of the barbell. Keep the buttocks fairly low and the arms locked. Lift the barbell about a foot from the floor by straightening up the body and pause in this position for a count of four seconds. Lift about another foot and again pause for a count of four. Then complete the movement by fully straightening up with the body erect and the barbell resting across the thighs. Lower to the floor, then stand up and rest for half a minute before repeating. Breathe naturally throughout.

Head strap exercise

For this it will be necessary to purchase or make a head harness — a band that fits over the head and on which discs can be attached. Stand in a bent-forward position, with the knees slightly bent and the hands resting on the bottom of the thighs for steadiness. Make the head movement by bending the head forwards and downwards as far as possible, then lifting upwards and backwards as far as possible. Only the head should move. As a variation, head circling can be done, alternating with clockwise and anti-clockwise movements. Special apparatus can also be used in a similar movement, as shown here.

Heels raise

Also known as Calf Raise. Using a block of wood about 2 in thick, stand on this so that the toes just rest on the edge with the heels on the floor. A barbell should be held across the back of the shoulders. Raise the body upwards as high as possible by rising on the toes. Lower the heels back to the floor and repeat.

High pull up

Stand with the feet apart about 18 in and grasp a barbell with a fairly wide grip, knuckles to the front. Adopt the starting position as for the Snatch, with the back straight, shoulders just forward of the barbell and arms locked. Pull the barbell upwards close to the body to about shoulders' height, keeping the elbows as high as possible and out to the side. Rise on the toes and stretch the body upwards to get maximum height. Lower to the starting position, pause a second or two and then repeat. Inhale on the pulling movement.

Incline bench press

This is a variation of Bench Press and is usually performed against an incline angle of 45°. A narrow grip will concentrate effort on the arms and shoulders, while a wider grip will put more emphasis on the upper chest. Make certain the Incline Bench is safely anchored. Partners will hand in the bar from stands. Take the weight on the upper chest and from there press it overhead, breathing in just before you start the action. Try to keep the chest as high as possible and be careful not to hollow your back as you push against the resistance.

Incline bench press with dumbbells

This is the same movement as a barbell, but instead one uses two dumbbells. Some body-builders prefer dumbbells as they find they provide a greater stretch to the chest.

Jumping squat

Hold a barbell behind the shoulders, keeping a firm grip with a downward pressure on the shoulders to 'lock' the barbell in position. Stand with feet held about 16 in apart and squat down to the lowest position possible. Immediately thrust upwards by leg pressure on the floor and jump clear of the floor as high as possible. Land on the toes, then allow the heels to touch the floor and continue down into the lower squat position. Immediately jump up again. Breathe as naturally as possible throughout. This is an exercise which should only be used by experienced performers and may, if done over long periods of time, have a harmful effect on the knees and spine. The stress will be greatly diminished if dumbbells are used.

Lateral raise lying

Lie supine on the bench with a dumbbell in each hand and the arms held out sideways from the shoulder, palms upwards. Keep the arms locked and raise them until they are upright above the shoulders. Lower back sideways to the floor again while inhaling. Pause for a second or two, then raise them again while exhaling. This exercise can be performed on the floor but the range of movement is not so great.

Lateral raise lying (bent arms)

The same movement as above, but with the arms slightly bent at the elbows (with forearms about 15° to 20° angle) and kept in this position throughout, which enables heavier weights to be used and takes some strain from the elbow joints.

Lateral raise – standing

Exactly the same movement as Lateral Raise – Bent Forward except that the body remains erect throughout the exercise.

Lateral raise – bent forward

Stand feet astride about 20 in or so, holding a dumbbell in each hand. Lean forward from the waist until the body is parallel with the floor and arms hanging directly downwards, knuckles facing outwards. Keep the arms straight and raise them sideways until they are parallel with the floor. Hold a second, then lower to the starting position. Breathe naturally throughout.

Leg circling

Hang on an overhead bar or wall bars in a gym with the legs held out in front at right angles to the body. Then perform circular movements while keeping the legs straight and toes pointed forwards.

Leg lunge – alternately (a variation of bouncing split squat)

Stand with feet together and a barbell held across the back of the shoulders. Start the movement by lunging forwards with the right leg and place the foot about 3 ft to 4 ft in front of the body into a position similar to the split position in the Snatch (see Chapter 17). Hold a second or two, then return to the starting position. Repeat the movement with the left leg and so on alternately. Breathe naturally throughout.

Leg press

A leg-press machine is the best apparatus for this movement, in which the weight is raised up and down in a fixed groove and has a stop to support the weight at a starting position which enables the trainee to lie on his/her back under the machine and place the feet under the weight. The weight is then pressed upwards until the legs lock.

Legs extension

A machine is usually employed for this exercise and the action is shown at the end of chapter 3. Alternatively attach an iron boot or discs to the foot and sit on a bench so that the lower leg hangs down without touching the floor. Now straighten the leg steadily and completely and fully tense the thigh muscles. Return steadily to the starting position and repeat for the required repetitions. Repeat with the other leg.

Legs raise

Start by lying supine, with the hands resting on the floor underneath the buttocks. Keeping the legs straight with the toes pointed forwards, steadily raise the legs until they are vertical. Pause a second, then steadily lower to the starting position and immediately repeat. A small weight or dumbbell can be held between the feet for added resistance. Breathe naturally throughout.

Nieder press

Stand erect, holding barbell at the shoulders in the same position as at the start of the standing Press. To perform the movement, vigorously thrust the barbell directly forwards to arms' length, then immediately return to the shoulders. It will be necessary to lean back a little as the thrust is made in order to preserve balance. Return to the upright position as the barbell is brought back to the shoulders. This exercise derives its name from Bill Nieder, the famous American shot-putter, who used it extensively to build up his putting power.

One arm lift over

Lie sideways on a mat, holding a dumbbell in the hand of the uppermost arm and resting the head in the hand of the free arm, the upper arm being placed on the floor. Hold the lifting arm stretched as far as possible away from the line of the body and as near parallel as possible with the floor. Then lift the weight on a locked arm until the arm is vertical above the shoulder. Repeat for the number of repetitions required, then perform with the other arm.

One arm press

Stand erect, feet apart about 16 in, holding a dumbbell at the shoulder. Keeping the body erect and the shoulders level, press the dumbbell to arm's length overhead. Lower to the shoulders. Inhale as the pressing movement is made. Repeat the required repetitions with the other arm.

One hand clean with dumbbell

Grasp the dumbbell (rod parallel with front of body) with knuckles facing to the rear. From a half-squat position with back flat and arm locked, pull the dumbbell to the shoulder in a swift, pulling and curling movement whilst lowering the body a little.

One arm swing

This is a competition lift and requires skilled technique to perform properly for this purpose. But for bodybuilding and strengthening a simpler version can be performed. With the feet about 20 in apart, place a dumbbell between the feet with the rod pointing directly forwards. Grasp the dumbbell in the normal starting position, back straight, arm locked and shoulders slightly in front of the centre of the dumbbell rod. Place the free hand on the corresponding thigh. Keep the lifting arm locked and with assistance by pressure with the free hand on the thigh, swing the dumbbell to arm's length overhead, straightening up the body as the dumbbell reaches the overhead position. Keep the arm locked and lower the dumbbell by squatting down again until it nearly touches the floor, then immediately pull back into another swing overhead. Repeat for the required number of repetitions without the dumbbell touching the floor. Repeat with the other arm. Inhale as the swing is made.

Overhead roll

Start by lying supine on the floor, with the arms placed beside the hips. Keeping the legs straight, steadily raise them upwards and backwards to touch the floor behind the head. If unable to do this, then go as far as possible, but endeavour, in time, to reach the floor. Return steadily to starting position, pause a second or two, then repeat.

Power clean

Starting position: This is the standard position for beginning many exercises. The eyes are looking up. The back is kept flat and the shoulders just forward of the bar. It is vital that the initial movement should be made using the force from the thighs to begin the upward progress of the weight.

Clean the barbell to the shoulders without using the orthodox split or squat to facilitate the movement. The knees should be bent just a little into a very slight squat position to receive the barbell at the shoulders, the object being to achieve the movement with minimum assistance from the legs and to use pulling power to the maximum.

This is an excellent exercise to develop all-round power in a dynamic movement and is highly recommended for all athletes and sportsmen. It is not difficult to learn and will often be an essential exercise in a schedule.

If you start getting lower back pain this is probably caused by hooking the bar over in an arch at the top of the pull. The bar hits the upper chest, which bends backwards, and the shock of this action is suffered by the lower back.

Power clean with dumbbells

The same movement as above, but using two dumbbells instead of a barbell. Keep the dumbbell rods facing forwards throughout the movement.

Power snatch

This has many similarities to a competitive snatch (for description see Chapter 17, 'The Technique of Olympic Weightlifting'), but without splitting or squatting underneath the bar. It is less difficult technically than the Olympic lift and one can handle less weight. Take a wide grip and adopt the 'get set' position in the usual way. With one even movement pull the bar overhead, swinging your hips through as it passes the waist. Do not press out the weight. If forced to struggle with the bar overhead then it is too heavy.

Preacher curls

For this exercise use a preacher bench. Larry Scott, 1965 and 1966 Mr Olympia, usually angled the bench at 80° and was largely responsible for its popularity. Rest the arms, palms uppermost, down the slope of the bench and slowly curl the weight to the shoulders. Always carry out this action slowly and with complete control.

Press behind neck

Clean the barbell to the shoulder, using a grip a little wider than shoulder-width, then place behind the neck to rest on the back of the shoulders. Stand erect with feet placed apart about 18 in and press the barbell to arms' length overhead. It will be necessary to move the head slightly forwards to allow the barbell to be pressed vertically, since the natural movement of the bar is forwards as it eases over the head. Lower to the starting position and repeat. Inhale as the press is begun.

Press on bench

See Chapter 20 for a detailed description of the competition lift. For bodybuilding purposes vary the movement by using different widths of grip, from shoulder width to a very wide grip. Inhale as the pressing movement is made. Dumbbells can also be used as a variation.

Press out from neck

Holding a dumbbell in each hand, lie on a bench with the head just over the edge. Starting position is with the dumbbells held close to each side of the neck. From here push the arms straight out backwards to arms' length, keeping them at shoulder width and parallel with the floor. Hold for a second, then pull back to the starting position.

Pull back

Hold a barbell with a shoulder-width grip behind the back, knuckles at the rear, while standing erect. Keep the arms locked and force the barbell backwards as far as possible, hold for a second, then steadily return to the starting position. For swimmers, body in piked position, do the same movement with hands overgrasped.

Pull over

Lie supine on the floor or on a bench with a light barbell (perhaps an empty barbell will be sufficient at first) held on straight arms above the shoulders. Steadily lower the barbell on straight arms behind the head until it touches the floor, then immediately return to the starting position. Inhale deeply as the barbell is lowered, exhale on return to the starting position. The movement can also be performed on a bench, with the shoulders resting on the back edge. In this case lower the barbell backwards as far as possible. Use a shoulder-width grip.

Pull over in back bridge

Assume the wrestler's bridge position, as described earlier. The barbell should be lying behind the head and grasped with a shoulder-width grip on straight arms. From this position, and keeping the arms straight throughout, pull it over until the arms are vertically above the shoulders. Lower steadily to the starting position, pause a second or two and repeat. Inhale as the barbell is lowered. The movement can also be performed with dumbbells.

Pull over with bent arms

Lie supine on the floor with a barbell held just behind the head, the arms bent with the elbows at about right angles with the upper arms, palms facing upwards. From this position raise the barbell until the arms are vertically above the shoulders. Lower back to the starting position. Use a shoulder-width grip. Inhale as the pull over is made.

Pull round sideways and over

Holding a dumbbell in each hand, lie on a bench with the head just over the edge. The starting position is with the arms extended backwards, parallel with the floor. Pull one arm out sideways, keeping it parallel with the floor, until it is in the opposite position to the start – that is, with the dumbbell beside the thigh. Then without pause raise the arm upwards and backwards until it reaches the starting position. As this sideways-and-backwards movement is being made, the other arm should be moved in a similar path, so that it follows the first arm. Thus the complete movement is made by one arm following the other in alternate fashion.

Roller bar winding

Secure a weight (about 2.5 kg or so) on a strong piece of thick string and secure the other end to the middle of a piece of wood or metal (about 1 ft long). Hold the rod straight out in front of the body so that it is level with the shoulders, with the weight hanging down on the string so that it is about a foot from the floor. Now wind up the weight by rolling the rod with the hands until the weight is fully wound up to the rod. Unwind it by reversing the movement until it is again hanging down from the rod on the full length of the string. Repeat the movement by winding up the weight with a reverse hand and wrist movement. This exercise can be carried out, as pictured here, using a machine.

Roman chair sit-ups

A Roman Chair is a special apparatus for abdominal work. Anchor your feet under the padded stays while sitting comfortably. Then slowly let your upper body rock backwards before sitting up. Usually your hands are folded across the chest. The advantage of the movement is that you can go below parallel, thereby exercising the abdominals over a great range.

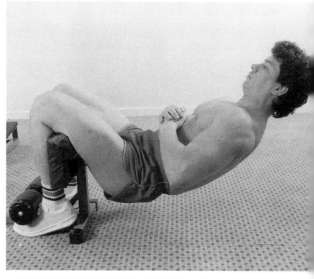

Seated calf raise

A similar exercise to Standing Calf Raises on a machine (see end of chapter 3), but this works the soleus rather than the gastrocnemius muscle. The seated exercise is also performed on a slightly different apparatus.

Seated dumbbell curl

Sit on an exercise bench. With the dumbbells hanging on either side of the body slowly curl the weights into the shoulder. The movement can be done either with both dumbbells being raised simultaneously or alternately, lifting one as the other is lowered.

Shrugs

Stand erect with feet about 20 in apart. The barbell can be resting either on the front or behind the thighs, with a hand spacing about shoulder-width apart. With the arms locked, raise the shoulders as high as possible. Then rotate them backwards and finally downwards so thoroughly exercising the trapezius muscle.

Side press

Stand erect and hold a dumbbell at the right shoulder in the starting position of the One Arm Press. Press the dumbbell to arm's length whilst bending the body from the waist to the left. When the arm is locked overhead straighten up the body and lower the dumbbell to the shoulder for the next repetition. Repeat with the other arm. Inhale as the Press is made.

Single arm rowing

Hold a dumbbell in one hand, then lean forwards from the waist and rest the free hand on a chair or something similar for support. The legs may be slightly bent for comfort, with one foot placed a little in front of the other. The hand holding the dumbbell should be hanging straight downwards with the body about parallel with the floor. Now pull the dumbbell up to the shoulder, at the same time shrugging the shoulder upwards to get maximum height of pull. Only the lifting arm should move, with all other body parts stationary. Lower back to starting position. Inhale as the weight is raised. Repeat with the other arm.

Squat (or deep knees bend)

Clean the barbell to the shoulders, then immediately lift over the head to rest on the back of the shoulders. Alternatively (and essential when heavier weights are handled) the barbell can be taken from squat stands or handed up to behind the shoulders by assistants. Stand with the feet apart about 18 in. Keeping the back flat, bend the knees and sink down until the tops of the thighs are parallel with the floor, keeping the heels flat on the floor. If difficult, then rest the heels on a block of wood 1 in or 2 in thick. But it is better to dispense with this aid as soon as possible, as one gets more supple and used to the movement. Perseverance and practice will eventually overcome this condition, which is caused by tight hamstrings and/or tightness in the ankle joints. Immediately the lowest point is reached, as described above, return to the upright position. The movement is made easier if one leans forward slightly, but be sure to maintain a straight (not vertical) back throughout. The full movement to the maximum low position can be practised, but it is advisable not to use very heavy weights in this low position. Use light-to-moderate weights, or with light weights for warming-up purposes. The Squat can also be performed by touching a bench or form of sufficient height so that when the bottom brushes it, the tops of the thighs are parallel with the floor. This is a safeguard against going into too low a position. Inhale as deeply as possible whilst lowering the body, exhale as the upright position is regained.

Step up on bench

Rest a barbell across the back of the shoulders and stand in front of a bench. Step up by placing the right foot on the bench, following with the left foot. Reverse the movement and return to the floor. Repeat, this time stepping up with the left foot, and continue for the required repetitions in alternate fashion. Breathe naturally throughout.

Straddle lift

Using a barbell, stand astride it with the left foot advanced and the rear foot taken back. Squat and grip the barbell with the right hand at the rear and with the left hand at the foot, the hand spacing being between 2 ft and 3 ft according to comfort and the size of the performer. Stand upright with the barbell between the legs to start, then lower the barbell *nearly* to the floor by squatting down and keeping the trunk upright. Immediately stand erect again and repeat. Breathe naturally throughout.

Swingbell curl – seated

Sit on a chair or bench with legs astride holding a swingbell (a dumbbell loaded with discs in the middle and secured by collars to allow the rod to be grasped with each hand outside the discs) with palms uppermost. Curl the dumbbell from a position between the legs to the shoulders by flexing the upper arms on the elbows, then lower back until the arms are straight. Breathe naturally throughout.

Triceps extension

Lie on a bench with the bar above the chest. The grip should be slightly wider than the width of the bench. Begin with the arms straight. From there lower the bar to behind the head, just touching the bench. The upper arms should not move and it is vital to keep the elbows in during the movement, which isolates the triceps.

Triceps press

Stand erect and hold a dumbbell in the right hand with the upper arm pointing upwards and the dumbbell resting in the middle of the top of the back. Keep the upper arm still and move only the forearm to raise the dumbbell and straighten the arm until the whole arm is vertical. Lower the dumbbell back to the starting position and repeat. Repeat with the other arm. Breathe naturally throughout.

Trunk extension

Lie on the stomach with hands by the sides. Lift head and shoulders a short way backwards, pressing the shoulder blades together. Hold for two seconds and lower slowly.

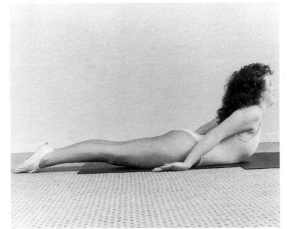

Trunk sidebends

Stand erect, feet placed about 18 in apart with a dumbbell held in one hand by the side of the thigh. Bend as far as possible from the waist to the side opposite from the dumbbell (making sure that it is a lateral bend only, not forwards as well), then bend over to the side of the arm holding the dumbbell. Continue the bending from one side to the other for the required repetitions. Alternate the movement by using the dumbbell in the other hand. Breathe naturally throughout.

Trunk twisting

Stand erect, feet astride about 18 in, holding a barbell behind the shoulders. Then twist the body to the right as far as possible whilst maintaining the hips facing forwards in the same position as at the start – do not allow the hips to twist round, only the upper body from the waist. After twisting to the right as far as possible, return and twist to the left and continue the left-right twist for the required repetitions.

Two hands clean

See Al Murray's chapter for detailed descriptions and diagrams of the Olympic movements, involving splitting and cleaning. For the Power Clean, see description earlier in this chapter.

Two hands clean from hang

Start by holding the barbell in the 'hang' position, held across the front of the thighs with body erect and feet about 8 in apart. Use a shoulder-width grip. Lower the barbell vertically downwards whilst squatting and maintaining a flat back until it is just below the knees, then immediately pull back into the split or squat position as described in the Two Hands Clean.

Two hands clean with dumbbells

Use the same style as described for the split or squat in Al Murray's chapter, but with a dumbbell in each hand instead of the barbell. The dumbbell rods should be kept parallel with each other throughout, and as they are pulled into the shoulders turn the front of the rods upwards and rest the discs on the deltoids to secure them in a solid position.

Two hands curl

Stand erect with a barbell held in front of the body across the thighs, using shoulder-width grip with palms facing forwards, feet astride about 18 in. Keep the upper arms close to the sides and fully bend the arms on the elbow joints to bring the barbell up to the chest. Consciously tense the biceps as the movement is performed. Inhale on the curling movement.

Two hands press

Using an approximate shoulder-width grip, clean the barbell to the shoulders and rest it on top of the chest. Stand erect, with the feet about 18 in apart, body and legs braced and with the forearms about vertical. Press the barbell to arms' length overhead whilst maintaining the upright position. The shoulders should be set back just sufficiently to allow the barbell to be pressed vertically close to the face. Inhale as the pressing movement starts. Only the arms should move. This is purely a bodybuilding movement and the main concern is not the amount of weight elevated, but the development of the deltoids and triceps.

Two hands press with dumbbells

This is a similar movement to the Press with barbell, but using a dumbbell in each hand. Clean the dumbbells to the shoulders, rods both facing forwards, and hold them with the rods level with the base of the throat and still parallel with each other. The back end of each rod can rest on the front of the deltoids. Keeping erect, press the dumbbells simultaneously and vertically to arms' length overhead, whilst inhaling. Alternatively, the dumbbells can be held wider apart, just outside the deltoids.

Two hands swing

Similar to the One Hand Swing, described earlier, this is a skilful competitive lift, virtually a Two Hands Snatch with dumbbells. Stand with feet about 8 in apart with a dumbbell at each side of each foot; the front discs of the bells should be level with the heels and the rods parallel with one another. Grasp the bells in the regular starting position, then pull up the dumbbells in a similar movement to the Snatch to arms' length overhead whilst splitting the legs fore and aft. The arms should be bent as soon as the bells pass knees' height and the bells kept fairly close to the body. The rods should be kept parallel throughout. In the competitive lift it is customary to use an additional preliminary movement of the bells before making the final lift, but for our purpose here this is not necessary.

Upright rowing

Grip the barbell with the hands spaced about 4 in apart, knuckles to the front. Stand erect, body braced, arms hanging straight down so that the barbell is resting across the thighs. Without moving the body at all pull the barbell upwards to the level of the chin. The elbows should be raised as high as possible with the wrists hanging downwards. Keep the barbell close to the body as it is raised, whilst inhaling.

Wrist curl

Sit on a chair or bench holding a barbell with shoulder-width grip, palms uppermost and with the elbows resting on the thighs just above the knees and the forearms parallel with the floor. Without moving the arms, raise the barbell upwards as far as possible by a wrist movement, then immediately lower back and downwards as far as possible. Only the hands should move and endeavour to make the range of movement as wide as possible.

Zottman curl

Hold a dumbbell by the side, standing erect, palm facing the front. Start the movement by curling the dumbbell across the body towards the opposite shoulder, rotating the palm towards the body. When the dumbbell reaches the opposite shoulder continue the movement across the upper chest to the shoulder of the lifting arm and at the same time rotate the palm to the front as far as possible until the bell is held in the concluding position of a One-arm Curl, but with the palm facing forwards. Lower the dumbbell to the starting position with the palm still facing forwards. Turn the palm again to the starting position for another repetition. You will see that the movement is a curling, twisting one for the forearm. Repeat with the other arm.

5
Manual Handling at Work and Play
George Hickling

George Hickling is a National Leader in Physical Education and was headquarters adviser (Central Council of Physical Recreation) on manual handling, and manual-handling consultant to the Industrial Welfare Society. He was at one time a BAWLA staff instructor and served on the Association's Central Council for a few years.

In spite of the mechanisation of materials handling in industry there is still a very large amount of manual handlng taking place. The remark has often been made about the experienced worker learning the best way to handle materials by his own efforts. Unfortunately, this is not true, as more man hours are lost in industry because of manual-handling accidents, particularly back troubles, than any other causes.

Many times I have called at the surgeries of industrial concerns to find workers being treated for cuts, contusions, minor fractures, hernias and strains of various parts of the body, usually the back, all because of faulty handling and lack of care.

In these days of increased productivity some thought has been given to alteration of layout, reduction of time operation and, in some cases, basic skill training. But where a man or woman is working in a condition of bodily strain, reducing the time factor per operation will result in greater strain and earlier onset of fatigue.

Few people know how to use their bodies correctly or economically. It is important that when such bodily movements requisite for pushing, pulling, lifting, lowering and carrying are carried out they should be performed with a minimum of effort and the maximum of physical efficiency and skill. Muscles which are wrongly used produce uneven development, loss of elasticity and a predisposition to injury and fatigue.

The approach to training is correct techniques of manual handling ideally should start in the school gymnasium and be followed up in technical colleges and industrial training centres for junior operatives and apprentices. The training at all times should be systematic and progressive.

In addition to the above, the older worker should not be overlooked; but he, too, should be instructed in the application of the skills to load and unload vehicles, the pushing and pulling of trucks, handling drums, casks and objects of all kinds of different weights, shapes and sizes.

Emphasis should at all times be placed on the correct use of technique until eventually the application becomes automatic. The fundamental positions for lifting and lowering depend on the position from which the object has to be lifted. Stand with the feet a comfortable distance apart (approximately hips' width) with one foot in advance of the other. Lower the body by relaxing the knees; the back should be kept straight throughout (Note: Straight does not mean vertical). Keep the arms close to the body.

Bending the back to pick up or lower cases causes unnecessary stiffening of the calves, lower back, lower abdomen, thighs and chest. When the bent-over position is adopted the work is performed by the muscles of the arms, shoulders and back.

With the feet in a parallel plane, pointing towards the object to be lifted, the body tends to fall forwards as the hands take the strain; the operative is unable to follow through with the weight as it is moved to its new position.

Chin tucked in

When teaching the fundamental lifting position a number of other factors must be taken into consideration, and the first one has a very strong bearing on the maintenance of a straight back.

This is the tucking in of the chin. When the hands move towards any object the head has a tendency to poke forwards; this relaxes the upper spine, thus developing a tendency for the buttocks to move backwards and upwards as the load is taken. In order to keep a straight back throughout the movement the operative should be encouraged to 'grow tall' and tuck in the chin before relaxing the knees.

The tucking in of the chin tends to shorten the sterno-cleido mastoid muscles. These in turn are attached to the first rib and collarbone and, in shortening, lift the rib box, thus imposing a lock action in the cervical and upper region of the spine and so controlling the tendency of the buttocks to move backwards and upwards.

Grip

The next principle to be considered is the use of a good grip. People rely on the strength of the fingers and thumbs when gripping and supporting objects, and while mentally the grip is being maintained, physically it is relaxing and objects begin to slide. This causes an unconscious tension in other muscle groups of the body, tension which leads to cumulative strain.

The full use of a broad, even grip is essential. This brings into use the full palmed surface of the hands and fingers. The interlacing of the fingers should be avoided, as this is dangerous. The shape of the proximal phalanges of the

fingers is such that when pressure is brought against the palms the grip locks and cannot be broken. Should the weight become unmanageable, the worker has to get rid of it by whatever means he may think fit, often causing accidents to others and damage to the object.

Position of the arms

When carrying objects the arms should be kept as straight as possible and close to the centre line of the body, whether the load be on the back, across the front of the body, or when pushing, pulling or lifting. The practice of winging the elbows should be strongly discouraged, as this causes tension in the whole of the shoulder girdle, a tendency to lean backwards and develops an overemphasis of the lumbar curve.

Proper feet position

Before the load is taken on to the body the feet should be placed in relation to the subsequent movement. The feet should point forwards for movement in that direction. If to the right, the right foot should point to the right and vice versa for the left. Many back injuries are caused by turning with a load and the feet fixed. The correct positioning of the feet plays a very important part in maintaining balance, also the follow-through when moving a weight from A to B.

Use of bodyweight

The observance of the principles outlined above makes it possible, when handling heavy weights, to make use of bodyweight to supplement, or even take place of, a muscular effort. The placing of the feet maintains balance and provides a check to over-balance should anything unforeseen occur. By transferring the bodyweight from one foot to the other the amount of muscular effort required to tilt a box, case or bale, or to initiate the trundling of a heavy drum or cask, is much reduced.

Balanced use of body

The importance of the balanced use of both sides of the body cannot be stressed too strongly. The continued use of one side of the body for the performance of such movements as lifting, lowering, levering, pushing, pulling, carrying, digging and striking, produces unilateral development, which in turn results in lopsidedness, lateral curvature of the spine, ill balance of the pelvis, and shortening of one leg in relation to the other. All of these can cause illness and injury, because of physical inability or disfunction of bodily processes.

Summing up

With the use of these principles it should be borne in mind that the stresses from handling the load are spread over many muscle groups and joints. Full use is made of momentum, thus producing smooth, rhythmic and well-coordinated movements, and eliminating snatched or jerky movements so productive of injury and wastage of energy.

The principles outlined above can be applied not only in the factory, but in the office, home, hospital and leisure-time activities, so making for a trouble-free and healthy existence.

6
Bodybuilding for Beginners
George Greenwood

A lifelong devotee to the cause of physical culture, the late George Greenwood was formerly bodybuilding adviser to a leading physical culture magazine for six years, during which time he answered some 50,000 training queries from readers. Before the last war he won various physical excellence awards and appeared in the final of Britain's best-developed man contest at the London Palladium in 1938. He was a good gymnast and swimmer, and despite a bullet wound in the chest won the heavyweight weightlifting championship of London in 1950. He was a fully qualified BAWLA referee when an amateur. As a freelance professional, he operated a photographic studio in Holborn, London, and wrote numerous courses on bodybuilding and magazine articles.

A few decades ago a man who engaged in specialised physical exercise was regarded as something of a 'crank'. The idea that physical culturists were a strange lot arose from some of the antics that the more fanatical adherents practised. People shuddered at the thought of a daily plunge into icy water, or a roll on the grass in the early morning dew; neither did they fancy struggling to elevate cumbersome iron barbells, clad only in the briefest of briefs.

But times, like the methods of training, have changed. The man in the street now readily appreciates the value of regular, progressive exercise. The term 'physical culturist' has been replaced by 'bodybuilder' or, if a man trains with modern-style weights, weight-trainer. Briefs have given place to ordinary swimming trunks or, better still, comfortable, fleecy-lined tracksuits. Cold baths and rolling in the dew are also things of the past. Indeed, today's keep-fit man is just the ordinary chap, aware of the importance of exercising his body to maintain good health and to develop a well-balanced physique.

So, before we begin, let me make one point perfectly clear. People will not think you are a bit peculiar if you practise bodybuilding. More likely than not your friends will want to join you, which is all to the good. Training in company with others is much more fun, and the spirit of friendly competition will encourage you to keep at it. Your exercise programme should be no novel experiment, but a part of your way of life. And how very worthwhile it will prove to be. Just a short spell of training a few times a week and you will be looking and feeling on top of the world; and, if you persevere, you will keep that way.

Various methods

The methods of keeping fit or developing the body are many and varied. If the aim is simply to keep fit, and develop a well-proportioned, though not excessively muscled physique, specialised training apparatus is not required, and you can achieve your goal through a daily routine of free-standing, easy-to-do exercises.

Men who aspire to physical perfection and require something a little more vigorous may choose to train with steel or rubber expanders or, what is by far the most popular effective method, progressive weight-training. In this chapter I shall deal only with non-apparatus work and elementary weight-training. Those who have a preference for expander exercises will find that illustrated exercise charts are supplied with most kits, and these can be relied upon to produce satisfactory results. But just a few words on the general aspects of training.

Sensible eating

Before embarking on any system of exercise it is important that you critically examine your general dietary habits and, if necessary, reorganise your larder. Some authorities say that correct eating is *the* key to good health, and that making planned exercise is quite unnecessary if you eat right. But I don't entirely agree with this. It is true that a properly balanced diet is essential to good health, but I maintain that exercise is equally important.

Correct eating aids functional efficiency and, of course, provides nourishment for the body as a whole. Exercise tones and strengthens the muscles, tendons and ligaments and keeps joints mobile and free. It follows that a combination of good dietary habits *and* sensible exercise is the complete answer to robust health and good physical development. This is not theory, but fact, as has been proved a thousand times over by men of all ages, in all walks of life, in all parts of the world. Bodybuilding really is a very fine thing, and I hope you will be proud to become a devotee.

A dietary plan

The chief food substances which go to make the bulk of our daily diet are carbohydrates, fats and proteins.

Carbohydrates provide the body with energy and may produce a certain amount of fat. They include foods of high starch and sugar content and, generally speaking, should not figure too largely in the bodybuilder's diet.

Fats include all fatty food substances – fat from meat, butter fat and all oils derived from animal or vegetable sources. Pure fat is the most concentrated form of energy food, but is rather indigestible and not recommended in large quantities.

Proteins. There is no known life without protein. In animals and man the muscular tissue is actually composed of protein, which means that an adequate supply of protein in your diet is necessary for the body's growth. Proteins derived from animal sources, known as first-class protein, and found in lean meat and the like, are of immense value to the bodybuilder; hence the popularity of thick, juicy steaks with American athletes.

A TABLE OF BODYBUILDING FOODS

Here is a simple chart which will help you to select the right kind of bodybuilding foods:

Steve Reeves – one of the most famous of USA bodybuilders

Rich in Carbohydrates	Rich in Fat	Rich in Protein
Sugar	Butter	Milk
Syrup	Milk	Nuts
Jams	Egg yolk	Lean meats
Flour	Cheese	Beef
Oatmeals	Peanuts	Mutton
White bread	Nuts	Fish
Raisins	Margarine	Poultry
Dates	Lard	Peas
Currants	Dripping	Beans
Dried peas	Bacon	Lentils
Honey	Pork	Sausages
Chocolates	Olive Oil	Protein food supplements

All forms of dairy produce should be taken in moderate quantities – particularly milk, butter, cheese and eggs. Drink at least one pint of fresh milk daily and replace tea and coffee with natural fruit juices. Milk is perhaps the most natural of all bodybuilding foods and will help you tremendously in your quest for a better physique.

ASSESSING YOUR OWN POTENTIALITIES

Although almost any man can vastly improve his muscular development and general physical appearance through a systematic programme of exercise, it is just not possible for each and every man to become a 'Hercules'. Some fellows are naturally slim, whilst others are naturally well built, and it is obvious that the latter types will find it easier to make the desired gains in development.

The question of height must also be considered. The short man cannot hope to become as heavy as a well-built, tall man. It is a matter of proportions, symmetry and overall balance. The 5 ft 6 in individual can develop just as pleasing a physique as the hefty 6 ft man, but on smaller lines, of course. The perfection chart that follows will serve as a useful guide and will give you a definite standard of measurements to aim for.

How to check your measurements

There is a right and wrong way to take your measurements. The following method is the one used by physique champions throughout the world when completing their entry forms for a physique contest.

Height. Stand barefooted, with your back to a wall, and have a friend rest a pencil on the top of your head and mark the wall in the correct place. You should, of course, stand perfectly upright.

Weight. Check your weight regularly, say every fortnight, on the same scales.

Neck. Around the thinnest part, muscles of the neck relaxed.

Chest (expanded). Inhale as fully as possible and spread the back muscles. The tape should pass around the top of the chest and must be level all round (a friend can assist by holding the tape in position at the back, as it may easily slip).

Waist. The thinnest part, standing normally upright.

Hips. The thickest part, at the level of the buttocks, muscles relaxed.

Biceps. Fully bend the arm, tensing biceps as strongly as possible. Pass the tape round the thickest part and be sure that it is level all round.

Forearm. The thickest part, fist clenched, arm straight.

Wrist. A useful guide to general bone girth. Place the tape round the wrist, just above the projecting knob of bone.

Thigh. At the thickest part, near the very top of the leg, muscles relaxed, standing upright.

Calf. Standing, muscles relaxed. Measure round the thickest part.

Always use a good, reliable tape measure and try not to cheat. Check your measurements every fortnight, and keep a record of your progress in a notebook. You will be surprised at the speed of your progress – if you train regularly.

Good development for men of light build

Height	Neck (in)	Chest (exp.) (in)	Waist (in)	Biceps (in)	Wrist (in)	Thigh (in)	Calf (in)
5 ft 4 in	14	38	27	12¾	6	19½	13
5 ft 5 in	14	38½	27½	13	6	20	13¼
5 ft 6 in	14	39	28	13	6¼	20	13½
5 ft 7 in	14½	40	28	13½	6¼	21	14
5 ft 8 in	15	41	28	13½	6½	21½	14¼
5 ft 9 in	15	42	28½	14	6½	22	14½
5 ft 10 in	15¼	42½	28½	14	6¾	22¼	14½
5 ft 11 in	15¼	43	29	14¼	7	22½	14¾
6 ft 0 in.	15½	43½	29	14½	7	22½	14¾

Good development for men of medium build

5 ft 4 in	14¾	42	28	13½	6½	21½	13¾
5 ft 5 in	15	42½	28½	13¾	6½	21¾	14
5 ft 6 in	15	43	29	14	6¾	22	14
5 ft 7 in	15½	44	29	14¼	6¾	22	14½
5 ft 8 in	15½	44½	29	14½	6¾	22½	14¾
5 ft 9 in	16	45	30	15	7	23	15
5 ft 10 in	16¼	45	30	15¼	7	23¼	15¼
5 ft 11 in	16¼	45½	30	15¼	7¼	23½	15½
6 ft 0 in	16½	46	30½	15½	7¼	23½	15¾

Good development for men of heavy build

5 ft 4 in	15½	44	29½	15	7¼	22½	15¼
5 ft 5 in	15¾	44½	29½	15¼	7¼	23	15½
5 ft 6 in	16	45	30	15½	7¼	23	15½
5 ft 7 in	16½	46	30	16	7½	23½	16
5 ft 8 in	17	46½	30½	16¼	7½	24	16
5 ft 9 in	17¼	47	31	16½	7½	24	16¼
5 ft 10 in	17¼	47½	31	16¾	7¾	24½	16½
5 ft 11 in	17½	48	32	17	7¾	25	17
6 ft 0 in	17¾	49	32½	17½	8	25½	17½

A SIMPLE NON-APPARATUS TRAINING PLAN

The following training plan – or course if you wish – has been designed to promote a high standard of physical fitness and build a well-muscled body. It must be understood that non-apparatus training will never build muscle as quickly, or to the same degree, as weight-training, but it will develop a wonderful physical foundation and a body to be proud of.

Shoulder mobiliser

This will set you 'at the ready' for the more strenuous movements that follow. Stand erect, feet apart, arms outstretched sideways in line with the shoulders. Now circle the arms smoothly in ever-increasing arcs until you are full-arm circling on the twelfth count. Perform two complete groups of twelve repetitions and breathe deeply throughout.

Cat stretch

This tones and strengthens the body as a whole and abdominals and back in particular. From the lower position (see illustration) raise the buttocks as high as possible and drop the head between the arms. Now return to the lower position, forcibly hollowing the spine and thrusting back the head. Breathe naturally. Perform two sets of twelve repetitions.

Dip between chair seats

One of the best-known exercises for strengthening and developing the large pectoral muscles on the front of the chest. It also increases chest expansion and deepens the rib box. Take up the position shown, feet on a chair, hands on chair seats just a little wider than shoulder width. Keeping the body rigid, bend the arms and lower the chest well down below the level of the chair seats. Press back to straight arms. Exhale as the body is lowered and inhale as the arms are straightened. Perform two groups of ten repetitions – increasing to three groups of ten as you become stronger.

The complete routine, with rests between exercises, should take about twenty minutes to perform, and it is recommended that you carry out this schedule daily, or at least four times a week. Pay attention to correct breathing and observe good style with every repetition.

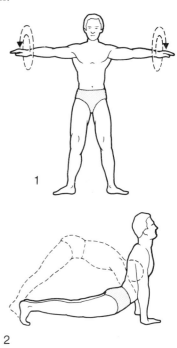

1

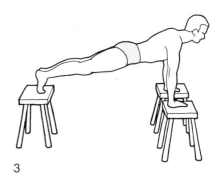

2

3

Squat (or deep knees bend)

Good for balance and muscular coordination, improves the efficiency of the lungs and strengthens the chest and legs. Stand erect, rise on the toes then sink down into the full knees-bend position, at the same time raising the arms sideways to overhead. Return to the starting position. Perform this movement fairly quickly in order to stimulate respiration. Perform two groups of twenty repetitions. Inhale as you rise, exhale as you lower.

4

Pull over

This is a grand movement for deepening the chest and developing the shoulder girdle. Lie on the back holding a heavy book or something similar, with the arms straight up over the chest. Inhale as deeply as possible, simultaneously lowering the straight arms back behind the head. Exhale as you return the arms to the starting position. Perform two groups of ten repetitions.

5

Wrestler's bridge

The object of this movement is to develop fully the neck muscles and to strengthen the back and spine. Lie on the back with the feet drawn up close to the buttocks. From this position arch the body until you are resting on the top of the head and feet only. Place a cushion under the head for comfort if need be. Return to the starting position. Perform two groups of eight repetitions.

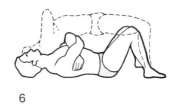

6

Posture improver

This movement helps enormously to rectify poor posture. With the legs straight, bend over from the waist and rest the hands on a table, as illustrated. Now drop the head well down between the arms and flatten the back. Make twelve little rebounds in this position, trying to get the head a little further down each time. Perform two groups of twelve repetitions.

7

Tummy toughener

This is one of the most effective exercises for reducing the waistline and building a firm, muscular abdomen. Lie on the back, feet together, legs straight. Now fully bend the knees and draw them well up to the chest. If you cannot manage to get them as far as that, just do the best you can. The *effort* will produce the desired effects and your tummy will soon become very much stronger. Exhale as the knees are drawn up and inhale as the legs are straightened out to the starting position. Perform two groups of ten repetitions.

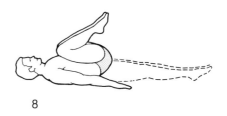

8

Controlled breathing

Stand with the heels about 12 in away from a wall, with the back of the head, shoulders and spine pressed flat against the wall. Place the hands on the lower borders of the ribs and carry out fifteen really deep breaths. Now place the hands on top of the chest and carry out fifteen full breaths, again trying to fill the lungs immediately under the hands. This is a wonderful tonic. Perform before an open window whenever possible.

Persevere with this simple, free-standing exercise schedule and in no time at all you will be feeling and looking a lot fitter and there will be a surprising change in your general standard of muscular development.

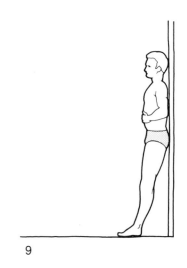

9

A BEGINNER'S WEIGHT-TRAINING COURSE

Weight-training is now regarded as the quickest and surest method of developing individual muscle groups or the body as a whole. It is now realised that lifting weights, in a properly prescribed manner and with a steady build up of resistance, not only strengthens the body, but also improves stamina, quickens reactions and gives more speed in athletic movements.

Weights can be used for a variety of purposes, from remedial muscular re-education to improved ability on the athletic track. The purpose here is to provide a straightforward sytem of weight-training exercises to produce rapid all-over gain in muscular development and to build a better physique coupled with a higher degree of strength and physical fitness.

Progressive weight-training represents exercise in its most concentrated form. The work is relatively severe and for this reason it is necessary to train only three times a week for the first few months. An ideal arrangement would be to train on Monday, Wednesday and Friday evenings. The rest days between allow for the repair and build-up of broken-down tissue.

Progress will be fast, particularly in the first few weeks, so do keep a careful record of your weight and bodily measurements. Nothing is more rewarding than visual progress and you will find that your strength will be increasing very rapidly, too, as you must also keep a note of the weights you are handling for each exercise. As you become stronger, so must you increase the weight resistance. This makes for fast gains in inches as well as strength. It has been said that there are 1001 different weight-training exercises to choose from and, although I have never wasted my time counting them, I am sure it must be true. Close analysis would reveal, however, that the majority of this vast number of movements are but variations on a basic theme. In other words, there are a dozen or so sound basic exercises that will fully develop the body; the rest are just novel varieties of the same action.

The exercises prescribed in this chapter are all tried-and-tested favourites. They have proved their worth and figure in the training routines of all great physique champions.

With regard to training equipment, you have one of two choices: (a) attend a weight-training club where everything is provided, or (b) purchase your own set of weights and train at home, in the spare room. Training at a club is really the best, as you will have a very wide range of apparatus to work on and you will also enjoy the company of fellow enthusiasts. Friendly rivalry will spur you on to greater efforts.

If you would rather train at home, with your own equipment, buy the heaviest set you can afford, as you will be needing it when your strength begins to take on real manly proportions. If possible, get a pal to train with you. You can help one another with some of the heavier exercises and encourage each other to 'keep at it'.

Here is your complete training programme, planned to produce good, all-round muscular development. See Chapter 4 for descriptions of the exercises.

Warm-up

The object of this warm-up movement is to get the muscles working freely and step up the circulation in readiness for the more concentrated movements that follow. Bend and grasp a light barbell with the hands about shoulders' width apart. Pull the barbell up to the level of the forehead, elbows high, chest well up. The impetus of this upwards pull should bring you up to your toes. Immediately lower the weight, almost to the feet, squatting down with the back straight, then perform the same action again, and so on for fifteen repetitions. Do not hold the breath but breathe naturally, through the mouth.

Arnold Schwarzenegger (Austria), winner of numerous major physique titles

Two hands curl

Object: To develop the biceps and other muscles of the upper arms. Two groups of ten repetitions with a weight that can just be handled without undue force.

Two hands press

Object: To develop shoulders, back and arms. Two groups of ten repetitions.

Upright rowing

Object: To develop the front part of the shoulder (deltoid) muscles and the upper arms. Two groups of ten repetitions.

Squat (or deep knees bend)

Object: One of the finest exercises for developing the legs, increasing lung efficiency and adding bodyweight. Two groups of fifteen repetitions.

Pull over

Object: To develop the muscles of the shoulder girdle generally and to enlarge the chest. Two groups of ten repetitions.

Press on bench

Object: To develop the pectorals on the upper chest, triceps and front of the deltoids. Two groups of twelve repetitions.

Single-arm rowing

Object: To develop the large latissimus dorsi muscles that sweep up from the waist to the armpits. It moulds and strengthens the arms and develops the upper back. Two groups of ten repetitions with each arm.

Alternate dumbbells press

Object: To build the shoulders, arms and back, and has a general strengthening effect on the upper body as a whole. Two groups of ten repetitions (five each arm).

Trunk sidebends

Object: To develop the lateral muscles of the trunk and strengthen the abdominal muscles generally. Two groups of ten repetitions with the right arm holding a dumbbell. Two groups with the left arm holding dumbbell.

ADVICE ON PROGRESSION

It will be noted that two groups of repetitions are recommended for the various exercises. The number suggested is about right for the average beginner, but after about a month's training the groups should be stepped up to three.

Increase the weight used gradually, just a few kilos every three or four weeks or when it is felt that increased strength will permit the heavier weight. Be sure to observe correct lifting style at all times during training. The best training kit to use is a fleecy-lined tracksuit or sweater and old trousers.

Championship Bodybuilding
Chris Lund

Chris Lund, who has been a practising body-builder for twenty-five years, is the editor of *Bodybuilding Monthly*, a magazine devoted to hardcore bodybuilding. He is also the European photo correspondent for *Muscle and Fitness* and *Flex* magazines, owned by Joe Weider, who together with his brother Ben set up the International Federation of Bodybuilders, the world governing body. Chris has interviewed and photographed almost every champion bodybuilder during the past ten years, making frequent visits to the United States where so many of the new developments have occurred. He was the photographer for many well-known books like *Hardcore Bodybuilding*, *High Intensity Bodybuilding* and *Super High Intensity Bodybuilding*.

There was a time when championship body-building meant secret, exotic exercises, mysterious routines and magical and expensive high-protein diets. But all that has changed. Now the exercises are the same. It's their performance that has changed and you may well be in for a surprise as far as nutrition is concerned.

What makes a championship bodybuilding routine stand out against another more traditional routine is its method of perform-ance, and in this chapter I will be outlining some of the routines that have been success-fully used by contemporary champions. The emphasis now is: intensity equals muscle growth. It is not what you do, but how hard you do it!

After you warm up, each set of every exer-cise must be pushed to the absolute limit — to a position where no more repetitions are possible. Anything less than this 100 per cent effort is wasted. You will not induce maximum muscular growth. You must constantly apply more and more intensity into your training as you slowly ascend the ladder to a champion-ship physique. Let me be honest about it: building muscle is hard. It is hard even for the genetic freaks — yes, such great professional bodybuilders as Casey Viator, Bertil Fox, Lee Haney, Albert Beckles, Tom Platz, Mike Mentzer and the countless other great phys-iques of our time. If it has been hard for them, then it is going to be as hard or even harder for you.

One way to increase intensity is to group two or more exercises together for the same body part. Two exercises performed back-to-back are commonly referred to as super sets. Three exercises done together are known as tri-sets, and more than three are called giant sets or cycle training. This form of training is hard, but it also produces results and is the quickest known way to build muscular size.

Pre-fatigue method

Another very popular advanced technique is the pre-fatigue method. With many conven-tional exercises it is not always possible for all the muscles to exert 100 per cent of their ability to contract because of the unavoidable involvement of other weaker muscles. For example, when performing incline pressing the work of the pectorals is limited because of the involvement of the weaker triceps. A point of failure in the Incline Press would be reached when the weaker triceps muscles fails, long before the failure of the bigger and stronger

Jack Delinger (USA), former NABBA Mr Universe

work closer to their maximum ability than would otherwise have been the case.

There must be absolutely no delay in going from the isolation exercise to the compound one, as even a three-second delay will allow the primary muscle group, the pectorals in this case, to recover up to 50 per cent of their strength, thus making the auxiliary muscle a weak link again. Once the isolation-compound cycle has been completed, then there can be a rest period for as long as is necessary before resuming with adequate training efficiency.

Further examples of pre-fatigue combinations are:

Lateral Raise Standing followed immediately by Press Behind Neck (deltoids); Triceps Press Downs followed immediately by Parallel Bar Dips (triceps); Two Hands Curl followed immediately by Chins to the front, palms facing you (biceps); Leg Extensions followed immediately by Squats (quadriceps); and Shoulder Shrugs followed immediately by Upright Rowing (trapezius).

pectorals. Similarly, when we work the latissimus dorsi with such conventional exercises as Rowing, Chins or Lat Machine Pull Downs, a point of muscular failure will be reached in the exercises when the strength of the weaker bicep muscles is used up, leaving fatigue, with the 'lats' largely unstimulated.

But weak links, such as the ones mentioned above, can be overcome by performing an isolation exercise on one muscle group prior to the performance of a compound exercise. Carrying an isolation exercise such as Dumbell Flying or Cable Crossovers to total failure will pre-fatigue the pectorals whilst preserving the strength of the weaker triceps. One follows the isolation exercise (so called because one muscle is isolated) with a compound exercise such as Dips or Incline Press which will allow the fresh triceps muscle to serve the pectorals, which are now exhausted. The triceps will have a temporary strength advantage over the pectorals, which will cause the pectorals to

THE CHEST ROUTINE OF ARNOLD SCHWARZENEGGER

Between 1970 and 1975 Arnold Schwarzenegger became the undisputed leader of championship bodybuilding by winning the Mr Olympia contest, six years in succession. A totally remarkable achievement, by any standards. He then retired from professional bodybuilding, although he returned again in 1980 to win the Mr Olympia title once more. Schwarzenegger advocated at least twenty sets per body part and was responsible for the super-strict-style training methods which are still in vogue today. A typical chest routine of his, which you can still observe being followed today by most advanced bodybuilders, was as follows:

Bench Press. Arnold always began his chest routine with this power-building exercise which builds thick lower pectoral muscles. He advocated a medium grip with the hands about 36 in apart so that his forearms remained vertical throughout the entire press. He usually performed five sets, increasing the weight with each set in the traditional pyramid fashion, and his repetitions were approximately fifteen, twelve, ten, eight, five.

Incline Press. Using a 45°-angled bench, Arnold preferred doing his inclines with a barbell rather than dumbbells because this allowed him to use much more weight. The inclines were used to build size and thickness to the upper-chest region, an often difficult area to induce growth. He used the same width grip (36 in) as he did in the regular Bench Press and again preferred five sets in a pyramid system, working up in weight and decreasing the repetitions with each set.

Lying Dumbbell Flying. This was one of Arnold's favourite chest exercises, which when executed correctly is unbeatable for building the central part of the pectorals. He was the master of this exercise and the dramatic way he executed this movement was one of the highlights of the highly acclaimed documentary film, *Pumping Iron*. Arnold often super-setted Dumbbell Flying with Parallel Bar Dips for a strenuous chest pre-fatigue routine.

Parallel Bar Dips. Using a heavy dumbbell attached to his waist with a dipping harness, Arnold used this great chest, shoulder and triceps builder to help develop the outer regions of his amazing chest.

Dumbbell Pull Over across a Bench. This completed his chest routine and was used primarily to build his rib box and serratus,

which are tiny, tooth-like muscles found just beneath the armpits. When fully developed they add those finishing, sculptor-like touches to a great physique.

To summarise: The Bench Press built Arnold's lower pectorals, the Incline Press built his upper pectorals, the Dumbbell Flying built his inner pectorals, the Dips built his outer pectorals and the Dumbbell Pull Overs built his rib box and serratus. Total chest development became Arnold's trademark.

MIKE MENTZER'S 'HEAVY DUTY' ROUTINE

When Arnold Schwarzenegger retired after the 1975 IFBB Mr Olympia contest there was suddenly a void in championship body-building. But then Mike Mentzer arrived with his new training method which he called

Mike Mentzer, who won the 1978 world heavyweight championship using the 'HEAVY DUTY' routine

'HEAVY DUTY'. Mike was an intelligent body-builder who scorned the twenty sets per body part and six-day-a-week training methods.

'HEAVY DUTY' meant training to complete failure – to a point where no more repetitions were possible, and sometimes even to a point where no amount of movement, no matter how slight, was possible. 'HEAVY DUTY' was a welcome relief from those long, arduous and tiresome six-day-a-week split routines. But the new method was hard, even brutal at times, and some bodybuilders certainly could not stand a great deal of it. Still, 'HEAVY DUTY' did cut normal training time in half. Instead of training six days a week for two and some-times even three hours at a time, Mentzer advocated no more than four workouts a week with a time limit on each of no more than one hour and fifteen minutes – a total of only six hours' training time per week.

A typical 'HEAVY DUTY' arm routine during this period was as follows:

Triceps:
Triceps Press Downs ⎱ One cycle to absolute
Parallel Bar Dips   ⎰   failure
Triceps Extensions: two sets to failure

Biceps:
Barbell Curls   ⎫
Chins to the front,   ⎬ One cycle to absolute
underhand grip   ⎭   failure
Preacher Curls: two sets to failure

The concept was simple. The first exercise in the cycle was carried out until no further movement was possible – to a point where you could not move the weight another inch. Immediately you moved on to the second exer-cise in the cycle and by applying the unused strength of this compound movement you were able to work the isolated muscle group even further.

In the case of the triceps cycle the unused strength in the shoulder and chest muscles enabled the Parallel Bar Dips to exhaust the triceps, already tired from the Press Downs.

The Dips took them beyond normal failure and as a result muscular growth was inevitable.

A similar policy was used in the biceps cycle. The biceps were tired after the Curls, but then immediately afterwards a set of regular-grip Chinning was executed. The larger and fresh muscles of the upper back enabled the biceps to be worked well beyond normal failure.

A back-up exercise was usually included after each cycle. In the case of the triceps, Mike performed two sets of triceps extensions to total failure and the biceps routine was completed with two sets of Preacher Curls, again to absolute failure. Four sets for triceps and four sets for biceps was a far, far cry from those twenty set routines.

Mentzer did not believe in doing many repetitions. Indeed, he always recommended around six positive repetitions, that is. Here's what he said about sets and repetitions: 'A weight should be chosen for each exercise that will allow approximately six strict repetitions. Never stop a set at any arbitrary number such as six. Instead, through sheer effort and deter-mination, a few more repetitions should be completed. Six is given here as a guide number, as any fewer than that will not tax your reserves enough, and too many – more than fifteen – will cause you to reach a point of cardio-respiratory failure before one of muscular failure.

'Once you have completed as many strict, positive repetitions as possible, have your training partner assist you in completing two more forced repetitions. His assistance should not enable you to perform these two repetitions easily, but should be just enough so that you can barely complete them. These forced repetitions will be brutally hard and should take up to six seconds just for the raising of the weight. The idea is to raise the intensity by exerting more of your ability. You will still not have exerted 100 per cent of your ability, as you will still have strength enough after the forced repetitions to perform negative repetitions, or a lowering of the weight.'

Negative resistance training

This brings us to the controversial training method known as 'Negative Resistance Training'. Arthur Jones was the first person to really promote the use of negative training. In 1973 he encouraged bodybuilders to accentuate the negative. He insisted that negative training built muscle and Mike Mentzer was the first advanced bodybuilder to apply this principle into his own championship bodybuilding training routine. The result was astounding increases in muscular size, but what did negative training mean? How could you apply it to your own routine?

It is generally accepted by exercise physioligists that there are three strength level positions involved in the repetition of an exercise. These are:

1. The positive part (the lifting part of the exercise), when the muscles move concentrically against the pull of gravity.
2. The isometric part (static position), when the muscles are holding a fixed position and defying the pull of gravity.
3. The negative part (the lowering part of the exercise), when the muscles are moving eccentrically, lengthening to allow gravity to help the action.

Using the Two Hands Curl as an example, lifting the barbell to the top would be the positive part. Holding the barbell in a static position under tension is the isometric part, and the lowering half of the Curl is the negative part. It is indisputable that negative strength is superior to positive strength – in other words, you can lower more weight than you can lift. Arthur Jones experimented with negative-only exercises and he tried to remove the positive part completely.

Using the outstanding physique champion Casey Viator, Jones had two training partners do the positive part of the movement by lifting the weight into the top position and then Viator concentrated as hard as possible on controlling the lowering, or negative portion.

Casey Viator, a leading American bodybuilder of the 1970s

Here is how Jones described his negative-only training principles:

'Up to this point in our experiments we have chosen to limit ourselves to the use of 'medium' or 'heavy' resistance – an amount of weight that Casey can barely hold, or cannot hold. Two or more assistants 'lift' the weight into the starting position and hold it until Casey is ready – then the helpers slowly and smoothly release the barbell so that Casey is holding it without assistance, or trying to hold it by himself.

'But since the weight is so heavy that Casey cannot hold it by himself, it gradually over-powers him and forces him to move. In a Curl he takes the weight at the top and then fights the barbell as it forces his arms to straighten – but he fights it all the way, constantly trying to stop the movement. At the bottom, when his arms are forced to be completely straight, the helpers again take the barbell out of his hands and lift it to the top, the starting position, for the next repetition.

'It is important that the weight is not too heavy. If the resistance was so high that his arms were jerked straight then injury might result. So the weight must be heavy enough to force movement against his maximum efforts to arrest the lowering of the weight – but not so heavy that the weight drops down quickly despite the lifter's efforts.

'We do not count repetitions, but do try to use a weight that will permit about ten or twelve. The set is finished when Casey finds it impossible to control the weight. When the weight starts moving fairly fast in spite of his efforts to stop it, then we call it quits.

'How fast? No exact time – in this case a bit of common sense must be applied. If it appears that a smooth, fairly slow movement is occurring 'under control', then it is probably safe to continue the set. But if the movement is out of control, then it is probably dangerous and we stop.

'How much weight should you use if you wish to experiment with such training? At first I would recommend a fairly light weight – one with which you could perform at least two or three positive repetitions. So if you can curl 55 kilos in good form for three repetitions then use that weight as a starting point. Do not actually perform the positive movements; simply use a weight that would permit such movements if you tried to do them.

'Have your helpers lift the weight into the top position and grip the barbell in the usual manner. Next, have the helpers smoothly release the weight. Then slowly let your arms straighten out. A properly performed repetition should probably take three or four seconds. The movement should not stop, but should be smooth and under full control. At first, if the weight is the right amount, you should be able to stop, or even reverse the movement. But do not stop the action.

'After several repetitions you will no longer be able to reverse the movement even if you tried. And after two or three more repetitions you could not even stop the movement. The set should end when you are unable to control the downward movement. How many sets? One set of each exercise. How many repetitions per set? Ten or twelve should be enough. How many exercises? Casey does one set of each of thirteen exercises. How long should such a workout last? Well, if your helpers can stand the pace you can be finished with the entire workout in fifteen to twenty minutes, or less.'

There was no doubt that 'negative-only' training worked. One look at the muscle mass of Casey Viator was sufficient proof. But the system was impractical, and it was just about impossible to locate two training partners prepared to do all the positive lifting throughout the entire workout.

Mike Mentzer had a different approach. He preferred to perform his negative repetitions after he had reached positive failure (usually after two forced repetitions).

'After the last forced repetition,' he explained, 'continue with the same weight, but concentrate now on negative repetitions by having your partner lift the barbell to the top position for you to lower.

'The first two of these negative repetitions will seem relatively easy, and you will be able to lower the weight slowly. You will even be able to halt the downward motion of the weight during these first few negatives as your static level of strength will be intact. As you proceed with the next few repetitions or so, the downwards speed will pick up and you will not have as much control. By this time your static strength will have been exhausted, although you will still have sufficient negative strength available to complete another two or more repetitions. The set should be finished when you find you can no longer control the downwards motion of the barbell, or even a repetition or two below, since it is dangerous to have a weight yank a muscle out of the contracted position.'

I do not know any championship bodybuilder currently applying negative-only repetitions in his training, but there are many who are using and benefiting from negative resistance. And one of these is Tom Platz.

THE SEVERE TRAINING SESSIONS OF TOM PLATZ

I have observed and photographed Tom Platz many, many times, but am still amazed at the severe training sessions that he forces himself to complete. He is living proof that high intensity equals muscle growth. Platz uses methods quite similar to those incorporated in the 'HEAVY DUTY' system, but his own championship bodybuilding requires more sets, more repetitions and more mind control. One of his favourite methods is:

Descending (or multi-weight) Sets. Descending sets are many sets in one. Using the Bench Press as an example, the trainee performs about six repetitions to failure. Then an assistant removes equal amounts of weight from each end of the barbell. Without rest, the

Tom Platz, winner of the 1978 world middleweight title

trainee continues with this lighter weight until he reaches failure again. The weight is then reduced again in the same manner and another set of several repetitions to failure is performed. As many as ten sets can be done in this manner, but usually three to five is as much as any normal person can stand. The pain from 'descending sets' is quite considerable.

Rest-pause Training.   Another favourite used by Platz which is probably the ultimate over-loading method in championship bodybuilding. It is extremely severe and demands caution, but Tom Platz seems to thrive on it. Basically, 'rest-pause' training allows you to perform a set of four to six repetitions with a weight that normally could be used for just one repetition. You achieve this phenomenon by taking ten to fifteen seconds' rest between each repetition. This enables you to follow with another repetition using the same weight. Therefore, each repetition becomes a maximum lift in itself. As Mentzer says: 'Where is it ordained that one repetition of a set must be followed immediately by another one?'

Putting the weight down for ten to fifteen seconds allows the blood in the muscle to return towards normal. This enables you to exert another maximum effort so that you can just complete a second repetition. The third one will also be difficult and you will find that you may have to reduce the starting weight by some 10 to 20 per cent, but it should still take maximum effort to complete the repetition. The same applies on the fourth repetition and, by now, you should really be feeling the demanding effects of this method of training. Four to six 'rest-pause' repetitions are enough for anyone, Mike Mentzer and Tom Platz included.

The mind plays a major role in Platz's routines. He frees it from any distractions some twenty minutes before his workout, and his attention to muscular effort is always 100 per cent. Training between 6.30 a.m. and 9.0

a.m. allows him to experience a workout free from many distractions. Unlike most other championship bodybuilders, Platz uses very few exercises in his routines. They are the same ones I have seen him do for years. He seems to have found the exercises that work best for him and he sticks with them. He takes four days to train his entire body, then rests on the fifth day. His routine is as follows:

First Day
(Back, rear deltoids, front deltoids, Abdominals)
1. Narrow-grip Chins using V-shaped handle
2. Bentover Dumbbell Laterals
3. Dumbells Pull Over Across Bench
4. Press Behind Neck
5. Dead Lift
6. Roman Chair Sit-ups
7. Incline Sit-ups
8. Trunk Twisting for fifteen minutes

Second Day
(Chest, middle deltoids, calves)
1. Dumbbell Incline Press
2. Incline Dumbbell Flying
3. Parallel Bar Dips
4. Lateral Raise – Standing
5. Calf Raise

Third Day
(Arms, Abdominals)
1. Seated Dumbbell Curl
2. Triceps Press Downs
3. Reverse Grip Dips
4. Wrist Curls
5. Roman Chair Sit-ups
6. Incline Sit-ups
7. Trunk Twisting for fifteen minutes

Fourth Day
(Legs)
1. Squat
2. Hack Lift
3. Leg Extensions
4. Leg Curl
5. Calf Raise on machine
6. Seated Calf Raise

Sets and repetitions are not given because Platz does not count them. Generally he uses the pyramid system, working up in weight then back down again. But he does at least five to eight sets per exercise and sometimes even goes as high as fifteen.

DIET

No chapter on championship bodybuilding would be complete without something on diet. Twenty-five years ago bodybuilders were encouraged to consume large quantities of protein. This was prior to the days of quality protein supplements and the solution to keeping your protein intake high was quite simple: increase your milk and egg intake.

If you wanted to gain muscle size it was then believed that you had to consume at least six pints of fresh milk and up to as many as twelve raw eggs daily. Of course you gained weight. There was no doubt about that. But the trouble was you also gained pure fat. The total calorie intake was phenomenal and the cholesterol level unacceptable. But in the early 1970s the low-carbohydrate diet began to be used. With this system you still fed the muscles huge quantities of protein, but starved away the fat by restricting and sometimes even totally eliminating all carbohydrates in your diet.

The end result was absolutely ridiculous. After having spent up to six months adding all that extra bulk to your body you now tried to remove it by severely restricting your carbohydrate intake. You certainly lost fat, but you also lost precious muscle as a direct side-effect. The current state of dietary practice is more sensible than it has ever been and concurs with the views currently preached by expert nutritionists.

A championship bodybuilder's diet now comprises a high carbohydrate intake, medium protein intake and very low fat. All wholesome foods such as nuts, grains, vegetables, all types of salad, fish, chicken, turkey, eggs, wholemeal bread, brown rice, brown pasta and oatmeal, etc., are staple foods found in the diet of 1980s championship bodybuilding. A typical championship bodybuilder's diet now consists of:

Breakfast. Bowl of oatmeal (porridge), two slices of wholemeal bread, two poached eggs, cup of herbal tea.

Lunch. Huge raw salad (lettuce, tomatoes, cucumber, green peppers, onions, raw carrots), one serving of fish (tuna is the favourite), one apple.

Dinner. Large serving of vegetables (green beans, cabbage, turnip, cauliflower, etc.), one large baked potato, one serving of either chicken, turkey or steak, fresh fruit.

Summary

A successful championship bodybuilding routine is based upon the following formula:
Intensity = muscle
Controlled
Calorie diet = reduction of body fat

The rest is up to you!

SECTION TWO

8
Weight-training for Athletics
Ron Pickering

Ron Pickering was the AAA national coach to Wales and South-west England for five and a half years until his appointment as recreational manager to the Lea Valley Regional Park, and was a former teacher (for eight years) of physical education at Wanstead County High School and Stratford Grammar School. He holds the Diploma of Physical Education from Carnegie College of Physical Education. Ron was an all-round athlete and games player before concentrating on coaching. He was coach to Olympic gold medallist Lynn Davies, former British internationals Mike Lindsay and Alan Carter, and weight-training adviser to several others. He was also the British team coach on a successful tour of the Soviet Union and Hungary in 1963. He is the author of the AAA handbook on weight-training, Strength Training for Athletics, also many articles on this subject and other aspects of athletic training. Ron, married to the former European gold medallist long jumper and Olympic hurdler, Jean Desforges, is now a regular television commentator on athletics.

Germany probably was the first nation to use systematic weight-training, in the preparation for track and field athletics at the 1936 Olympic Games. Whilst there may well have been political undertones behind this preparation, Teutonic thoroughness has given the lead to many new ideas in athletics. Since then the use of weight-training throughout the world has become the rule rather than the exception. In the heavy throwing events it is not unusual to find an athlete spending more time on developing strength than actually throwing the shot, discus or hammer.

The development has not come about merely because it is now fashionable to lift weights, but because much more is being learned by coaches, teachers and those qualified in sports medicine. Even more important is the fact that much of the information gained is quickly spread because of the tremendous interchange of information between coaches and physiologists of many nations. International coaching conferences, wider travel facilities and better translations of important papers have all done much to develop these new ideas.

Of course, every new idea has to be accepted by an authority and then given the impetus needed before it is accepted by all. From the earliest days of the Amateur Athletic Association's coaching scheme the inspired leadership of the then chief national coach, Geoff Dyson, gave the idea just that impetus, and since then every attempt has been made by coaches in athletics to keep in touch with recent trends.

One drawback to this picture of progress has been the confusion over some terminology and definitions. The most common example is the confusion over whether the activity itself should be called weightlifting or weight-training. I still receive letters from athletes asking for advice on a training schedule for weight-training, but *not* weightlifting.

Weightlifting is surely the well-established sport of competitive lifting, whilst weight-training is a training aid to different sports whilst using the same apparatus and often in much the same way. The difference in terms certainly does not, or should not, imply that weights are being handled in some different way or that resistances and repetitions are completely at variance with those handled by weightlifters.

Obviously the competitive lifter must spend considerable time and energy developing the complex skill of each lift, whereas the athlete must spend much of his available time on the skill of the athletic event rather than on lifting.

The athlete's first aim in using weights in training must be to benefit from the effects of the exercises and then to integrate this effect into the more important athletic event itself. Strength is not really a quality that can be stored for the winter and brought out for use next summer in the athletic season. Training for athletics has to be a combination of all aspects of athletic fitness and one aspect must not be divorced from another or its effect can be detrimental.

The athlete's armour of fitness must include SPEED, STAMINA, SUPPLENESS and SKILL as well as STRENGTH, and to neglect one aspect at the expense of another merely leaves a weak link in this armour.

What is strength?

Having, I hope, clarified the confusion between weight-training and weightlifting, we must now try to be more precise as to what is strength and how it can benefit the athlete.

Probably the easiest definition of strength is: 'The capacity of a muscle to exert force against resistance.' Adamson[1] has further defined it as: 'The ultimate capacity of a muscle to exert tension.'

Both these definitions give a clear indication that strength is concerned with maximum performance of one or more muscle groups. Fatigue is not the limiting factor in this expression of strength, but just the capacity of the muscle to create more force or tension against resistance.

This obviously is the need of the competitive weightlifter when attempting a new best performance; but even this is not only a measure of his strength but also of his skill,

his confidence and, of course, the extent to which he has been motivated. A more accurate measure of strength can be obtained by using dynamometers or tensionmeters – instruments which measure force – but, again, motivation can play an important part.

If we want to measure the capacity of a group of muscles to continue working and withstanding fatigue as long as possible we call this MUSCULAR ENDURANCE. This, like pure STRENGTH, is vital to the needs of the athlete, and testing the exhaustion of various muscle groups in activities such as Chins, Dips, Press-ups and Abdominal Curls shows this capacity. You don't really have to convince the steeple-chaser or 400-metre hurdler that his exertions not only cause him to puff and pant, but also cause his arms, legs, shoulders and so on to ache with fatigue.

The third aspect of STRENGTH, and probably the most important as far as athletics is concerned, is when strength can combine with SPEED to give an explosive contraction we call POWER. Force X velocity combine to give power, and a free translation of this law sums up the ability to get away to a fast start to reach the first hurdle first, to lift at take off when jumping, or to accelerate the shot.

All the empirical evidence available shows conclusively that through the judicious use of weight-training we can effectively improve STRENGTH, LOCAL MUSCULAR ENDURANCE and POWER, all of which are vital to the athlete.

Some athletic events, such as middle-distance running, depend primarily on GENERAL ENDURANCE or STAMINA. This is a measure of an efficient heart and lungs and their capacity to supply oxygen to the whole body. Endurance activities such as long-distance running develop this capacity, but even systematic, frequent weight-training has little or no effect on general endurance. I point this out intentionally as some athletes tend to regard weight-training as the panacea of all ills and forget that it does not cater for this aspect of fitness.

Having then established our needs and our

aims, we must set out to incorporate them in a training programme which effectively fulfils the needs of each individual athlete.

A TRAINING GUIDE

The specific needs of an individual athlete can only be arrived at by the coach working in the weight-training room with the athlete, measuring his performance againt his previous performance and assessing his needs from practical experience.

It is quite impossible for anyone to write out a training schedule that would suit everyone's needs. Even a separate schedule for sprinters, jumpers and throwers as I have listed in this chapter can only at best be a guide to the athlete or coach and must be changed to suit the needs of the individual.

However, we can be guided by certain principles in planning a training programme.

How often?

Frequency obviously will vary with circumstances, facilities and time available. It will also vary considerably from event to event, as the needs of the thrower are far greater than those of the marathon runner. In world-class athletics it is doubtful if there are any throwers who do not use intensive weight-training. Indeed, the number of great jumpers and sprinters who do not is fast becoming less, and many who do not use weight-training may well employ other forms of strength-training. In certain events, such as the high jump and triple jump, the greatly increased strength of the athletes has been responsible for a complete change of technique.

Habits in weight-training are themselves fast changing, and whereas until recently the winter or off season was regarded as the time to build up strength, it is now common practice for weight-training to be used all the year round. The emphasis may still be on the building up of strength during the winter, but because there is a reduction in strength levels

during the competitive season, sufficient weight-training is done in an attempt to maintain those levels.

Again I must emphasise that the athlete *must* run, jump, vault or throw throughout the whole year so that any strength gains can be integrated into the skill of the event itself. This is still often neglected.

Also neglected is specific work on mobility and suppleness. A great deal of work has been done to quash the myth about weightlifters being slow, sluggish and muscle-bound. The work carried out by Zorbas and Karpovitch[2] as well as many others[3] has shown that the reverse is true. In measuring the arm and shoulder speed of 300 non-lifters and 300 weightlifters (including champions) the lifters had the fastest movements.

Even so, it is not enough for the athlete to rely on weight-training to produce suppleness and mobility. The effective output of work is governed by the range over which force is applied. FORCE X DISTANCE = WORK. This aspect of fitness, like strength-training, must be systematic and just as thorough.

Warming up

Even the long-established practice of warming up has become a subject of controversy in recent times, with some physiologists claiming that it is not really essential and others insisting that the lack of it is responsible for a greater rate of injury.

Obviously there is need for further research, but until the physiologists can agree it is strongly advocated that a thorough warm-up should precede any weight-training session.

No one has yet disproved that a warm, stretched muscle gives a greater response to a stimulus than a cold, unstretched one – and this is certainly sufficient to ensure that warming up is included.

There is also a possibility that its inclusion might tie up beneficially with research concerning the speed of muscular contraction. It may well be that in heavy lifting, where the contraction is strong but relatively slow, the work is done by a specific type of muscle fibres (red fibres). The responsibility for fast muscular contraction may lie with the other type (white fibres). There is a possibility that if only heavy resistance work is used, the need of the fast contraction fibres (white) may be inhibited.

This is not to say that high-resistance work is bad, but in order to avoid this possibility it seems only sensible to include a fast set of repetitions with a very light weight at the beginning and end of each exercise. The extra time involved would be only a matter of minutes.

A severe weight-training session can and should be very fatiguing. There will be a considerable build-up of waste products within the working muscles and it is these waste products, such as lactic acid, acid phosphates and carbon dioxide, which inhibit the further contraction of those muscles. This fatigue causes stiffness, dull aches, and even muscle cramps, and it can be guarded against by cooling down at the end of each weight-training session. A quick game of basketball or volleyball, or even ten minutes' gymnastics, is ideal, as it changes the activity and therefore the muscles involved. This brings a fresh blood supply to the areas of fatigue, which has the effect of flushing away the waste products.

METHODS OF WEIGHT-TRAINING

Sets and repetitions

Much of the evidence on the structure of a weight-training schedule is empirical, based on experience rather then scientific evidence. However, the work of two eminent medical men, De Lorme and Watkins[4], has had considerable influence on schedule-building.

Their work on the rehabilitation of wounded US Servicemen during the Second World War resulted in the definition and the book of the same name, *Progressive Resistance Exercise*. Their work on reconditioning wasted muscles led them to suggest a training dose of three sets of ten repetitions with an increased weight on each set. This became the basis of the pyramid system which many athletes now use, and it also became a general guide to coaches.

The coaches and lifters have been experimenting ever since with the various possibilities of sets and repetitions and include as well as the pyramid system the multi-weight system, progressive multi-weight, intermediate lifting and super sets.

The most favoured amongst athletes and athletic coaches where strength and power is the main aim is the pyramid system. If the need is for more muscular endurance then three sets of eight or ten repetitions would be used, or such activities as circuit-training or target-training.

The pyramid system

In this method progression is maintained by adding extra weight as the repetitions decrease – for example:

5 repetitions with 70 kg, then rest, followed by
4 repetitions with 75 kg, then rest, followed by
3 repetitions with 80 kg, then rest, followed by
2 repetitions with 85 kg

If successful, the lifter then attempts not just one lift at 90 kg, but two; if successful again, a further 5 kg can be added. It is important that the athlete should not predetermine what he is capable of lifting, but allow the pyramid to be continually progressive.

In the schedule above, if the two attempts at 90 kg are successful it can be seen that the work output is sixteen lifts totalling 1240 kg which averages 77 kg per lift. As the athlete becomes more experienced in his lifting, he can improve the quality of his lifting by cutting down on the quantity.

Thus his schedule may now read:

3 repetitions with 80 kg
2 repetitions with 85 kg
2 repetitions with 90 kg
1 lift with 95 kg

Work output is now eight lifts totalling 685 kg, but averaging just over 85 kg per lift.

Because athletes vary so much in size and suitability in design for lifting – that is, the shorter man with short levers having an advantage over the taller man with long levers – it is now important to relate the quality of the lifting with the athlete's own bodyweight rather than compare two athletes with one another. If the athlete's bodyweight fluctuates considerably during a season, then it is obvious that this will affect his lifting potential.

1. If John Smith's work output is twelve lifts totalling 1080 kg, his average lift is 90 kg. If his bodyweight is 70 kg this amounts to 1.3 times bodyweight per lift.
2. If Bob Brown's work output is twelve lifts totalling 1200 kg, which equals 100 kg per lift, yet Brown weighs 90 kg, this would amount to 1.1 times bodyweight per lift. This means that Smith, the lighter man, is doing better-quality work for his bodyweight.

However, it should be pointed out that in world-class weightlifting it is not uncommon to find the smaller man superior to his heavier colleagues when compared in this way. A major reason for this is because of the mechanical advantages of the smaller man with short levers.

SCHEDULE-BUILDING

The exercises (for full descriptions see chapter 4)

As the repetition of almost any exercise will develop muscular endurance, the main emphasis in weight-training for athletics must be on greatly improving the quality of power. The power we refer to in athletics usually means leg power, and in most of the power-building exercises listed below it is the legs which initiate the movement and make the greatest contribution to the lift.

The principal power-building exercises used in athletics are:

1. The two hands clean and its many variations

Remembering that athletes aim primarily for the effects of the exercise rather than spending a great deal of time on developing the skill of each lift to reach new maximum performances, the following are examples of exercises commonly included in training schedules.

(a) *Power Clean.* This is the basic Clean, which is often the first exercise taught, and is performed without a split or squat under the barbell.

(b) *Clean with Split or Squat.* As the athlete becomes more used to handling the barbell he may learn a reasonable technique of splitting or squatting under the barbell, in which case it can be included in his schedule.

(c) *High Pull Up.* The barbell is pulled high to the top of the chest without being arrested at the shoulders.

(d) *Two Hands Clean from Hang.* The barbell is pulled to the shoulders from a position of 'hang' just below the knees with the arms fully extended.

(e) *Halting Dead Lift.* This is a good power-building exercise as well as being a good preparation for progression in the Clean.

2. The two hands snatch

An excellent, fast-moving exercise, using the whole body and legs, and which can be done without a very advanced technique, although, of course, progress is faster as skill improves. The Snatch can also be performed from the 'hang' position.

3. The squat and its many variations

This exercise has probably caused more controversy than any other in weight-training. Evidence suggests that when squatting with heavy weights in the full squat position, that is as far as one can go down, there is the possibility of injury to the knee joints and the lower back. For this reason it is strongly recommended that squatting is done with the lifter lowering until his seat touches a bench or strong chair to avoid squatting too low.

Because enormous weights can be lifted in this way it is not recommended that the lifter works on a pyramid system working up to a single maximum lift. This tends to encourage bad posture and leaves the athlete vulnerable to injury. It is far better to use a leg-pressing machine, which completely stabilises the back, leaving the lift entirely to the legs.

Other alternatives are:

(a) *Front Squat*. Where the barbell is supported at the chest. One possible disadvantage here is that the athlete has to be particularly mobile and strong in the arms and shoulders in order to support the barbell at the chest.

(b) *Jumping Squat*. As the name implies, this entails a vertical jump from the squat position whilst the barbell is held firmly against the back of the shoulders.

(c) *Bouncing Split Squat*. This is highly recommended for sprinters, jumpers and throwers alike, as it employs a fast, explosive leg movement under resistance. Again the barbell must be held firmly down on the shoulders and the back must be kept straight throughout. The split jumping must be fast and rhythmic, with the fullest range of movement in the legs. It is extremely effective for improving leg power and flexibility of the hips.

4. Step up

Another excellent exercise for building up leg power which avoids some of the controversial issues over squatting. The height of the bench should not exceed 18 in and resistance should be added only when the exercise can be done well and reasonably fast. As in squatting, it can be harmful to work up to an absolute maximum. An aggressive attitude to raise the barbell at all costs can cause harmful postural changes.

5. Heels raise

This exercise is designed to give maximum range of ankle extension and is therefore ideal for sprinters and jumpers. The lifter should stand with the barbell held at the back of the shoulders on a block of wood at least 2 in high to give maximum range of ankle flexion and extension.

ASSISTANCE EXERCISES

Having concentrated on the principal power-building exercises, attention must now be given to exercising other parts of the body. Many of the following exercises strengthen parts which are specific to various events, and although great upper body strength may not appear to be needed in some events, it is essential for progress in the heavy power-building exercises.

Frequently I am asked why international sprinters and jumpers include such exercises as the Press on Bench in their schedules, and I have to explain how difficult it is to clean, say, one and a half times bodyweight without arms and shoulders that are trained as well as the legs.

Like the power exercises, these are common weightlifting exercises used often by competitive weightlifters, bodybuilders and many others in sport who feel the need for additional strength to complement their other training.

The following is a list of exercises used by athletes in weight-training schedules to supplement their power-training, but the list is by no means comprehensive (for detailed descriptions see Chapter 4).

Two Hands Press
Two Hands Clean and Jerk
Press on Bench
Press behind Neck
Two Hands Dead Lift
Straddle Lift
Two Hands Curl
Two Hands Press with Dumbbells
Pull Over, bent and straight arms
Lateral Raise Lying
Triceps Stretch
Abdominal Curl

It should be pointed out that many athletes supplement their weight-training programmes with other forms of strength-training. These may include expander exercises, isometric training, bench weight-training and particularly gymnastics.

SPRINTERS AND HURDLERS

The vital need of all sprinters and hurdlers is tremendous leg power, necessary for a fast, explosive start, and the capacity to maintain the fastest possible leg speed. Power is the rate of doing work. It is the weight that can be lifted over a given distance in a given period of time. A powerful sprinter is not only strong; he is one who can use his strength with great speed. By increasing his strength, the athlete can raise the same weight much more quickly over the same distance in the same time, thus increasing his power.

The speed of muscular movement depends on the condition of the muscles, how well the skill of the movement has been learned, and on heredity. There is a saying in athletics: 'You cannot make a Derby winner out of a carthorse.' And this is true. Some athletes have an inherent gift of being able to move faster than others.

However, as well as improving power, weight-training can improve muscle condition and thus affect their speed of movement.

A Suggested Two-week Beginner's Schedule for Sprinters and Hurdlers

Exercises	Repetitions	Increase	Rest	Times per Fortnight	Target	Comments
Power Clean	5–4–3–2–2	by 5 kg	3–4 min.	5	bodywt	Start with set of 10 fast repetitions with 1/3 bodywt.
Press on Bench	5–4–3–2–2	by 5 kg	3–4 min.	5	bodywt	Wide grip for greater mobility.
Step Up	3 × 10	by 5 kg	4–5 min.	5	bodywt	Full extension on standing up.
Abdominal Curl	3 × 12	by 2.5 kg	4–5 min.	5	—	Back lying, feet fixed.
Squat	3 × 8	by 5 kg	4–5 min.	5	bodywt	Lower to touch bench with seat. Keep back straight.

Each session should include some gymnastic work and also some resistance running, either with a partner whilst wearing a belt or on sand-dunes.

The first six months or so of weight-training, if it has been taught well and supervised closely, will build a tremendous confidence in handling weights and the athlete will then be able to gradually move on to a more advanced schedule.

A Suggested Two-Week Schedule for Advanced Sprinters and Hurdlers

Exercises	Repetitions	Increase	Rest	Times per Fortnight	Target	Comments
Power Clean	3–3–2–2	by 5 kg	3–4 min.	6	1½ × bodywt	Learn split technique.
Alternate Dumbbells Press	4 × 8	by 2.5 kg	3–4 min.	6	—	Experiment with weight, but full arm extension vital.
Press on Bench	3–2–2–1	by 5 kg	3–4 min.	4	1½ × bodywt.	Wide grip.
Heels Raise	3 × 10	by 10 kg	4–5 min.	4	2 × bodywt	Full ankle extension
Squat	4 × 5	by 10 kg	4–5 min.	4	2 × bodywt	
Bouncing Split Squat	3 × 12	by 5 kg	4–5 min.	6	bodywt	Fast, explosive splitting.
Two Hands Snatch	4 × 4	by 5 kg	4–5 min.	4	—	Experiment with weight.
High Pull Up	3 × 5	by 5 kg	4–5 min.	4	1½ × bodywt	
Step Up	3 × 10	by 5 kg	5–6 min.	4	2 × bodywt.	

Again it is very important to include other resistance-training activities. The athlete must not forget to pay particular attention to mobility, especially in the ankle, knee and hip joints. Obviously this is vitally important to the hurdlers.

JUMPING

A Suggested Two-Week Beginner's Schedule for Jumpers

Exercises	Repetitions	Increase	Rest	Times per Fortnight	Target	Comments
Power Clean	5–4–3–2–2	by 5 kg	3–4 min.	6	bodywt	Start with a set of 10 fast repetitions with $^1/_3$ × bodywt.
Bouncing Split Squat	3 × 10	by 5 kg	4–5 min.	6	half bodywt	Straight back and good legs mobility.
Squat	3 × 6	by 5 kg	4–5 min.	6	bodywt	—
Step Up	3 × 10	by 5 kg	4–5 min.	6	bodywt	Full extension on standing up
Press on Bench	5–4–3–2–2	by 5 kg	3–4 min	6	bodywt	Wide grip.
Abdominal Curl with Trunk Twisting	3 × 10	—	4–5 min.	6	3 × 20	Performed on inclined bench with raised feet fixed.

There are numerous resistance exercises that the jumper can use to build up leg power that are closely related to jumping itself. Bouncing, skipping and hopping through sand or wearing a weighted jacket, or even doing these activities with a barbell or weighted sandbag across the shoulders, can supplement the weight-training. All are excellent for toughening the ankle and knee joints and are ideal preparation for jumping.

Strength is playing a more important part in changing techniques in jumping events and it is no longer sufficient to be tall, gangling and springy to excel in the high jump. In both long and triple jumping, similar efforts are being made to 'produce' athletes who can match the great 'natural' athletes.

Where strength is related to bodyweight, the jumpers probably rate stronger than any other group of athletes. They, like sprinters and hurdlers, must pay particular attention to suppleness, so should include frequent gymnastic sessions in their training. They should also include games like volleyball and basketball, which demand great agility, rapid acceleration and a great deal of jumping.

All jumpers should measure their leg power at frequent intervals in the simple standing jumps. Standing broad jumps and vertical jump or Sargent jump are excellent tests of leg power. Standing triple jump and the various standing high jumps demand rather more skill, but are excellent activities which not only measure but help to improve leg power. Successive hops or jumps measured for distance or speed can also provide the essential variety in training, which in turn provides the incentive for harder work.

A Suggested Two-week Advanced Jumper's Schedule

Exercise	Repetitions	Increase	Rest	Times per Fortnight	Target	Comments
Clean with Split	3–3–2–2–2	by 5 kg	3–4 min.	6	1½ × bodywt.	Power Clean may be used as an alternative.
Press on Bench	3–2–2–2	by 5 kg	3–4 min.	4	1½ × bodwt.	Wide grip.
Heels Raise	4 × 6	by 10 kg	4–5 min.	4	2 × bodywt.	Maximum ankle flexion and extension. Use 3-in block.
Bouncing Split Squat	3 × 10	by 5 kg	4–5 min.	4	1¼ × bodywt.	Fast, full split.
Halting High Dead Lift	3 × 6	by 10 kg	4–5 min.	4	2 × bodywt	
Jumping Squat	4 × 4	by 5 kg	4–5 min.	4	1½ × bodywt	Keep barbell pulled well down, keep back straight.
Two Hands Snatch	3–2–2–2	by 5 kg	3–4 min.	4	bodywt	Learn good technique.
Abdominal Curl (inclined)	3 × 15	by 2.5 kg	3–4 min.	6	12.5 kg	Also use with trunk twisting.
Leg Circling	4 × 4	—	4–5 min.	4	—	
Step Up	3 × 8	by 10 kg	4–5 min.	4	2 × bodywt	Alternate with Squat.
Squat	3 × 6	by 10 kg	4–5 min.	4	2 × bodywt	

N. B. pole vault

It should be pointed out that I have included pole vault in the jumping group as the weight-training programmes for this event would be much the same. It is the supplementary strength-training activities that will differ. These should include a great deal more gymnastic work, especially work on ropes, beams and the high bar, together, of course, with skill training or pole-vaulting.

THROWING

Force is the product of mass × acceleration. *Work* is the product of force × distance.

These two mechanical laws are an important guide to the type of weight-training schedule the thrower should do. Obviously there must be no loss of mobility, as this would reduce the range over which the force can be applied. Equally obvious is the fact that the thrower needs mass to produce this force and power to provide the acceleration.

The coach must decide whether the thrower needs a greater number of repetitions, such as used by the bodybuilidng fraternity, in order to add more bulk, but must also keep a close watch to see that there is no loss of mobility.

The very large thrower may not like the idea of doing gymnastics or similar activities like low hurdling and sprinting, but they should be an essential part of his training programme.

Where possible, simple tests of mobility should be given to the thrower to make him conscious of the need not only to maintain but to improve suppleness.

Weight-training for field events has become essential for international success and Fatima Whitbread, the 1984 Olympic bronze medallist, is one person who has benefited

A Suggested Two-week Beginner's Schedule for Throwers

Exercise	Repetitions	Increase	Rest	Times per Fortnight	Target	Comments
Two Hands Clean	4–3–2–2	by 5 kg	3–4 min.	8	1¼ bodywt.	Warm-up to include fast set of 10 repetitions with ½ bodywt.
Press on Bench	5–4–3–2–2	by 5 kg	3–4 min.	8	1½ bodywt	Wide grip.
Alternate Dumbbells Press	3 × 8	by 2.5 kg	3–4 min.	8	—	Experiment with weight.
Two Hands Curl	4 × 5	by 5 kg	3–4 min.	8	—	Experiment with weight.
Squat	3 × 8	by 5 kg	4–5 min.	8	1½ × bodywt.	Keep back straight.
Bouncing Split Squat	3 × 8	by 5 kg	4–5 min.	8	bodywt.	
Press Behind Neck	4–3–2–2–2	by 5 kg	3–4 min.	4	—	Experiment with weight.

During each weight-training session every thrower should include one or two exercises which are specific to his throw, such as the Nieder Press for shot, Lateral Raise for discus, Halting Dead Lift for hammer and Triceps Press or Pull Over for javelin.

The number of training sessions will vary with each thrower, who may lift up to five times a week during the winter, especially if throwing conditions are bad. However, it is a bad fault among throwers that they do not throw often enough during the off season, and every effort should be made to train at least twice a week to improve technique.

As with jumpers, there are many throwing activities that can be used in training which give variety as well as the desired effect of improving strength and mobility. Light shots (3 kg, 4 kg and 5 kg) can be thrown by the javelin-throwers using the same throwing action. Similarly, heavy shots (9 kg and 10 kg) and specially made heavy discoi can be used as part of the strengthening build-up. Throwing with overweight implements will not, however, improve the technique of the actual event and so it should be practised only in limited amounts, especially during the competitive season. It is perhaps better to do a variety of throwing activities which often can provide a basis for a good competition among a group of throwers. These are as follows:

1. Throwing a 16-lb shot overhead forwards for distance.
2. Throwing a 16-lb shot overhead backwards for distance.
3. Putting the shot with the 'wrong' hand.
4. Pushing the shot with two hands from the chest.
5. Throwing the shot two-handed with hammer turn.
6. Throwing the shot one-handed with discus turn.
7. Throwing the shot underhand from beneath the knees.

As well as joining in these events the hammer-throwers can include the traditional Scottish heavy events of throwing the 28-lb and 35-lb hammer for distance and throwing the 56-lb ringweight for height and distance. All these, along with many other possibilities, can provide competition between throwers and do much to add interest to what otherwise can often be routine training.

MIDDLE- AND LONG-DISTANCE RUNNING

In this chapter I have tried to show that the quality we call strength is a very complex matter which has to be integrated with many other qualities of athletic fitness before it can better the athlete. This is certainly true in middle- and long-distance running.

We know that for these athletes there are no substitutes for running itself. It is also true to say that for every Sebastian Coe who trained with weights there are equally great champions who never used them.

Weight-training, even when done systematically and frequently, will not improve general endurance or stamina, but only muscular endurance and strength.

Inevitably then the question is raised: should middle- and long-distance athletes do weight-training? The answer, of course, can only be one of opinion when so much depends on the individual athlete. Some world-class runners already weigh around 168 lb and possess fine physiques by any standards. Obviously they have little need for additional strength and certainly they do not want any extra bodyweight to lessen the economy of running.

But what of the many runners who do not inherit this muscular armour? In the foreseeable future the 800-metre runner is going to have to run sub-50 seconds for each 400 metres to break the world record. This surely will need the strength and power of a sprinter.

Anyone who has run the so-called 'man-killer' steeplechase will tell you that it is not just heart and lungs that feel fatigue, but arms, legs and shoulders that need tremendous muscular endurance.

So the needs of each athlete will vary amongst individuals and from event to event. It will range from the explosive sprinting of the great 800-metre runner to the supreme stamina of the marathon runner, and physiques will vary just as much.

Tragically it seems that it is often those who need greater strength who are physically and emotionally unsuited to weight-training. The ectomorphic long-distance runner often has a distinct feeling of insecurity when attempting to lift weights alongside his shot-putting colleague. By the same token, of course, the heavy thrower does not like to do his endurance work running round the track alongside the marathon men.

The answer, then, is surely for the coach to find ways that his athletes will find acceptable and palatable, for most athletes will agree that additional strength can only add to performance and will never be a disadvantage.

Sugaring the pill

Some middle-distance runners will be quite happy to lift weights along the same lines as the sprinters and hurdlers, but others are happy only if their strength-training is closely related to running. Suggest to the runner that he runs in heavy boots or in a weighted jacket and he will be delighted to add variety to his running. Similarly, running on sand-dunes or

A Suggested Two-week Advanced Thrower's Schedule

Exercise	Repetitions	Increase	Rest	Times per Fortnight	Target	Comments
Two Hands Clean and Jerk	3–2–2–1–1	by 5 kg	3–4 min.	8	1½ × bodywt	Target will be higher if good technique is learned.
Press on Bench	3–2–2–1–1	by 5 kg	3–4 min.	8	2 × bodywt	Wide grip.
Halting Dead Lift	4 × 4	by 5 kg	3–4 min.	4	2 × bodywt	Alternate with Snatch.
Two Hands Snatch	3–2–2–1–1	by 5 kg	3–4 min.	4	bodywt	—
Two Hands Curl	4 × 5	by 5 kg	3–4 min.	4	¾ bodywt.	—
Squat	4 × 4	by 10 kg	4–5 min.	8	2 × bodywt	Weight depends on apparatus available
Abdominal Curl	3 × 12	by 2.5 kg	4–5 min.	8	—	Feet attached to inclined bench.
Bouncing Split Squat	3 × 8	by 5 kg	4–5 min.	8	bodywt	Fast, explosive splitting.
Step Up	3 × 8	by 10 kg	4–5 min.	4	2 × bodywt.	16-in Bench.
Nieder Press	4 × 2	by 5 kg	3–4 min.	4	1½ × bodywt	Experiment with weight. Use one of these three last exercises according to specific event.
Lateral Raise Lying with Bent Arms	4 × 6	by 2.5 kg	3–4 min.	4		NB Additional exercises, and particularly additional repetitions, may be required for building up bodyweight.
Pull Over with Bent Arms	4 × 6	by 5 kg	3–4 min.	4		

in deep snow is equally as acceptable, as much will depend on the coach using his initiative and imagination.

The best results can come only from a flexible training schedule set by a coach who knows (a) the individual needs of the athlete, and (b) the physical needs of the event itself. The coach and athlete must keep an open mind on new ideas without necessarily jumping on the bandwagon of every suggestion or trend that comes along.

The training, especially for top-class athletes, may well be tough, exacting work, but should be the more satisfying for being so. Even so, success must not be measured by the tape and stopwatch, for real athletic fitness is in itself its own reward.

In conclusion I will quote John P. Jesse, an eminent American coach and authority on strength-training. 'There is no short cut to strength development, as there is none for the development of skill, agility or endurance in an athlete. No amount of fancy gimmicks or equipment or adoption of alleged time-saving fads will substitute for a long-term programme of hard work that is required to develop the quality of strength needed by an athlete for optimum performance in his speciality. Greater progress in track and field performances during the past fifteen years has been the result of harder work by the athletes, not by resorting to short cuts and less work.'

This I most heartily endorse.

REFERENCES

1. Adamson, Graham, Senior lecturer, Department of Physical Education, University of Leeds.
2. Zorbas and Karpovitch, *Research Quarterly*, 22, 1951. Comparison of speed of rotary movement of the arm in weightlifters and non-weightlifters.
3. B., Wilkin, *Research Quarterly*, 23, October 1952. The effect of weight-training on speed of movement.
4. De Lorme and Watkins, *Progressive Resistance Exercise*. Appleton, Century, Crofts.

9
Weight-training for Swimming
Brian Crompton

International swimming coach Brian Compton, for many years a master at the City of London School, has made a particular study of the value of weight-training for swimming. He qualified in physical education at Loughborough College with a first-class honours diploma. He was the director of coaching to Middlesex land-conditioning courses and has also been a coach and lecturer on land-conditioning at the ASA Loughborough and the Southern Counties ASA courses. Among the swimming stars he has advised are Elizabeth Long, John Martin-Dye, Sue Soper, Darryl Jones, John Gordon and Cliff Battle.

Various forms of weight-training exercises have been used throughout the world during the past forty to fifty years. At the present time all the major swimming nations use some form of weight-training programme. In order to compete on equal terms with these nations Britain must conduct a vigorous land-conditioning programme of her own. In addition to this, in order to supplement our meagre swimming facilities, Britain must ensure that young swimmers are working harder on land than her opponents.

I believe that we have evolved a much more beneficial weight-training programme than many of the major swimming nations, including America and Australia.

We have many swimming pools throughout the country, but too often baths managers or baths committees do not make any provision for training facilities.

REQUIREMENTS OF A TOP-CLASS SWIMMER

(a) Skill in a particular stroke.
(b) Mental attitude in the actual race and towards training.
(c) 'X' factor – that spark of speed genius.
(d) Endurance or stamina to maintain high-quality performances.
(e) Mobility – the ability to move muscles and joints throughout their full range.
(f) Strength, which is the important factor in speed-swimming.

The last three points can be covered on land, especially (f).

BASIC LAND-CONDITIONING PROGRAMME (1½–2 hours)

Warm Up: Free-standing, mobilising, games, etc. 5 minutes
Weight-training: Mainly heavy weights 1 hour
Circuit-training: Or any other endurance work 15–20 minutes
Mobilising: Suppling and stretching exercises 10 minutes

Should training time be very limited, spend most of it on weight-training.

GENERAL WEIGHT-TRAINING PROGRAMME FOR THE YEAR

Close Season (October–January)

Best results are obtained from three sessions per week on alternate days. Use three groups of eight to ten repetitions per group, with a speedy and vicious approach to each repetition. Warm up steadily until using very heavy weights. Devote one session per week to performing single lifts on each exercise with maximum weights. Occasionally have an endurance session, using three sets of twenty to thirty repetitions.

Pre-competitive period (February–April)

Still work on three sessions per week as often as possible, with the same groups and repetitions. Use very heavy weights during February and March, performing single lifts on each exercise with maximum weights every two weeks. During April gradually reduce the weights, but attempt to increase the speed and viciousness of contractions.

Do endurance work and intermediary contractions about every two weeks; also have a few sessions on isometric contractions (these can be done at home). Have some sessions using very light weights and extremely fast contractions.

Competitive period (May–early August)

Attempt to maintain the strength gained, working once or twice per week. Still work on three groups of eight to ten repetitions. Use the maximum possible speed in every repetition with light weights. Do occasional work with heavy weights when an important race is pending. Have fairly regular endurance and isometric contractions. Still do one session per week up to the national championships.

DETAILED WEIGHT-TRAINING SCHEDULES FOR EACH STROKE

(See Chapter 4 for detailed descriptions of exercises)
Basic work for all strokes

High Pull Up. General exercise and for breathing.

Abdominal Curl. To strengthen abdominal muscles.
Cat Stretch. Mainly to strengthen lower back (see page 96 for description).

Exercises for back stroke

Pull Round Sideways and Over. This is the most important exercise for the back stroke.
Press on Bench, Also use occasionally with the feet raised on an inclined bench, when the movement is beneficial for 'S' pull.
Press Out from Neck. Very good for ensuring a firm and vigorous 'catch' position.
Squat. Extremely beneficial for starts and turns. Use very heavy weights, squatting to a point where the tops of the thighs are parallel with the floor. As an alternative, use Jumping Squats.
Pull Over. Use both flat and inclined benches. The movement can also be varied by using a dumbbell in each hand and working the arms alternately.
One Arm Lift Over.

Exercises for breast stroke

Squat. Lower to the thighs parallel position, using really heavy weights. Also do Jumping Squats.
Press on Bench. Use a flat bench.
Pull Over. Again, use both flat and inclined benches.
Pull Back. Excellent for the important underwater stroke in starting and turning.
Full Squat. This movement, squatting as low as possible, strengthens the legs' drive throughout the complete range of the breast-stroke kick and is beneficial for starts and turns.
Bent-over Rowing. Strengthens the important finish to the stroke.
Pull Over on Mat. Use very heavy weights. The weight can even be bounced off the mat to achieve the required number of repetitions. This system brings a rapid increase in strength.

EXERCISES FOR THE FRONT CRAWL AND BUTTERFLY

Pull Over on Inclined Bench. This is most beneficial for both strokes. Alternate pull overs with a dumbbell in each hand is the best method to use, but it can also be done with a barbell.

Press on Bench. I have found the inclined bench varieties very beneficial. Use the movement with both the feet and head raised as varieties.

Front Squat. Perform with the barbell held at the shoulders.

Pull Back. This is important to develop the pull-push phase in the strokes.

Bent-over Rowing.

Note that the basic exercises for all strokes, detailed earlier, are best placed in the middle of the schedule.

I would now like to discuss some of the prevalent criticisms of weight-training for swimmers. These criticisms are very largely offered by coaches, officials and administrators within the sport. I would say that without exception all these people have little or no knowledge of this subject or its values.

(a)   Fear that swimmers will become too muscular. This is especially so concerning women. Muscularity will result, certainly, if the swimmers spent as much time on weight-training as they did in the water. But two to three hours of weight-training a week will have no adverse effect, even if continued for several years.

(b)   Insufficient time to do weight-training. The real question is: does the swimmer or his/her coach wish to practise weight-training? If so, then both the swimmer and coach will find the time. The work can be done at home, even before breakfast, in the garage or shed, or during the lunch hour, and so on.

(c)   No specialised knowledge. This is up to the coach to rectify. He must look for help in books, at demonstrations, at coaching courses, observe other groups at work, or write to other coaches for help. He must search for the knowledge, then have the confidence to put it to work.

(d)   No facilities or apparatus. The answer here is to make your own apparatus if necessary, or to improvise, if it is not possible to attend a weight-training club.

I hope that this chapter will prompt swimmers and coaches to do more of this type of work; to use heavy weights and to have confidence in heavy weights. Ignore those who condemn this activity. Experts on the subject do not. Land conditioning, and especially weight-training, for swimmers will form a major part of our programmes until such times as we get better swimming-training facilities. When that time arrives this activity will continue to be most important.

10
Weight-training for Wrestling
Jack Ingle

Jack Ingle was formerly a senior instructor and a stalwart of the British Amateur Wrestling Association, a director of sport at the King George's House YMCA, London SW9, and an official of the International Amateur Wrestling Federation. He started free-style wrestling in 1936 after spending a year practising ju-jitsu. During his seven years of Army service he became a PT instructor and unarmed combat specialist. Jack wrestled in many places during this time, and gained a lot of experience in India and wrestled in many British national championships. He was the founder of a famous South London Wrestling and weight-training club – the United – in Stockwell and was mainly responsible for the founding of junior wrestling in the BAWA, which was recognised by the Greater London Council. Hundreds of lads between the ages of twelve and seventeen enjoy serious championship competition thanks to Jack's diligent work in this field.

Amateur wrestling, the most ancient of combat sports, promotes a high degree of physical fitness, the participants raising their standards of strength, suppleness, stamina and mental alertness to well above average.

After a wrestler has absorbed a considerable amount of technical know-how, and is keen to improve his competitive standard, he must seek ways to improve his physical condition to enable him to apply his wrestling knowledge with better effect. There are numerous methods of raising a wrestler's general standard of fitness, but in this chapter I shall concentrate on the sure way to improve strength by the use of weight-training.

In the past there has been considerable prejudice against weight-training as an advantageous method of training for mat men. Statements have been made that it tends to slow one down and causes muscle-binding, but beyond all doubt these have been proved wrong by looking at the wrestling competition records over the past two or three decades, and also by the fact that I have trained a lot more than 100 wrestlers to championship status and more than a dozen or so to representation at Olympic Games, Commonwealth Games and world championships. Weight-training played a major part in aiding these men to reach the peak of the wrestling world.

tler's programme depends primarily on what time he has available for the sport and on the temperament of the individual. A keen man who is prepared to train seriously obviously will be willing to make sacrifices and devote the majority of his leisure time to wrestling practice and additional forms of exercise. The average person from the working class who puts in a five-day working week and devotes two or three evenings a week to wrestling practice is usually prepared to participate in two additional sessions of weight-training providing they are not long schedules.

The workout should not exceed one hour, excluding the changes and showering time. It is advantageous to encourage the wrestler to associate the particular lifts he is performing with comparative wrestling movements, which will serve to stimulate his interest and promote the drive he requires to obtain the best results from the lifting schedule.

To illustrate this association of lifting movements with wrestling movements I have listed a number of examples under five headings: Gripping Power, Pushing Power, Pulling Power, Lifting Power and Bridging Power. All these categories can benefit from sensible weight-training schedules. The lifts listed are not the only beneficial ones, but because of limited space I must confine them to approximately six per section. See Chapter 4 for descriptions of exercises.

GRIPPING POWER

Gripping power is an indispensable quality a wrestler must attain to enable him to apply holds which his opponent will find virtually impossible to break. As gripping is used in the majority of throws and holds I shall not mention more than two examples in which this strength is put to a test – cradle holds and crotch holds.

Lifts for Gripping Power
(a) Barbell Windmill Rotating
(b) Barbell One Hand Seesaw Movement
(c) Two Hands Dead Lift
(d) Zottman Curl
(e) Roller Bar Winding
(f) Wrist Curl

PUSHING POWER

To provide the strength to dictate moves in standing initial hold, for pushing off holds preparatory to making leg attacks or Lancashire turns to get behind opponent. Also to fight from the prone position on the mat to the ground defence position.

Lifts for Pushing Power
(a) Swingbell Triceps Stretch
(b) Alternate Dumbbells Press
(c) Triceps Press
(d) Press on Bench
(e) Press from Behind Neck
(f) Parallel Bar Dips

PULLING POWER

To aid leg attacks, arm drags and chancery drag downs, pulling power provides the strength to take holds such as the further-arm more forcefully, also leg pick-ups from the ground attack position.

Lifts for Pulling Power
(a) Two Hands Curl
(b) Bent-over Rowing
(c) Alternate Dumbbells Curl
(d) Swingbell Curl seated
(e) Chinning the Bar

LIFTING POWER

For all pick-up attacks in both standing and ground wrestling such as double-thigh pick-up, front crotch and shoulder pick-up, near-leg pick-up into crotch turn from ground attack position.

Lifts for Lifting Power
(a) Two Hands Clean and Jerk
(b) Power Clean with Dumbbells
(c) Squat
(d) Two Hands Dead Lift
(e) High Pull-up
(f) Hack Lift
(g) Heels Raise

BRIDGING POWER

Used in both defence and attack moves, calling for great neck strength. In defence, wrestler's bridge position when lifting the back off the mat, often with the opponent's weight being lifted, too. Used in attack with suplex and porro throws.

Lifts for Bridging Power
(a) Pull Over in Back Bridge
(b) Alternate Pull Over in Back Bridge
(c) Flying Movement in Back Bridge
(d) Flying Movement in Front Bridge
(e) Front Bridge with Neck Rotating
(f) Head Strap Exercises

These movements, with the exception of (f), provide the effect of wrestling whilst executing a bridge, as a wrestler is often called upon to do during contests.

Many wrestling coaches teach resistance exercises which require two or more men to perform the various movements, utilising the bodyweight of a partner to obtain the extra effort needed to strengthen the wrestlers. When there are no partners available, then the weight-training equipment is indispensable.

There is a well-known saying that 'the proof of the pudding is in the eating', and in the remainder of this chapter I will deal with weight-training schedules which have been tried and tested. They have been proved to be beneficial to wrestlers who combine them with their normal session of calisthenics and wrestling practice.

The first training schedule is one for the wrestler who prefers to spend most of his time on the mat and does his calisthenics period quite willingly, but insists that his weight-training time is kept to a minimum. He takes it rather like one takes bitter medicine which does one good — real fast.

Although normally I do not put a name to the schedule this one is an exception and is called the 'Fast Four'.

SCHEDULE ONE

(a) Two Hands Clean   6 reps   2 groups
    and Jerk

(b) Squat   6 reps   2 groups

(c) Two Hands Dead Lift   6 reps   2 groups

(d) Two-way Bridging   10 reps   2 groups
    (one group a back-bridging lift;
    one group a front-bridging lift)

This fast-four workout has often served to whet the appetite of a wrestler who has not previously used weight-training for a further crack at this training medium.

SCHEDULE TWO

(a) Power Clean with Barbell	8 reps	3 groups
(b) Cheat Curl with Dumbbells	8 reps	3 groups
(c) Jumping Squat	12 reps	3 groups
(d) Triceps Press	8 reps	3 groups
(e) Bent-over Rowing	8 reps	3 groups
(f) Pull Over in Back Bridge	8 reps	3 groups

Schedule two has increased power without increasing bodyweight after a thirteen week lifting period.

SCHEDULE THREE

Before starting this schedule ascertain what maximum weight can be lifted for two groups of six repetitions for each of the exercises, which must not be altered during the course. But the number of groups will alter, as shown at the end of the exercise list.

(a) Press Behind Neck	6 reps	2 groups
(b) Cheat Curl with Barbell	6 reps	2 groups
(c) Press on Bench	6 reps	2 groups
(d) Squat	6 reps	2 groups
(e) Chair Dips with Raised Legs	As many repetitions as possible in 3 groups	
(f) Parallel Bar Dips	6 reps	2 groups

In the first and second weeks use the repetitions and groups as shown above, with two training sessions. In the third and fourth weeks use three groups, with two training sessions. In the fifth, sixth and seventh weeks

Right: Noel Loban, who in 1984 became the first Briton to win an Olympic medal in wrestling in 32 years when he finished third in the Los Angeles Olympics, trained with weights both in Britain and USA, where he was National Collegiate champion

use three groups, with three training sessions. In the eighth, ninth and tenth weeks use four groups, with three training sessions. In the eleventh week use five groups, with four training sessions. And in the twelfth week use six groups, with four training sessions.

This schedule is used to increase the bodyweight and strength of the wrestler who is light in his weight class but is too heavy to train down to the lower weight class without feeling distressed.

In one instance nearly 5 kg bodyweight was gained by a top-class wrestler, plus a considerable gain in strength. The success he had in his new weight class proved the beneficial effect of his work put in on weight-training.

SCHEDULE FOUR

This is a useful schedule for quickly strengthening the wrestler's upper body and in particular his neck, which in wrestling plays an extremely important part, both in attack and defence.

(a)	Press Behind Neck	6 reps	2 groups
(b)	Flying Movement in Front Bridge	10 reps	1 group
(c)	Pull over in Back Bridge with Dumbbells	10 reps	1 group
(d)	High Pull Up	6 reps	2 groups
(e)	Flying Movement in Back Bridge	10 reps	1 group
(f)	Front Bridge Neck Rotating	10 reps	1 group

These weight-training schedule examples have proved to be beneficial to wrestlers, and are just a few of the many that could be given. But this need not restrict wrestlers to these four schedules. With careful thought numerous schedules can be devised from the exercises listed, remembering to take into account one's specific requirements.

In conclusion I am short-listing some very important DOS and DO NOTS which I trust will serve to ensure that benefit will be derived from this form of additional training.

DO NOT use weightlifting equipment before receiving basic lifting technique from a qualified instructor.

DO NOT be a 'fritter lifter', but follow your chosen schedule strictly.

DO NOT perform the lifts in any other way than the correct one; in this way you will ensure absolute safety and avoid any possible injury.

DO remember to breathe freely during the exercises, bearing in mind to inhale prior to making the effort.

DO try to work out with a partner if possible.

DO put plenty of drive into your work; minimise the talking and get cracking, just as you would do on the mat.

DO remember to fit in two weight-training sessions if you wrestle an average of three wrestling sessions each week, or perform a part of your weight-training schedule each day if you are a four- and five-times-a-week wrestling practice man.

DO adjust your calorie intake to compensate for the extra energy expenditure which will occur when weight-training.

11

Weight-training for Football
Bill Watson

Bill Watson, who was British middleweight weightlifting champion in 1946 and 1947 and competed in the 1948 Olympic Games, is generally regarded as a top-line expert on weight-training applied to football. He has assisted many leading English clubs, such as Tottenham Hotspur, Burnley and West Ham, including the year when Spurs won both the League championship and the FA cup. Bill Nicholson, the Spurs manager, paid tribute to the value of Bill's training by saying: 'It is not just coincidence that we have been successful at Tottenham for the four years that Bill Watson has been with us, as I believe that his training has been one of the most important contributions towards making our players sound in body, mind and spirit.'

Since 1954 I have devised and developed a new and revolutionary approach to physical fitness. This form of training concentrates on the basic qualities essential to good performances on the field of sport and starts from the very first movement to improve balance, speed, timing, flexibility, stamina and agility. As a former British weightlifting champion, record holder and agility coach, I was able to demonstrate to and interest top-level physical-training coaches and convince them that sensible weight-training would improve an athlete's performance.

Looking back some twenty-five years or so you can take as an example the fabulous Spurs football team and their remarkable level of success over a comparatively long period. Just look at their records in the period when I was mainly connected with them and advising on their weight-training. First Division champions and FA Cup winners in 1960–61; FA Cup Winners again in 1963. Spurs became the first British team to triumph in a European tournament and they were very near the top of the League again, along with Burnley, another fine team that I have been privileged to train. A mention must, of course, be made of West Ham. This team won the FA Cup in 1964 and extensively used weight-training methods. Bill Nicholson, former manager of Spurs, who wrote the foreword for my book *Agility Fitness*, declared that my training methods could be adapted to many sports. He also went on to say that my training required concentration and willpower, packed a high work-rate into a short period of time and maintained enthusiasm throughout.

During the football season of eight to nine months I plan a routine to strengthen the internal organs, improve the circulation and develop lung endurance. Also to strengthen the muscles, ligaments and tendons, using exercises to progressively stretch the muscles so that the body becomes more supple and flexible.

I use exercises to develop timing, coordination and balance. Special exercises are used to strengthen the abdominals, as in football the mid-section must have a high degree of fitness.

I have devised ten exercises to develop all-round fitness, agility and strength. The instructions must be followed carefully with vigour, energy and devotion. Using this course for at least twice a week will bring great improvement in all fitness qualities.

Exercise 1. Astride-form jumping with a dumbbell of about 7.5 kg held in each hand at the shoulders. Leap on to a bench and at the same time thrust the dumbbells overhead. Immediately jump to the floor again, returning the dumbbells to the shoulders. Inhale deeply before you leap, and exhale during the upwards jump. This exercise will strengthen the shoulders, increase agility and stamina. Start with two sets of five repetitions and increase by five repetitions each week.

1

Exercise 2. Take up the half-squat position, holding two 5 kg dumbbells in the 'hang' position. Leap forwards as far and as high as possible. Inhale before leaping, exhale as the leap is made. This exercise will increase leg drive and strength, acceleration and add power to the hips, knees and ankles. Perform ten jumps forwards and ten jumps backwards. Increase by five repetitions each week. Make a definite effort to improve your leap every performance.

2

Exercise 3. The starting position is with the feet about 18 in apart, with the left foot resting on a 12-in high bench. Hold a 7.5 kg dumbbell in each hand. Bend sideways to the left and then, quickly and vigorously, bend as far as possible to the right. The dumbbells should swing upwards and downwards alternately – as you bend to the left the dumbbell in the right hand swings upwards, and as you bend to the right swing the left arm upwards. Breathing should be in your own time. Perform fifteen repetitions with the left foot on bench and fifteen with the right foot. Increase by six repetitions each side every week. The dumbbells should remain at 7.5 kg. This exercise will increase the strength of the oblique abdominals.

Exercise 4. The starting position is with the right foot resting lightly on a bench or form, with the arms bent to bring them in line with the hips, holding a 7.5 kg dumbbell in each hand. Change step – that is, jump over the form sideways so that your left foot is now on the form and the right foot on the floor.

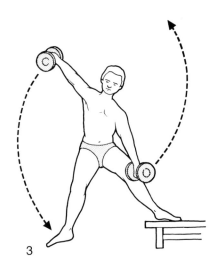

3

Perform the movement at speed, and as lightly as possible. Keep the dumbbells in the hang position the entire time and make a conscious effort to speed up the motion. Perform two sets of twenty repetitions. Increase by adding four repetitions each week. The dumbbells should remain at 7.5 kg. This exercise will increase agility, balance and strength to the leg abductors.

Exercise 5. Hold a 7.5 kg dumbbell in each hand. The starting position is in the full squat, feet slightly apart (heels raised), with the arms hanging by the sides. Holding the squat position, swing the right dumbbell overhead and back again to the starting position. Repeat with the left arm. Inhale on the upwards swing, exhale on the downwards swing. This exercise will improve balance and coordination and strengthen the shoulders. Perform two sets of twenty repetitions with each arm, carrying out the movement with alternate arms. Increase by three repetitions each week. The dumbbells should remain at 7.5 kg.

Exercise 6. Start by lying on your back on the floor, feet together and holding a 5 kg. dumbbell between them, arms by the sides. Raise the legs slowly until they are vertical, pause, then lower them slowly back to the floor. Exhale as the legs are raised and inhale as they are lowered. Perform two sets of ten repetitions for the first week then increase by two repetitions per week. The dumbbell must remain at 5 kg. This exercise will strengthen the abdominal muscles and leg extensors.

Exercise 7. Lie flat on your back on the floor with legs extended and feet together. One 5 kg dumbbell should be held in both hands. Sit up smartly and at the same time draw the left knee up towards the chest and push the dumbbell forwards to reach out for the right foot, then return to the starting position. Perform the movement again, but this time draw the right knee up towards the chest and stretch out for the left foot. Perform two sets of thirty repetitions non-stop, adding four

4

5

6

7

repetitions per week. The dumbbell should
remain at 5 kg. This exercise will quickly
develop power in the leg extensors, the quadriceps. It will also strengthen the abdominal
muscles.

Exercise 8.   Sit on the floor with legs as wide
apart as possible holding a 5 kg dumbbell in
each hand at the shoulders. Then start
punching forwards with alternate arms as fast
as possible. Endeavour to continually increase
your speed in punching. Breathing should be
in your own time. Repeat as many movements
as possible in ten seconds, increasing by two
seconds each week. This wonderful exercise
will quickly develop powerful shoulders and
chest muscles and will also build endurance.
The dumbbells should remain at 5 kg each.

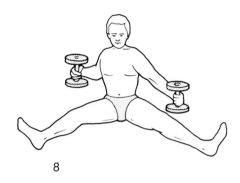

8

Exercise 9.   Stand with the feet astride with
a 5 kg dumbbell in each hand at the sides in
the hang position. Unlock the knees and bend
backwards, aiming to touch the heels with the
dumbbells. It is important not to squat down
too much, but to perform more of a back
extension exercise. At first it may not be possible to reach, or even get near, your heels
without losing balance. But do not worry
about this. Once the movement is mastered a
wonderful feeling of power will be felt in the
legs and the whole of the body. Start by doing
only six movements, increasing by four
repetitions each week. The dumbbells should
remain at 5 kg. This exercise is excellent for
the legs and for increasing flexibility in the
lower back. It will also help to prevent sprains
and pulled muscles.

9

Exercise 10.   Jumping squats is a very good
movement to round off the training session,
and I always use it in all my routines. Hold a
7.5 kg dumbbell in each hand, arms hanging
loosely by the sides. Inhale deeply and at the
same time sink into a full squat. From this
position immediately leap high into the air,
drawing the knees up to the chest. Exhale as
the leap is made. As you come down again
drop immediately to the squat position. The
whole movement is then repeated.

10

Start with three sets of ten repetitions and add three repetitions each week. Rest for one minute between each set. Occasionally see how many repetitions can be performed without resting. This exercise will build stamina, endurance, power, balance, coordination and explosive speed. The dumbbells must remain at 7.5 kg each.

Having prepared this special three months' course for your sport, I am confident that you will follow it faithfully and reach a new peak of fitness. Stamina and staying power are needed in good measure to give one's best in any sport. These routines I have set you are tough and get even tougher as you progress, but this is the only way to reach the top.

AGILITY FEATS

When this course is finished it is a good plan to try out your new-found agility-strength on certain feats.

Jumping between forms. This is one of the most severe movements, in which the student stands between two sets of forms placed one on top of the other. Three forms high on each side is what most of the players I have trained can do. From the starting position the movement is a high leap into the air. In flight the feet come up to land on the top forms. From this position leap back to the floor again. If you then feel confident of your ability, repeat the exercise several times. Some of the Spurs and West Ham players could leap on to four forms. But I don't recommend this without many months of training. Dumbbells are not used in these movements.

Chair-jumping. This feat is to leap over chairs from a standing position. Stand about 2 ft away from the chair with the seat facing you. When you have landed on the other side, turn and leap back. Repeat several times.

Side-jumping over forms. The starting position is sideways on to four normal gym forms. From an initial spring the student leaps sideways to clear the combined width of the four forms. Perform several times, and do not increase the width of the forms until you have the confidence and ability to do so.

12
Weight-training for Rowing and Sculling
Jim Railton

Jim Railton, the Rowing Correspondent of The Times, was appointed the first-ever Director of Training to the Amateur Rowing Association in 1964. In this capacity he reorganised training in three major rowing establishments – Eton, Oxford and Cambridge Universities – as well as supervising training programmes for clubs, universities, colleges and schools throughout the country. Jim was educated at Liverpool Collegiate School and Loughborough College (1956–59) as a specialist in physical education. He held the British junior 100 yards record and represented the country at athletics. He is now Director of Physical Education at Oxford University, which he combines with reporting rowing. He has covered several Olympic Games and world championships.

The ideal oarsman requires the strength of a weightlifter and the stamina of a distance athlete. Add to this flexibility, power, a high degree of muscular endurance, top it with precise skill and technique required to harness these fitness components to move the boat, and the ideal oarsman or sculler is realised. Although this is quite a demand, every oarsman and sculler must work both on the land and the water to develop all the qualities required by the sport. He must work conscientiously to eliminate specific areas of weakness and develop to the maximum all the factors that contribute to moving the boat faster over any given racing distance.

An unfortunate baptism

The most neglected fitness component in British rowing for many years was the development of strength. Weight-training, involving the use of heavy resistance, had been wrongly associated with muscle-bound and slow-moving athletes. Indeed, weight-training as an aid to athletics had an unfortunate baptism in this country and was generally introduced as a form of remedial exercise performed with lightly loaded barbells. One may argue that weight-training is remedial in that it caters for specific areas of weakness in the individual, but when strength is a basic requirement in the sport then it will only be acquired, developed or released through moving weights on the threshold of maximum.

One of the greatest rowing coaches of all time, Steve Fairbairn, advocated heavy weight-training as far back as the 1930s. He wrote: 'Rowing fits one for weightlifting, and so weightlifting will fit one for rowing.' Unfortunately this advice was ignored and it was our continental rivals, some twenty-five years later, who were to demonstrate its value in the training and development of oarsmen. In 1965 British oarsmen and coaches were treated to a demonstration of power rowing when Olympic champions Vesper BC (USA) were defeated by Ratzeburg RC (West Germany) in the final of the Grand Challenge Cup at Henley. Both these crews were products of the heavy weight-training school. Since then British rowing has learned from their example.

Strength era in rowing

The most influential figure in international rowing was the Ratzeburg coach Karl Adam, a former boxer and hammer thrower, who never rowed or sculled in his life In 1956 he was responsible for the rise to fame of the small West German club of Ratzeburg RC, and he introduced new ideas to the sport.

Adam's main training principles were: The application of interval training as used by successful track athletes to obtain peak fitness and racing condition in the boat, and the development of strength endurance on the land by applying the methods of the weightlifter.

His theme was strength on the land and fitness in the boat. Between 1956 and 1965 Ratzeburg won three European titles, the 1960 Olympic title and the 1964 silver medal and the world championship in eights.

The Ratzeburg model

A basic Ratzeburg land-training session consisted of the following activities and exercises:

Warm Up. Callisthenics, skipping, medicine-ball exercises, rope-climbing without feet and flexibility exercises.
Main Lifts. Two Hands Snatch, Two Hands Clean (split style), Full Squat. Use three sets of five repetitions in each of the basic lifts.

Games, additional gymnastics and weight-training activities

The Ratzburg oarsmen trained on three evenings a week and the weights moved were some 80 per cent of maximum (calculated by maximum lift tests). The programme varies very little from this content, but over the years Adam was able to eliminate conditioning work such as running, leaving this factor to be developed by the skilful application of interval training.

Strength endurance

The Ratzeburg oarsmen moved the weights in a manner that developed both strength and

muscular endurance. The barbell was moved swiftly and rest periods between sets were cut down to a minimum. In some exercises the barbell did not touch the floor between repetitions and this really required strength-endurance with the heavy loads which were moved. Adam believed that the technique employed by the competitive weightlifter was the best, and the oarsmen were encouraged to acquire the necessary skills required for weightlifting.

In 1963, the Vesper BC of Philadelphia launched a campaign to recapture the Olympic eights title for the United States. The Americans had won every eights title in Olympic regattas from the 1920 Games until their run of successes was broken by Ratzeburg in 1960. With financial backing from millionaire Jack Kelly jnr the services of a former Ratzeburg oarsman Dietrich Rose, a good intake of college graduate material and an intelligent and driving coach in Al Rosenberg, the necessary ingredients for success were available.

The winter training programme of Vesper was decidedly Adam-influenced but with intelligent improvisations. See Chapter 4 for descriptions of exercises.

Vesper BC Schedule 1963–64

Squat Jump	20 reps	1 set
Two Hands Snatch	5 reps	5 sets
Squat Jump	20 reps	1 set
Two Hands Clean (split style)	5 reps	5 sets
Squat Jump	20 reps	1 set
Squat (top of thighs parallel with floor)	5 reps	5 sets
Squat Jump	20 reps	3 sets

Frequency: three times a week.
Training loads: 80 per cent of maximum in basic lifts.

The inclusion of 120 squat jumps performed with two 15 lb dumbbells nurtured vital leg endurance, and Rosenburg maintained conditioning training by including runs of from one to five miles on non-weight-training days. In the 1964 Olympic Regatta, Ratzeburg suffered one of its rare defeats, losing the title to Vesper. During 1965, Ratzeburg, however, once again gained world supremacy, beating Vesper in three straight races at Henley, Ratzeburg and Duisburg. The example of these two crews has been an enormous influence in subsequent years. The 1965 Boat Race was the first one between heavy weight-training crews. Oxford, beaten by six and a half lengths in the 1964 race, reformed its land-training programme and lifted heavy weights on three evenings a week throughout the winter and early spring. The only alterations from the basic 'Ratzeburg Model' were the Two Hands Clean and Jerk instead of the technically difficult Snatch, the Half Squat to diminish chances of knee-joint injury and controlled interval running to assist condition while training on techniques during the Michaelmas term. Subsequent British crews followed the trend towards heavy weight-training.

Muscular requirements in rowing and sculling

Before listing recommended weight-training exercises some discussion is necessary on the muscular action involved.

The principal muscle groups concerned in moving the boat are the extensors of the thighs and the pulling muscles of the upper back and arms. The extent to which these muscle groups are utilised is determined largely by the rig employed. The longer the slide, the greater the leg emphasis and the shorter the body swing. The shorter the slide the greater the body swing and the less the role played by the legs. The coach must consider this when devising the training schedule.

The oarsman requires a connective strength so that the force exerted by these muscles is transmitted, without interruption, to the blade. Any weak link in this transmission detracts from the force available when the blade enters the water.

The most critical position is the 'catch', or beginning, when the blade enters the water and the oarsman through his connective strength transmits a force to the blade and levers the boat through the water. The 'get-set' position in weight-training – when the lifter prepares to raise the barbell from the floor – correlates well with the beginning in rowing, and massive body movements initiated from this position are ideal for oarsmen and scullers.

RECOMMENDED WEIGHT-TRAINING ACTIVITIES

Warm-up activities

Various forms of callisthenics and flexibility exercises, gymnastics, movement on wall bars or beams, skipping, medicine-ball work, etc. Weight-training exercise: the High Pull Up.

Main lifts

This section always provides most of the schedule. All movements are comprehensive muscle exercises involving the principal rowing muscles: Two Hands Snatch, Two Hands Clean and Jerk, Power Clean, Split Clean, High Pull Up, Squat, Dead Lift, Leg Press, Bench Stepping with heavily loaded barbell and Halting Dead Lift.

Exercises for specific muscle groups

Arms and upper body: Rope-climbing, with or without moving feet, Chinning the Bar, Bent-over Rowing, Upright Rowing, Single-arm Rowing, Lat Machine Pull Down.
Lower Back: Dorsal Raise (hyperextension exercise) with isometric hold.
Legs: Squat Jumps (mainly muscular endurance activity), Bench Jumps.

Steven Redgrave, Britain's outstanding oarsman of the 1980s, having won both Olympic and Commonwealth titles, is a regular user of weights in training

Abdominal/ilio-psoas: Various forms of sit-ups and leg-raising activities.

SCHEDULES

There are many possible variations in schedule structure and the following models will serve as a guide. The schedule is divided into three distinct parts: Warm-up; Main Lifts; Subsidiary lifts and exercises. The selection for these sections should be taken from the list already given.

Basic schedule

(a) Callisthenics, etc., and some flexibility work; High Pull Up.
(b) Main lifts – Two Hands Snatch or Clean and Jerk; Power Clean, Split Clean or High Pull Up; Squat or Two Hands Dead Lift.
(c) Rope-climb, with or without using feet; Abdominal Curl; Squat Jumps, etc. In the above section (c), arrange activities so that some form of anatomical order is followed: e.g., arms, lower back, legs, etc.

Most of these activities start with the 'get-set' position, when the lifter prepares to raise the barbell from the floor. This is as important in weight-training as the catch in rowing and sculling. The performer must be in an efficient lifting position with a flat back, linked up to form an effective chain of action. The get-set and catch correlate in many ways, and the coach should look for mistakes such as seat-showing, lunging, sitting back from the weight and rounding the back, all of which may occur in moving the weight incorrectly.

By arranging the schedule in the (a), (b) and (c) form, the main lifts are reached when the performer has had a thorough warm-up and should be ready to tackle the hard work required for the main lifts. The lifts in section B are best arranged so that there is a progression from the lesser resistance moved in the Two Hands Snatch to the intermediate weight of the Cleans and finally to the heavier loads moved in the Squat.

Alternative lifts are given in section (b) to use when the weight plateau cannot be broken. This also offsets frustration and adds variety to the schedule. The Clean and Jerk, using the split position, is a good alternative lift for the difficult Two Hands Snatch and acts as a transition lift to the Snatch after the oarsman has gained some lifting experience.

Sets and repetitions

For beginners the safe system of three sets of eight repetitions is recommended for all main lifts. The weight should be increased each time the oarsman proves his ability to cope with the higher loads, and the criterion for this is to achieve ten repetitions in the third set. The weight should be increased at this stage by 2.5 kg or 5 kg each session.

Eventually in each of the lifts the oarsman will reach a plateau or point of no improvement. As soon as this occurs in any lift adjust the training dose to three sets of five repetitions and increase the weight only if five or six repetitions can be achieved in the third set.

The experienced weight-trainer should work at the beginning of the season for two or three weeks with three sets of eight repetitions. After this he should quickly work at resistance levels near to his maximum. This can be calculated by giving maximum lift tests in each of the main lifts after the first few weeks of training and then at periodic intervals – e.g., every two weeks or six sessions and continually adjusting the training load to 75 to 80 per cent of

maximum. The training dose recommended at this stage is three to five sets of five repetitions.

The lifts recommended for section (c) consist of both strength and muscular endurance activities and should be treated accordingly.

Upright Rowing Bent-over Rowing	8 reps	3 sets
Squat Jump Bench Jump	25 reps	3 sets
Rope-climb	Test for maximum and set training dose at $3 \times \frac{1}{2}$ maximum	

STARTING WEIGHTS FOR BEGINNERS

One has to be extremely cautious about setting starting weights in the case of the beginner. To start with, he has to be educated in the motor movements required and motor education varies considerably. The coach has to use his common sense, and if necessary some movements may be performed at the start with token weights only.

Suggested Weights – Main Lifts
Two Hands Snatch   ¼ bodyweight
Two Hands Clean   ½ bodyweight plus 5 kg
Squat   bodyweight plus 5 kg

FREQUENCY OF TRAINING SESSIONS

When following a heavy weight-training programme, alternate days are recommended. The oarsman will feel saturated after a training session and will require a full day's rest from the weights.

If the full schedule cannot be completed because of time, the following daily system is recommended:

Day one   (a) and (b) sections
Day two   (a) and (c) sections
Day three   (a) and (b) sections
            and so on

By following this pattern the heavy lifts are included only on alternate days and each session has a short but thorough warm-up.

LIGHT OR HEAVY WEIGHTS?

The accepted formula for muscular endurance is high repetitions with light or moderate resistance. If muscular endurance were the only requirement of the sport then circuits well loaded with weights or specially devised, light weight-training schedules would be the answer. I consider, however, that strength and power are also essential yet have been the most neglected requirements.

The problem in many cases has been the system of circuit or weight-training employed and the fears of the possible side-effects of strength-training on speed, endurance, flexibility and so on. Many British rowing clubs in the past have followed basic circuit-training programmes involving the use of extremely moderate, if any, resistance — and although a reasonable level of general fitness has been developed the basic requirements of the sport have hardly been met. Other leading clubs have employed heavy resistances in their circuits and in most cases have produced the more successful crews at a national level.

The difference between the strength-endurance training and advanced circuit-training may be subtle but is sufficient to merit the extra few lengths necessary for international success. The successes of crews attempting strength-endurance training programmes for the first time in this country are sufficient to indicate the advantages of strength-endurance training.

In advanced circuit-training, weights are never on the threshold of maximum, and muscular endurance is given priority over strength. In the strength-endurance training advocated in this chapter strength is given priority and it is found that muscular endurance increases at almost the same rate when allied to rowing training. One distinction is, however, necessary. Although the oarsman is advised to acquire the skills of a weightlifter, a specific and functional system of training is required. Pure strength-training with constant attempts at maximum lifts becomes questionable. The oarsman must pursue a programme involving dynamic movement with occasional maximum tests to calculate training loads. His programme must involve series of repetitions to nurture a high strength-endurance level.

There are occasions when muscular-endurance training is indicated. Oarsmen with high strength levels but poor muscular endurance obviously require muscular-endurance work. Activities such as the Squat or Bench Jumps for the leg extensors, or pulling movements for the arms, may be ideally integrated into a strength-endurance programme.

13
Weight-training for Judo
Syd Hoare

Syd Hoare, who represented Britain as a middleweight at the 1964 Tokyo Olympic Games, lived in Japan studying judo for three and a half years. He practised at the Kodokan, the mecca of judo, and used the excellent weight-training facilities there. He won a silver medal at the 1965 European Championships in the Open category. Syd was appointed chief instructor of the famous London Budokwai in 1967 and his training methods helped the club to one of its most successful eras – highlighted by producing two European and three British Open champions in 1970. He now runs gymnasiums in London and was elected chairman of the British Judo Association in 1985.

Judo, a regular part of the Olympic programme, is a hard, exacting sport. Judo competitors need great skill, timing, stamina and strength and, as in any other combat sport, skill being equal the stronger and fitter man will win. There are four methods in judo by which one can win a contest outright.

1. To throw the opponent on to his back with some impetus.
2. Apply a strangle or a choke.
3. Apply a lock on the elbow joint.
4. Hold the opponent immobilised on the ground for thirty seconds.

All these cover an enormous range of technique. The first problem for the judoman, therefore, is to develop skill. He must learn how to defeat the tall and thin man, the short and fat man, the fast attacker, the slow defender, and so on.

The traditional form of judo training is 'free practice' – that is to say, continuous fighting with many men over a period of some two hours daily. This type of training is very severe and builds excellent stamina and strength. However, it can be limiting if one does not use many techniques. To develop all-round peak condition the judoman must include in his training running, weight-training and gymnastics for greater stamina, balanced strength and agility.

There are two main divisions in judo – standing combat and ground-work. The physical needs of these differ slightly. In ground-work there is an obvious need for great strength. The movements into various hold-downs and locks demand control of the opponent. Timing and speed are not as essential as in standing work.

Strength is definitely needed in escaping from a hold-down or from an inferior position. In standing work the need is for explosive attacks whilst being careful to defend against the opponent's attacks. In modern competition with weight divisions, where the judoman will fight someone his own size and weight, the stronger and fiercer attacker should win. I believe that weight-training for judomen should start about the first to second dan stage.

With beginners there is a tendency to substitute strength for skill. The stronger ones usually have the advantage in the beginning, but often fail to develop sufficient skill. Time devoted to weight-training depends on how much time the judoman spends at judo. With a full judo-training programme of, say, two hours daily on six days a week, there is little time for weight-training. However, perhaps twice a week for an hour at a time should not exhaust the judo exponent too much. Where the quality and quantity of training opposition are insufficient, then time devoted to weight-training could be safely increased.

Now to consider the techniques of weight-training for judo. All parts of the body are used in judo and some more than others, depending on the techniques used. Therefore, all the usual weight-training exercises are essential. The judoman must have a balanced physique. Apart from the usual exercises, I give here a list which have some particular benefit for judo and an explanation of their application. See Chapter 4 for descriptions of the exercises.

UPPER BODY

The first obvious part for strengthening is the upper body. The two judo contestants stand holding each other at arms' length and in the course of a contest the arms, shoulders and upper back come in for a lot of heavy work. Also, most throwing actions start in this area. In throwing techniques the first major action is to pull the arms into one's body and for this, apart from using heavy wall-pulleys, the best weight-training exercise is Bent-over Rowing, using a dumbbell. In right-sided throwing one arm does most of the work, so dumbbells are necessary, and a fast, sharp movement is essential to simulate the snap of balance-breaking.

With a straight pull it is often necessary to get the opponent coming up off his feet — that is, instead of pulling with his elbows moving into the side of the body the elbows move upwards and outwards. This movement can be seen in the springing hip throw and can almost be copied by Upright Rowing with a narrow grip. To back up the arms' movement, back strength is essential and this can be developed by heavy cleaning with dumbbells. The normal Press on Bench movement is hardly used in judo. When a man attacks he usually aims to hit near or below one's centre of gravity, and to defend against this low attack it is necessary to push the man off — not straight out from the shoulders, but in a line from the solar plexus or lower, keeping the elbows into the sides.

The arms and shoulders come in for a lot of strain, especially in defence trying to push the attacker away. To strengthen this movement, the Press on Bench with Dumbbells, keeping the elbows into the sides and with the dumbbells parallel with the body, is helpful. In groundwork the body can come under fire from any direction, so all the usual exercises must be included, as these parts of the body come in for a lot of work in the constant gripping and changing of arm positions.

NECK

The wrestler's bridge position is not so necessary in judo as in wrestling as it is not essential to keep the shoulders off the mat. Most bridging is done in a different way — from the shoulders. However, the neck has to resist a lot in the form of strangle attacks, and as the head and neck are essential parts to control in groundwork attacking, it is wise to develop a strong neck as an aid in escaping from such control. Bridging and some weight-training work with a head harness are helpful.

LOWER BACK

Good morning exercise, two hands dead lift, two hands clean

There is a lot of pull from the standard judo collar grip down to the ground, and the lower back takes most of the strain. Also, support for the throwing action starting in the arms must come from the back. The above exercises directly strengthen this part. Cleaning particularly helps in developing some of that explosive movement necessary for attack.

Neil Adams, 1981 world light-middleweight champion and twice Olympic silver medallist, presses a bar overhead

STOMACH

Abdominal curl with twist, abdominal curl (with weight)

There is a considerable amount of twisting of the trunk in judo attack, so Abdominal Curls with Twist is a good conditioner. It is necessary in many throws, once one has manoeuvred into position, to complete the throwing action by curling forward (shoulder throw), and when one has great resistance to this it is essential to have strong stomach muscles. The Abdominal Curl on an inclined bench (feet raised) with weight behind the head is excellent.

LEGS

Squat, front squat, back lift, leg press

There are many strange leg positions in judo which are difficult to devise exercises for. In leg sweeps, speed and timing are more essential to the throw than power. In a few of the major throws it is necessary to balance on one leg and lift or sweep the opponent up with the other in a variety of movements. Exercises with an iron shoe, lifting the leg forwards, to the side and to the rear are useful. However, I think a lot of weight is necessary and it is difficult to load the shoes up too much. Squats on one leg will strengthen the balancing leg. All the usual thigh and calf exercises must also be included for complete leg development.

The number of repetitions and groups used depends on one's aim. For stamina, high repetitions are best and for strength low repetitions with heavier weights. I have used heavy weights and not felt any slowing down at all in my techniques. For the judoman wishing to start weight-training I would recommend an all-round programme for a few months to condition the body, and then gradually incorporate some particular exercises to strengthen one's favourite throwing movements.

14
Weight-training for Rugby
John Taylor

John Taylor, Rugby Correspondent of the *Mail on Sunday*, was one of the most distinguished members of the highly successful London Welsh, Wales and British Lions teams in the early 1970s. A graduate of Loughborough College in 1966, he taught physical education and history at Elliott School, Putney, until 1971. During this period, he was also a visiting lecturer at St Mary's College, Strawberry Hill. As a player, he represented Wales twenty-six times between 1967 and 1974 and played in all four Test Matches in New Zealand for the 1971 British Lions when they beat the All Blacks for the only time in history. He also toured South Africa with the Lions in 1968. On leaving teaching John worked in a leading sports promotions agency before becoming a full-time journalist in 1978. After three years as a rugby reporter for the *Sunday Telegraph* he moved to the *Mail on Sunday* in 1982. He has also been ITV's gymnastics commentator since 1979 and has presented other television programmes. He wrote, produced and presented the recent rugby coaching series, 'Try, Try Again'.

When it comes to fitness, Rugby Union players are the least dedicated and least scientific of all athletes. In some cases, even at the very top level, they have a cheek to call themselves athletes at all. In most clubs there is no objectivity in the evaluation of fitness. Serious players, the members of the first-team squad, will go through the motions twice a week with players from the fourth and fifth teams. Often the level of work is determined by the lowest common denominator instead of being pitched to suit the requirements of the best players.

Many club rugby players take part in the game for the social enjoyment they reap from it. Their real reason for attending 'training' is to enjoy a few beers afterwards with their mates. The Rugby Union Clubhouse is a euphemism for the 'pub'. For these players the philosophy that 'We play the game to stay fit; we don't get fit to play the game' is very real. That is fine for the player who has no aspiration to be at the top level. There will always be a place for the strictly recreational players, but to try to put that approach on a pedestal and claim that the game is being ruined because people now take it too seriously is to do a disservice to the sport. It is nonsense to suggest that the game at a lower level will be made less enjoyable because the top players are striving for perfection.

As a student at Loughborough I soon became acutely aware of the lack of fitness of rugby players compared with specialists in other sports. In practical lectures encompassing team games, gymnastics, athletics and swimming we also showed up badly. Living in the same halls of residence I was able to compare the life-styles with other sportsmen because, contrary to popular belief, most of the actual course was spent in lecture rooms and not on the training fields, so that serious work in your specialist sport had to be done in leisure time. It was all too obvious that the level of commitment of games players in general and rugby players in particular did not measure up to many individual sportsmen.

Athletes and swimmers would laugh as we cursed our twice-weekly sessions – they would work at least as hard twice a day every day.

Rugby is very good at hiding behind a barrage of half-truths and downright lies when the question of fitness is raised. The recovery period needed after a physical game is one reason often used to excuse players. The reality is that almost every player in the world would benefit from a more rigorous conditioning programme.

If general fitness is poor, strength work is almost completely neglected. This is partly because the typical rugby club has neither the facilities nor the expertise needed. Bath, the 1985 John Player Cup winners, whose organisation and approach are under the direction of Tom Hudson, is one exception and there are a few others. The absence of strength conditioning is largely because of the myths that have been handed down about the specialist sort of strength, unique to rugby players, which must be learned for the various positions.

Props are generally excused other duties so long as they can scrummage well. For this they must serve a long apprenticeship, learning secret techniques that only come from wrestling with an acknowledged master. Anxious to maintain their hard-won reputations, the masters scorn pure strength. Second rows must similarly spend time developing leg power and upper-body strength in the proven way, through lifting weights, and they also totally neglect speed work. The result is that any contribution from the front five in the loose, the athletic part of the game, is unusual and considered a bonus.

All the claptrap uttered about forward play has largely been exposed by the popularisation of American football in this country. Through a rigorous conditioning programme, the Americans have proved that men weighing more than 130 kg (20 stones 6 pounds) can still be athletic. The latest phenomenon, William Perry of the Chicago Bears, weighs more than 135 kg, but can still sprint forty yards in less than five seconds. In this country Geoff Capes has also proved that big men need not be immobile. I would back either of these two

men in the scrum against any rugby prop in the world today even though they would lose out on technique.

The only excuse that rugby players can offer, with some justification, is that the calendar of matches during the season is too congested to embark on a concentrated weight-training programme. Players are often expected to play between forty and fifty games during an eight-month period, which is why skills as well as conditioning suffer. However, if a player is in the ideal situation of practising twice a week (usually Tuesday and Thursday) and playing once a week on a Saturday, weights should still form part of the conditioning programme. Thirty minutes spent before or after the main session will give an excellent foundation on which to build.

I would recommend a simple three-exercise session aimed at strength improvement rather than endurance. Cardiovascular and local muscular endurance should both be incorporated into normal training. Press on Bench (4 × 5) followed by Abdominal Curls (4 × 10), with a weight behind the neck if possible, finishing with Half Squats (4 × 5) was always a rewarding and very beneficial mini-circuit for me.

But the real work must be done in the close season. It needs dedication because I suggest that three sessions weekly is the minimum, but it will be well worth the effort. One of the great joys of weight-training is that you can measure your improvement exactly; the other is that it happens very rapidly.

Gerald Davies, for me the greatest three-quarter of his generation, and I worked together one summer for a twelve-week period. We managed three one-hour sessions three times a week and concentrated on all-round strength improvement. The results astounded both of us. On several exercises we doubled our weights. I began with bench pressing 60 kg and reached 125 kg. I was also using 275 kg in Half Squats on a power rack. After that it was merely a question of topping up that strength. I am convinced that the summer of

Maurice Colclough, England second row forward and captain, is pictured here working out on a Multigym

weight-training in my twenty-first year was the reason I was playing international rugby six months later. At under 89 kg (14 stones) and playing in the back row at under six feet tall, I needed all the power I could get. Gerald also remembers the enormous confidence boost his extra strength gave him. He had always had pace, but with greater power he was able to ride tackles and hand people off as well.

In general the chapter on weight-training for athletics by Ron Pickering provides all the basic work for the rugby player. For the concentrated period of training during the summer I would also recommend the pyramid system, fully explained both in that chapter and in John Goodbody's one on the scientific basis of weight-training.

The exception is the Squat. Here the weights are so great (or very quickly will be) that there is too much risk involved in going for the maximums for the non-specialist lifter. The schedules for throwers would provide a good basis of work for the forwards. Almost everything that is suitable for them applies to rugby — even the point about using the weight-training techniques of the bodybuilders, explained in the chapters on bodybuilding, to add extra bulk if required. In addition, some extra shoulder and back strength exercises would be beneficial. Two or three of the following (regularly alternated) could be used: High Pull Up, Good Morning exercise, Lateral Raise Lying, Alternate Pull Over, Pull Over, Lat Machine Pull Down.

Tackling always puts great strain on the upper arms and shoulders. Most injuries incurred in tackling happen because of bad technique, but if the tackler hits his man wrongly extra strength will often compensate and allow him to get away with it. Mauling is impossible without good strength in this area and binding at rucks and scrums is less effective.

The backs should base their training on the schedules recommended for sprinters — after all, many of the very best backs are also successful track athletes. For example, the flying Welsh winger J. J. Williams was a Commonwealth Games sprinter. Once again, because of the physical contact at high speed, the very essence of the game, it is a wise precaution to put extra emphasis on shoulder strength.

To conclude, I return to my opening remarks. Rugby players are light years behind other athletes in their use of weight-training, but they stand to gain more from it than most other sportsmen. The revolution will almost certainly not stem from the clubs, so it must come from the individual player. Stop finding excuses and go to it!

SECTION THREE

15
A Brief History of Weightlifting
George Kirkley

George Kirkley has a vast experience of all aspects of weightlifting, extending to more than fifty years, as a competitor, referee and coach. He has won many divisional and county titles and has closely approached British record standard on several of the official lifts. As a referee he has officiated at numerous world championships, Olympic Games, European championships, international matches, British championships and other events. George, who has been a professional journalist for nearly forty years, is a prolific weightlifting writer, reporter and photographer and was a former editor of a leading British weightlifting magazine. He has served on the BAWLA technical committee (assistant secretary) and for five years was chairman of the BAWLA referees' examining board. He is also a British senior coach. He practised hand-balancing in addition to his lifting activities, and for several years appeared with his partner in a hand-to-hand balancing act in variety shows, cabaret, pantomime and other such functions, as an amateur.

There have been so many 'unofficial' championships, so much exaggeration, obscurity, rumour and derision that it is difficult to present a clear, accurate picture of early weightlifting history. However, it seems that the first attempt at international competition was made in 1893 when a 'world championship' was staged at the Cafe Monico, Piccadilly, London. Englishman Lawrence Levy was the winner after a series of tests largely involving repetition or alternate pressing of 56 lb (25 kg) and 84 lb (39 kg) weights with each hand.

From then the picture starts to become a little clearer, although the late 1890s and the early 1900s were littered with a series of unofficial world championships running at irregular intervals, until the International Weightlifting Federation (IWF) was formed in 1920 to bring some official status to the sport. The IWF was set up by Frenchman Jules Roset and formulated the different lifts and competition rules.

Three years after the 1893 'world championships', the 1896 Olympic Games in Athens (a makeshift tournament inspired by a French nobleman, Baron Pierre de Coubertin) weightlifting made its contribution to reviving the four-yearly championships. Only one weight category was held, won by Launceston Elliott of Britain with a Right Hand Lift of 71 kg, with Viggo Jensen of Denmark winning the Two Hand event with 111.5 kg.

There was no weightlifting event in the Paris Olympic Games of 1900, but in 1904 in St Louis, USA, the sport was revived, with Oscar Ostoff (USA) winning the One Hand Jerk gold medal with 86.75 kg, and Perikles Kakousis of Greece taking the the Two Hands Jerk event with 111.67 kg.

Again, weightlifting was not included in the 1908 Olympics (London) and 1912 (Stockholm).

Fourteen countries entered the Antwerp Olympic Games in 1920 (the first after World War I) and the sport was now becoming firmly established. The lifts were the One Hand Snatch, One Hand Clean and Jerk (opposite hand) and the Two Hands Clean and Jerk, and the best total of the fifty-three competitors was put up by Ernest Cadine of France with 290 kg at light-heavyweight.

The 1924 Games (Paris) saw the addition of the Two Hands Clean and Press and the Two Hands Snatch to make the number of lifts five. Charles Rigoulot of France totalled 502.5 kg at light-heavyweight to take the gold medal.

The Amsterdam Games of 1928, with the lifts restricted to the double-handed movements of Press, Snatch and Jerk, attracted ninety-two competitors from nineteen countries. These lifts remained until 1972, when at the Munich Congress the Press was removed following a long period of controversy and the sometimes bitter ill-feeling caused by inconsistent and often weak refereeing, together with interminable arguments between team officials, coaches, the Jury of Appeal and others. This move was a pity in many ways, but largely I blame the referees and the Jury of Appeal who often were clearly motivated by political considerations.

The IWF now recognises only the Snatch and Jerk for the purposes of all championships and records, although many countries recognise other lifts.

The British Amateur Weight Lifters' Association (BAWLA), formed in 1911, recognises thirty two lifts (at one time it was forty four). The most popular are the Olympic set and the Power set (Squat, Press on Bench and Two hands Dead Lift). It is perhaps a pity that the IWF does not now encourage any movements other than the Olympic set, as this restricts the number of lifters who want high-class competition.

The International Powerlifting Federation (IPF) was established in 1973 to organise annual world and European championships and other major events. There was some disquiet about this move as the 'Olympic only' view was that these two movements combine true athletic/strength ability. Undoubtedly this is true. The Snatch and Jerk are the best two-handed movements in weightlifting, but there is no reason why other lifts should not be encouraged, particularly as this would influence large numbers of lifters throughout the world to enter more competitions. When one thinks of gymnastics, for example, at the Olympic Games, with its many different events, I belive that weightlifting as a sport would benefit if more lifts were included in world championships and possibly in the Olympic Games, too. Different events could have different lifters.

The three Olympic lifts which formed the official set in 1928 also brought a new concept to weightlifting as a whole. It made the weightlifter specialise either on the Olympic set or on general all-round strength work. Whereas previously a regular weight-trainer could do well on a number of lifts and also have an outstanding physique, lifters then aspired to top-class performances in one of the branches of weight-training – Olympic weightlifting, all-round lifting or physique building.

This gradually became more pronounced, so that now a decision on what the individual wishes to specialise in has to be made early in his weightlifting career if his full potential is to be reached. Obviously a top Olympic lifter will also have a good physique, but it will not be as good as one who trains specifically with that end in view. Conversely, the bodybuilding star will be strong, but not as strong as one who concentrates on Olympic weightlifting, all-round lifting or powerlifting. The method of training in each field is quite different.

Because of the clash in training methods, weight-trainers, with the specialisation on the three Olympic lifts, began to move in large numbers towards physique contests in which the object was a perfectly formed, symmetrical body at the expense of strength, speed and technique.

The 1930s saw the beginning of the physique craze, but it did not really take a hold on weight-trainers until the 1940s, when the Mr Universe competitions began and the National Amateur Bodybuilders' Association (NABBA) was formed in Britain to regularise physique contests. Strangely, the first Mr Universe winner in 1946 was Steve Stanko, who was also an outstanding weightlifter and the first man ever to total 1000 lb on the Olympic lifts.

The trend, however, was pronounced and it grew as bodybuilding mushroomed in popularity. Such men as John Grimek, Clancy Ross, Steve Reeves (later a film star), Reg Park, another film actor, and Jack Delinger became the ultimate in bodybuilding as they annexed physique titles. During the 1970s, the Austrian Arnold Schwarzenegger attracted enormous attention to the activity. He also became a film star.

Thus the regularising of the lifts in 1928 had far-reaching consequences. It sowed the seeds for the eventual split between Olympic weightlifters and bodybuilders, with the powerlifters hovering rather uncertainly in between. In Britain and the USA this caused rifts between the two sects to the benefit of no one and the denigration of weight-training. The struggle had been largely in these two countries because when the Iron Curtain countries entered the weightlifting field they did it entirely on the competitive weightlifting side.

I believe that most fair-minded people will agree that the former wrangles between BAWLA and NABBA were unfortunate and futile. Weightlifting should be – and is now largely – separate from bodybuilding. The only connection between them is that bodybuilders use weights to develop their physique.

But all this was in the future when the Olympic Games weightlifting really started as we know it in 1928. There were still five class weights. The bantamweight class began with the 1947 world championships and the mid-heavyweight class in 1951. Other classes to be added to make the ten now operating were the flyweights and super-heavyweights in 1969 and the 100 kg class (not named) in 1977.

The interest in Olympic weightlifting really grew after World War II, but there were many notable lifters in the 1930s who are worth a mention. Frenchman Louis Hostin won the 1932 (Los Angeles) and 1936 (Berlin) light-heavyweight crowns, setting Olympic Games' records in the process.

The Egyptians performed well in this period, especially at the 1936 Games, with lightweight Mohammed Mesbah and middleweight Khadr el Touni capturing gold medals and other awards by placing second and third at featherweight and third at light-heavyweight. This did not please the Germans, who were looking for gold medals to give another polish to the rampant swastika, but they had to settle for only one gold (Joseph Manger in the heavyweight class) and four other place medals.

One interesting winner in Los Angeles was Jaroslav Skobla of Czechoslovakia, who took the heavyweight title. His son Jiri was to become Europe's leading shot-putter during the 1950s. Juroslav's compatriot, Vaclav Psenicka, won silver medals in the heavyweight class in both Los Angeles and Berlin. He also had a son who was good enough to compete in world championships.

Ron Walker was Britain's leading competitor in this period and undoubtedly one of our greatest-ever lifters, not only on the Olympic lifts but on most of the others, too. He held a majority of the British records on the wide range of lifts then recognised – forty two.

Although Walker lifted at heavyweight for the majority of his career, most times he weighed little more than 90 kg and had this class been operating then there is little doubt that he would have been world champion at that weight. Walker died tragically in the late 1940s at only forty one.

Although, as I said earlier, Egypt enjoyed great success in the 1936 Olympics, they were more prominent in the 1940s. Men like featherweight Mahmoud Fayad (Olympic champion and twice world champion), Touni (whom I remember watching in many tense encounters with the USA's Pete George) and lightweights Ibrahim Shams and Attia Hamouda were probably the best in this era. Shams was reputed to be the world's fastest-moving lifter. One wag commented he moved

One of the fastest-ever Olympic weightlifters, Ibrahim Shams of Egypt, former world and Olympic champion

so quickly that at night he switched off the light and was in bed before the room was dark.

Since World War II, but particularly in the past two or three decades, lifting standards have risen tremendously. One major reason is the increasing number of countries competing in major championships. Another is the more intensive and scientific training by many of the leading nations. And, of course, there are the drugs, which I will discuss later.

The European Eastern Bloc countries have particularly benefited from this need for greater concentration on preparation. They have established careful medical control over their lifters and been able to assist competitors on a larger scale than has been possible in democratic countries. Also they have financially aided lifters, who rarely have been distracted from their duty to represent their country at sport by the need to earn money.

Success in international lifting has, therefore, steadily become the prerogative of the Communist countries. Thus, in 1946, when the world championships were resumed in Paris, with the Soviet Union being the sole representatives, they took five of the possible fifteen medals. In 1975 the Communist countries won twenty three of the possible twenty seven. Nor is this statistic a gross exception. At the 1976 Olympic Games there were only five medallists who were not members of the Eastern European states.

The Soviet Union was usually dominant until recent years, when Bulgaria began pressing hard for a bigger share of the honours. The Soviet Union's vast population, facilities and inclination for big periods of the year to practise indoor sports because of the weather, has resulted in considerable depth in most of the weight classes. Official figures released in 1984 showed that the Soviets had 330,000 competitive lifters, 7,500 coaches and thousands of voluntary instructors. Only three times has the Soviet Union been beaten in team championships at world meetings (official) and Olympic Games (unofficial) – in 1965 by Poland and in 1972 and 1985 by Bulgaria.

It has been in the heaviest division that the Soviet Union's status has been renowned. But for many years the USA excelled. John Davis, who most times weighed only around 105 kg, won every title from 1946 to 1952. In 1949, despite his small hands, he lifted the famous Apollon railway wheels connected by a two-inch-thick axle weighing 165 kg, only previously lifted by Apollon himself in the 1890s and another Frenchman, Charles Rigoulot. Another American who cleaned and jerked the wheels was Norbert Schemansky (he made three repetitions from the shoulders). Schemansky won a record four Olympic medals, although he missed the 1956 Games because of a severe back injury. He was the 1954 world heavyweight champion and a bronze medallist in this category in the 1964 Olympics.

Schemansky was succeeded by Paul Anderson, whose colossal build of 165 kg pre-empted the massive physiques of super-heavyweights in the 1970s. Before retiring, initially to perform in night clubs and subsequently promoting Christianity and doing a lot of work for boys' clubs, he was the 1956 Olympic champion after winning the world title in the previous year.

Since 1956 the Soviet Union has only four times lost the distinction of possessing the 'World's Strongest Man' – in 1969, when Leonid Zhabotinsky was off form, supposedly through injury, and relinquished the first super-heavyweight title, on its introduction, to the USA's Joe Dube; in 1978, when Vasily Alexeev had to retire injured to leave the title in the grip of Jurgen Heuser of East Germany; in 1984, when the Soviets did not compete in Los Angeles; and in 1985, when the Bulgarian Antonio Krastev pushed the two Soviet lifters into second and fourth places.

The first of these great Soviets was Yuri Vlasov, Olympic and world champion from 1959 to 1963 and the first man to clean and jerk 200 kg, in 1960. Vlasov, a bespectacled, studious man, a qualified engineer and with a genuine interest in philosophy, had a collection of short stories published – probably because of his standing rather than because they contained any literary merit. He lost the 1964 Olympic crown to Zhabotinsky, whose unusual strength was first apparent as a schoolboy when he hurled to the ground a pedigree bull weighing half a ton.

'Zhabo' was given to clutching his back as if in pain early in the competition. But on completing the winning lift, his face would dissolve in an enormous smile, the pain seemingly forgotten.

Alexeev took the world title in 1970, when he also became the first man to clean and jerk 500 lb, and subsequently completed a series of eight consecutive victories in Olympic Games and world championships. He broke eighty world records in his career. Only the Americans John Davis and Tommy Kono approached Alexeev's record of invincibility in any category of the sport since World War II.

In the other weight divisions the Soviet Union has been almost as consistently formidable. One man who has had enormous influence in the Soviet Union, both as a lifter and a coach, is Dr Arcady Vorobyev, formerly a deep-sea diver in the Black Sea Fleet. He was a splendidly successful lifter, twice Olympic and four times world champion at light-heavyweight and mid-heavyweight, and subsequently appointed chief coach of the Soviet Federation. He is also a respected author of many books on the sport. Vorobyev's contemporaries included the late Gregori Novak, perhaps the first of the Soviet Union's outstanding representatives. I well remember him enthralling the vast audience in 1946 at the Paris world championships on my first visit to such a competition. Trofim Lomakin was another, who initially attracted attention by throwing a grenade a record seventy metres when a young airman during the War. There was also Rudy Plyukfelder, a Soviet of German extraction who was initially banned from exercising because of a heart disease, but trained himself to win both the world and Olympic light-heavyweight crowns.

Only an injury sustained the day before the event prevented him from winning another Olympic gold medal in 1960.

Among the lighter men worthy of mention were the brilliant featherweight pair, Ivan Udodov and Raphael Chimiskyan, lightweights Nikolai Kostilev (one of the finest, fastest snatchers I have ever seen) and Vladimir Kaplunov, middleweight Victor Kurentsov, and bantamweight Vladimir Stogov, who won five world and six European titles between 1955 and 1961.

In recent years, perhaps the most colourful and popular Soviet competitor has been mid-heavyweight David Rigert, who was coached by Plyukfelder. After winning the 1971 European and world championships, he was a firm favourite for the 1972 Olympic title. But he failed with all his Snatches and was eliminated.

Rigert went quite berserk after his failures, literally tearing his hair out and beating his head against a wall. It took all the might of the Soviet coaches and trainers to subdue Rigert and give him a sedative. On awakening he went berserk again, so terrible was his grief, and was finally sent home. In 1977, when he was in a Soviet training camp, he became drunk and was involved in a brawl, subsequently taken into custody and banned from competing for a year.

It is said that lightning never strikes twice in the same spot, but Rigert proved this wrong. After he had got the Munich failures out of his system by winning the 1976 Montreal gold medal and breaking world records following his 1977 suspension, he was struck again at the 1980 Moscow Games when once more he failed with all his Snatches – almost ending a bizarre, colourful career in ignominious fashion. But despite all his troubles, he was generally accepted as 'the lifters' lifter' and was a most popular figure on the world's lifting platforms.

During the 1960s the Poles were particularly prominent. Ireneusz Palinski, Olympic light-heavyweight and world mid-heavyweight champion; lightweights Marian Zelinski and

Zbigniew Kaczmarek; flyweight Zygmunt Smalcerz; light-heavyweight Norbert Ozimek; all were magnificent competitors. But for most weightlifting enthusiasts their finest lifter – and one of the most accomplished of all time – was lightweight Waldemar Baszanowski. His epic contests with Zielinski and the Soviets Kaplunov and Lopatin were as exciting a series of events as any in this period.

Baszanowski's slim build – he could amost have been mistaken for a gymnast – and technical proficiency made him a distinguished figure in the sport. If the general public preferred Vlasov and Zhabotinsky during this era, weightlifters invariably admired Baszanoski far more. He won two Olympic and three world titles with his neat, fast style and tremendous pulling power.

It was Bulgaria who were to make an even greater contribution than Poland to the development of the sport. They discovered that the body did not need two days' rest between heavy training sessions, as had hitherto been accepted. Their lifters began training daily and then twice a day. At the 1972 Olympic Games Bulgaria caused one of the biggest upsets in the sport by defeating the Soviet Union in the unofficial team contest. They maintained their status by producing even more lifters of international distinction – men like Nedelcho Kolev, Khristo Plachkov and the staggeringly precocious Valentin Khristov, who at the world junior championships in 1975 broke eighteen World records – all the junior and senior Bulgarian, European and world records. Khristov won the 1976 Olympic heavyweight title with a 400 kg total, only to have his gold medal taken away when a dope test for anabolic steroids proved positive. Seven other lifters at these Games were disqualified, including Kaczmarek, winner of the lightweight category.

Although there had been massive disqualificatios at the 1970 world championships, these resulted from tests for stimulants. The 1976 disqualifications were for steroids, the body-building drug, which everyone knew many competitors had been taking for some years.

Although four Communist lifters were disqualified in Montreal, the other three were from Western countries who were desperately trying to keep up with the improvement of competitors from Eastern Europe. Two of them were from the USA, who probably more than any other nation were distressed at the supremacy of the Iron Curtain countries. The USA had been world team champions from 1938 to 1953 and during the 1950s had a series of fascinatingly close contests with the Soviet Union. But they have never subsequently enjoyed the eminence they had during this era, with their number of phenomenal heavyweights; Stan Stanczyk, who became the first man to win three successive world titles at different bodyweights; middleweight Pete George; featherweight Ike Berger and, above them all, the extraordinary Tommy Kono.

The Americans have never replaced Kono who, between 1952 and 1959, was invincible in Olympic Games and world championships. Not since then has the USA had a competitor who was indisputably the best lifter in a category. Kono was the only lifter in history to set world records in four different weight divisions. His ability to rise to the occasion, despite some comparatively indifferent training achievements and his amazing strength of body and mind, gave him a long run of triumphs.

The one non-Communist country to be consistently among the highest places in the lighter divisions has been Japan. Her most famous lifters were the two brothers, Yoshinobu and Yoshiyuki Miyake, who both took world titles. Yoshinobu was also twice Olympic featherweight gold medallist. Another country to enjoy success has been Iran, ranging from Mahmoud Namdjou in the

Above right: Tommy Kono (USA) – eight times world or Olympic champion and one of the greatest-ever weightlifters

Below right: Yoshinobu Miyake (Japan), former world and Olympic champion

late 1940s and early 1950s to Mohammad Nassiri in the 1960s and 1970s.

In more recent years the Soviet Union and Bulgaria have largely dominated the scene with a long series of battles for team supremacy, throwing up such outstanding lifters as Yurik Vardanyan (who broke five world records in the 1980 Olympic Games), Sultan Rakhmanov and Anatoli Pisarenko for the Soviet Union; Stefan Topurov (who became the first lifter to clean and jerk three times bodyweight), Mincho Pachov, Blagoi Blagoev, Neno Terzi-iski, Yanko Rusev and the latest discovery Naum Shalamanov, who was breaking junior and senior world records in his middle-teens and became senior featherweight world champion in 1985 at only eighteen, for Bulgaria. At most world championships it has been the Soviets and the Bulgars providing the main battles, with the rest of the world nowhere.

Rakhmanov was the first successor to Alexeev who, after being semi-retired for almost a year, strode off the platform at the 1980 Olympic Games jeered by some of his own countrymen after he had 'done a Rigert' by failing with all his Snatches. This was a sorry sight, only emphasising the terrible mistake it was to bring back Alexeev into the limelight when obviously he was not in good condition.

Rakhmanov won the world title in 1979 and the Olympic crown in 1980, but his place as the Soviet number one was taken by an exciting, stream-lined super-heavyweight of only around 121 kg, Pisarenko, who took world titles in 1981, 1982 and 1983 before getting a life-ban in 1985 for dealing in steroids.

Rusev, at only eighteen, broke the feather-weight junior and senior world records on the Jerk at his first appearance in the 1977 world championships and took the silver medal in the total. He subsequently had a good run of successes at lightweight and middleweight before retiring in 1984 to become one of Bulgaria's leading coaches.

The British Commonwealth has rarely been able to challenge the Eastern Europeans, although Canadian Doug Hepburn brought off a major upset in 1953 to defeat John Davis for the world heavyweight title, despite being handicapped by having a club foot and with-ered right leg. But he did not compete again at this level.

Louis Martin, who was born in Jamaica but later represented Britain, had a longer career. He took four world mid-heavyweight titles and Olympic silver and bronze medals in a series of performances that inspired everyone who saw him. A charming, immensely friendly man, given to sudden explosions of enthusiasm and happiness, Martin retired in 1970 after winning his third successive Commonwealth Games title. Unfortunately, the Common-wealth has never produced anyone else of similar calibre, although we do have some good performers in Australia, Canada, and particularly Britain.

Here, we have many young lifters who have mainly risen from the schoolboy ranks and have put up some creditable performances in Olympic Games, world and European cham-pionships and Commonwealth Games – men like Dean Willey, Dave Morgan, Newton Burrowes, Dave Mercer and the Pinsent brothers, Steve and Peter, to mention just a few.

Australia actually provided an Olympic Games gold medallist in Dean Lukin, who won the super-heavyweight class in 1984, whilst Australian Robert Kabbas took the silver medal in the light-heavyweight class at the same meeting.

British lifters did particularly well in Los Angeles, with Mercer winning a bronze at mid-heavyweight and Willey (lightweight), Morgan (middleweight) and Burrowes (light-heavy-weight) taking fourth places. Canadian Jacques Demers won the silver medal at middleweight.

Some people have said that the absence of the Soviet Union, together with other Eastern European countries who supported the Soviets in their boycott, made it a lot easier for some of the lesser lights to win medals. This is, of course, perfectly true. But remember that these medallists went to Los Angeles to take on the opposition and were worthy successes on the day. They did all that could be expected of them, so we must give them full credit for that.

So all in all, the standard of Commonwealth lifting is fairly solid these days, even though the prospect of unearthing another Louis Martin might not be very bright.

CAN WE BEAT THE DRUGS PROBLEM?

The biggest blot on the pages of weightlifting history is, of course, the widespread drug abuse. It is common knowledge that a lot (even most) of the world's top lifters and a good proportion of the lesser ones, too, take drugs of some kind to boost their performances.

The first real scare at world championships came in 1970 when several competitors were found guilty of taking amphetamines (short-term pep drugs) and were disqualified. At the 1976 Olympic Games eight were disqualified for taking anabolic steroids. But drug-taking had been going on for a long time before 1970 and over the years has grown into what can only be described as sordid, disgraceful and heart-breaking for those of us 'old fashioned'

enough to regard sport as something pleasant, relaxing and, above all, HONEST.

It now seems that some countries have discovered means of beating drugs tests carried out at major championships and many other events. Certainly the current rate of detection is very low. At the 1980 Olympic Games, for example, there was not one positive test, although few people will believe that all competitors were 'clean'.

The difficulty in detecting the use of drugs has been of advantage to those countries prepared to support medical research to discover ways of avoiding detection. Those who have adopted a strictly ethical line have been at a great disadvantage, even though morally they are right.

If sport is to return to its natural state, with progress and performance standards governed by hard training, dedication and other legitimate aids, then somehow the drugs problem has to be solved. Those people, whoever they are, who discover new drugs, with ways of avoiding detection, from time to time and those who make them available to athletes (the 'pushers') have a lot to answer for.

Our only hope seems to be that the scientists and chemists will eventually produce a formula that will stamp out this practice once and for all.

16
Olympic Weightlifting for Beginners
George Kirkley

Although competitive weightlifting is firmly established as a regular part of the Olympic Games programme and is practised in considerably more than a hundred countries, here in Britain it is truly a 'Cinderella' sport, largely ignored by the media, considered by some sports editors and journalists I know to be 'unimaginative' and has little support from the general public. This is in complete contrast to the situation in some other nations, particularly in the Soviet Union, Bulgaria and a few other Eastern European countries, where the sport has quite a good following coupled with massive State support and encouragement.

I believe one major reason why some critics label it unimaginative is because by and large they have never lifted weights themselves and so fail to appreciate the sport's finer points. I have always said that to fully understand what weightlifting is all about one must have been an active participant. Certainly I, together with countless others I know, have found it a fascinating, worthwhile pastime.

The first step

I believe that the first step for a beginner is to join a good club where he can get personal instruction from a qualified coach. Weightlifting is a sport that demands a high degree of technical skill on many of the lifts, so it is essential that from the very start the movements are acquired with all possible skill so that progress in lifting ability will not be retarded by efforts made in crude style.

In Britain thirty two lifts are officially recognised by the governing body, the British Amateur Weight Lifters' Association (BAWLA), although the most popular ones are the Olympic set (Two Hands Snatch and Two Hands Clean and Jerk) and the Power Set (Squat, Press on Bench and Two Hands Dead Lift), which I have covered elsewhere.

A perusal of Chapter 17 by Al Murray will give the trainee the basic principles of the best methods of performance on the Snatch and Jerk. But however well one may learn from a textbook, personal instruction is essential for the best results. For an intelligent trainee it would be possible to make fair progress by absorbing the technical know-how from Al's chapter and diligently applying it. However, unless watched by a qualified instructor, technical faults may creep into one's style that if persisted in could become difficult to eliminate.

A good coach who can analyse technical movements and see any basic faults can correct them on the spot. So I advise the beginner to seek out the service of such a man. Generally this is best done by joining a club, as most of them have one or two qualified men.

When to start

One of the first considerations is the best age to start competitive weightlifting. I am no believer in rushing youngsters into this tough, demanding sport too early. My own conception of a boy's early physical activities is that he should indulge in a variety of sports and pastimes – play football, cricket, practise gymnastics, cycle, run, swim, and so on for a few years, all activities that will give him a good physical foundation. I did most of these things myself from the age of eleven, then, after concentrating on football for several years, started to lift weights at nineteen. But youngsters mature earlier these days and many lads of fourteen are probably more grown up than those of seventeen or so forty or fifty years ago.

In Chapter 19, John Lear reveals how the Bulgarians (one of the two top lifting nations) introduce young boys of twelve to weightlifting under their State system. This works well enough in Bulgaria and some other Eastern Bloc countries, but I do not believe it could ever work here. We don't have the facilities or resources to administer such a system. Neither, as a nation, do we have the same desire to follow such a regime for lads of that age.

In my days the average age one started weightlifting was seventeen or so. Anyone wanting to start much younger than that was generally frowned upon. Nowadays, of course, more and more young boys in their early teens are positively encouraged to start competitive lifting. Indeed, over the past two decades or so schoolboy lifting has taken a strong root and the BAWLA British schoolboy championships (13–16) finals regularly attract more than 100 contestants. Many BAWLA officials believe that the future national champions must come from the schoolboy ranks, and there are many good examples of former schoolboy stars making their marks in top events like the Olympic Games, world and European championships and the Commonwealth Games.

At the other end of the scale some lifters don't take the plunge until their late teens or early twenties, and many of these I know have shown good results. But generally better results come when an earlier start is made.

I would say that, on average, thirteen to fourteen is a good age to start weightlifting, particularly for an ambitious and naturally talented youngster. The standards are so high now that an early start is almost essential if one is to become a champion. It is much easier, too, for a youngster to make an early start these days. A more enlightened outlook, more encouragement from the medical profession and greater opportunities to get good coaching and experience through such schemes as run by BAWLA, all give the youngster a good start over the one in my early days.

But at whatever age one starts I must emphasise the need for proper guidance and a curb on over-enthusiasm. The latter (in the case of a youngster) can so easily result in the lad 'burning' himself out after a year or two because of trying to achieve too much in too little a time and then giving up the sport altogether. Steady, regular progress should be the aim, with no attempt to rush things in the first year or so of training. A good foundation built steadily is a long-term policy that will pay rich future dividends.

Physical requirements

Broadly speaking, training for Olympic lifting can be divided into two main phases; (a) the direct cultivation of more physical power, and (b) the improvement of lifting technique. There are, of course, other relevant factors, such as speed, balance, coordination, courage, the correct mental outlook and the like, all essential components of the complete weightlifter. A perfect combination of them all produces the maximum platform performance.

Although, as I have said, weightlifting demands a high degree of technical skill, unquestionably the most important requirement is great strength. No one ever became a world champion, or even a good-class performer, without great strength. Every world champion possesses great strength. Some have excellent technique, most have good or reasonable technique, and a few are champions despite the fact that they lack good technique. But none became a champion with just moderate strength. Even if a weightlifter has perfect or near-perfect technical skill, heavy or record weights cannot be lifted unless this skill is allied to great strength. Many, many lifters have good technical skill, but because they are simply not strong enough they never reach the top grade.

A very strong man with only moderate technique will almost always be better than the perfect technician with only moderate strength. But, of course, the stronger man would be even better if he improved his technique so that he could fully exploit his strength. It is possible for some performers to improve their lifting totals simply by improving their technique and without getting any stronger at all. However, once a high degree of technical skill has been achieved the only way in which a man can lift heavier weights is by getting stronger.

I believe, too, that for the majority there is more scope for developing strength than in acquiring more skill. With most lifters a limit of technical skill is soon reached. Many never acquire a high degree of skill because of natural, inherent physical disadvantages. But there is ample scope for *everyone* to get stronger – and over a longer period of time, too. Most of us have only a limited amount of time for training and it is wise to apportion this to the best advantage. It is essential, of course, for anyone lacking in skill, speed and so on to spend a lot of time in improving these qualities. But don't make the mistake of spending *too much* time – time that perhaps could be better spent on the development of more sheer strength.

Ideally, the best method of training is to constantly adjust one's programme so that both the development of strength and the cultivation or maintenance of technical skill receive attention as necessary. Often one may find that lifts are being lost in competition not because of any lack of sheer physical strength, but simply because of faulty technique. Then, a good proportion of training time should be spent on improving skill and speed of movement. At other times one may be lifting with good skill, but cannot make progress in lifting heavier weights. Then is the time to train mainly for greater strength. All the time a balance must be kept between these two factors of strength and skill and one's training adjusted accordingly.

The importance of mobility

An Olympic weightlifter must have good mobility of joints, particularly at the shoulders, hips and ankles, so that he can easily adopt the best technical positions. For example, tightness in the shoulders (when the locked arms cannot easily be held overhead with the hands directly over the ear) will make it difficult to jerk and hold the barbell overhead in the correct position, which should be at a point directly over the head, shoulders and hips, with the trunk upright.

Tight shoulders, too, are a definite handicap for those who wish to use the squat style of snatching. Lack of mobility around the hip joints will also make it difficult to adopt the upright trunk position so essential for good split snatching and jerking ability; whilst a similar condition in the ankle joints will prevent full use being made of such manoeuvres as pushing the front knee well forwards when split snatching and cleaning, and also forcing the rear heel backwards in a low split position to avoid the rear knee touching the platform.

Accordingly it is wise, before starting on training schedules, to ascertain one's degree of mobility and then, if necessary, practising remedial exercises to improve the condition.

Using an empty barbell, try to adopt the technical positions described in Al Murray's chapter, preferably with the help of someone to check for you. If it is found that the positions can be adopted without difficulty than there will be little wrong with your mobility. If not, then an analysis must be made accordingly.

Gentle forcing into the positions should be made in groups of several repetitions. For example, get as near as possible to the split Snatch position without physical discomfort.

Then, if the trunk is not held upright, perhaps with the hips too far to the rear, gently force the hips forwards, together with the front knee, to bring the trunk nearer the upright position. Hold for a second or two in the forced position, then relax and return to the original position. Pause for a second or two, then again force nearer to the correct position. Repeat another two or three times, then replace the barbell and rest for a few moments. Perform another two or three groups of repetitions, each time trying to force a little nearer to the correct position. Continued practice will show gradual improvement. Practise these forcing movements in all positions that cannot easily be adopted.

Tightness in the shoulder girdle is probably the greatest handicap to safe overhead lifting, and a good remedial exercise is the following.

Lie on a bench with the shoulders at the back edge, holding an empty barbell at arms' length over the face, using a shoulder-width grip. Lower steadily backwards (keeping the arms locked) as far as possible, whilst inhaling, then return to the starting position. Repeat for six repetitions in three or four groups, trying each time to stretch back a little further. Also try the movement with a wider handgrip, as used in the Snatch, and also using an alternate movement with a dumbbell in each hand.

As a free exercise, try shoulder circling. Hold the arms out sideways parallel with the floor, then start to make small circles with the hands, gradually widening the movements until quite large circles are being made, all the time trying to make the shoulder girdle looser and looser.

I have given you just a few of the many movements that can be practised to improve mobility. With one's own knowledge and some thought many more movements can be devised.

The first stages

In many cases, particularly when the beginner is naturally weak and underweight, it is advisable to spend a few months on a general bodybuilding schedule before starting on Olympic lifting proper. A perusal of George Greenwood's chapter will give one a basic schedule that will be very suitable. This preliminary work will build up some strength and development and accustom the muscular system to handling weights, all very useful before getting down to the business of developing actual weightlifting ability.

Before actually starting competitive lifting, make sure that you have the right kit. A lifter's boots are very important, so go to a reputable sports shop and choose the best you can afford. They must be strong and pliable with a good rubber sole that will not slip on the platform during the vital movements of the lifts. A good, modern-style competition costume is an essential, together with a strong jock-strap or tight-fitting trunks, and a warm, fleecy-lined track suit for training.

In the case of those who have already practised some form of physical activity, this preliminary period is perhaps not so necessary, but could still be carried out with some advantage.

When one makes a start on actual Olympic lifting it is wise to spend the first few months learning the technical movements with very light weights, concentrating on moving into the positions with as much accuracy as possible and performing the movements very fast. For some, it will take a long time before the lifts can be performed with smooth, flowing, rhythmic movements because of a lack of natural athletic ability. For others, who possess a good degree of this latter ability, good technical positions will be attained more rapidly. But on no account should progress to handling heavy and near-limit weights be made until a reasonable degree of technical ability is attained. On average, a period of some one-to-two months should be spent on positional work with very light weights. Some may require less time than this. Others will need perhaps a longer period. But however long the period may be it will be well spent.

On the Snatch, perform one lift, recover to

the concluding position and hold the barbell overhead for a second or two. Then lower it to the platform, adopt the starting position again and repeat the lift. Work in groups of four or five repetitions.

On the Clean and Jerk, regard this as two separate lifts. First make a clean to the shoulders and recover to the erect position ready for the jerk. Then lower the barbell to the platform, adopt the starting position again and repeat, again in groups of four or five repetitions. Follow the same procedure for the jerk part of the lift, making the repetitions from the shoulders.

Frequency of training

I recommend that the number of training sessions for a beginner should, for the first few weeks, be three times weekly, say Monday, Wednesday and Friday, stepping this up to four times a week by adding a Sunday session. Certainly the periods should not be less than three, as training only once or twice a week would be largely a waste of time and severely limit the rate of progress. Anyone with ambitions to be a champion or a top-line performer will have to train hard, very hard, eventually working up to a minimum of five periods a week, if, of course, this is possible. A lot depends on the amount of work done at each session. If one is only able to devote, say, an hour or an hour and a half to a session, then maximum progress cannot be expected. Allowing time for a proper warm-up, then a schedule on the two lifts, followed by some 'assistance' exercises, I would say that a minimum period of some two hours is necessary.

The value of speed

Earlier I mentioned that the lifting movements should be performed FAST. I cannot emphasise too strongly the value of speed to an Olympic lifter, and during one's career frequent periods of training should be devoted primarily to the cultivation of more speed. Many lifters have a full, natural measure of this valuable asset. Others, not so favourably endowed by nature, are more sluggish in their movements and must endeavour, by assiduous training, to cultivate a greater degree of speed.

Training for speed means, quite often, the use of comparatively light weights. I think it is wrong for a lifter or coach to despise the use of light weights (as indeed some do) in training. Heavy work in plenty there must be, to develop stronger muscles and tendons. But there are times when spells of training with light-to-moderate weights, primarily aimed at building up speed, are essential. Of course, speed work should also be done at times with heavier weights because it is with the heavy weights in competition that you need the speed.

For the beginner, it is a wise policy to develop this greed for speed right from the start – to make it a habit. Likewise, when the legs and body are moved into the split or squat positions they must move at maximum speed to achieve maximum results. Any sluggishness at a vital stage of the lift that is not enforced solely by virtue of the heaviness of the weight and causes a failure, means that one's full potential is not being reached.

Apart from speed of movement, speed of reaction and adjustment – for example, the ability to adjust quickly from a technical position that is not quite 'in the groove' – is most valuable and can often save a lift that otherwise might have been lost by a slower moving or slower thinking performer.

I always have vivid recollections of a former British middleweight champion, Jim Halliday, who was a grand performer and competitor and very fast and volatile. But his technical positions were not always good and very often he would fix a weight overhead with either his body or the barbell out of position – or perhaps both. Many a lifter, finding himself in the same position, would assuredly have lost the lift, yet Jim, almost invariably, by a lightning-like adjustment of position, managed to recover and save the lift.

It can be said, of course, that such adjustment would not be necessary if the technical position was good in the first place. That is so. But one must face the fact that perfect technical positions are not always achieved with limit or near-limit weights, and the ability to adjust a lift to a safe position is very useful indeed. I am speaking now of technical positions that ARE possible to retrieve; that is, positions that are not too far from the ideal. Quite often, when a lift is well out of position, no amount of adjustment or manoeuvring can save it – and obviously perfect positional lifting must be aimed at.

The driving force for greater speed comes from the mind and conscious efforts must be made to move fast – and FASTER. I have always considered it a good training policy to endeavour to make each succeeding lift a little faster than the previous one. Only by such application cam maximum speed be cultivated . . . particularly so in the case of the stolid type of lifter, whose movements generally are naturally slow.

In training for speed improvement, use single lifts on the Snatch and Clean and Jerk with mainly light-to-moderate weights (with only occasionally using heavier ones) concentrating on an 'explosive' effort of maximum speed of movement combined with perfection of position.

Repetitions and resistance

To develop any physical quality, training must consist largely of similar movements and exertions. Olympic weightlifting is a sport that demands short and sharp explosive efforts, interspersed with brief rest periods. The quality of stamina, as employed in such activities as track athletics, swimming and cycling, for example, is not required.

The Olympic lifter must direct his training towards developing the quality of being able to concentrate his energy (both physical and mental) on this brief explosion of power. High repetitions will not develop this power to maximum extent, but will tend to develop the quality of being able to perform high repetitions and to increase muscular size rather than strength. Low repetitions (threes, twos and singles) are essential for the development of the qualities required – *with heavy weights*. In competition, only three attempts are allowed on any one lift – all with near-limit and limit weights.

In the beginner's schedules that follow later it will be seen that most of the weights handled are light to moderate. This is recommended because a beginner's muscular system is not fully toned and accustomed to handling heavier weights. The use of light weights – gradually progressing to heavier ones – is the best method of accustoming the muscles to the technical movements required. As I said earlier, it is important to avoid the use of heavy weights while learning these movements. Later, when progression has been made, training schedules must assume a different character, with a large proportion of training time devoted to lifting heavy weights in low repetitions.

Warming up

Before starting a training session it is essential to warm up thoroughly. No track or field athlete, no gymnast, no circus athlete and the like starts his performance before warming up, and the same sensible principle applies equally to a weightlifter. It is obviously important before a competition and is still essential before training, so that the possibility of sustaining a 'pulled' muscle or some other muscular strain is minimised. 'Cold' muscles are susceptible to some strain and, furthermore, if some light lifting movements are performed first to achieve a 'pattern', a muscular rhythm is attained which makes it easier to go straight into the schedules with maximum ease.

First, I advise a few minutes spent on free-standing exercises, such as trunk twisting and bending, 'running on the spot', free squats, or even a minute or two of skipping. Then move on to a few light repetition Presses and Snatches with emphasis on speed of movement.

Physiologically, too, it is a good plan to 'cool down' after the lifting session with some light Snatches and some more trunk and abdominal movements.

Training must be progressive

Progress can be made only if the work performed is progressively harder. That is, as the muscles gradually get stronger, they must be given heavier work to coax them to get even stronger. If, for example, a lift or exercise was performed always with a fixed weight, the muscles employed in the movement would get stronger for a limited period only and would remain at that strength unless the weight handled was increased. It is only by the steady, continued use of heavier and heavier weights that the muscles are strengthened. This progression need not be rapid. Indeed, I advise against that. Experience has taught me that strong muscles developed over a long period will retain their strength for a long time, too, which is a quality well worth possessing. The development of great strength, for the majority, cannot be achieved 'overnight'. It is a job that demands patience and perseverance and training on proved, sensible lines.

SCHEDULES FOR THE BEGINNER

After a month or so of practising the Olympic movements with very light weights, as advised earlier, it will be time to move on to more methodical and planned schedules. There are many, many schedules that can be compiled, with many variations of repetitions, groups and resistances, and as one progresses thought must be given to changing these from time to time to find out exactly what type of schedule brings the best results.

Every lifter will not respond exactly to the same type of schedule, and a subtle variation here and there often can bring better results. Experiments will have to be made, together with self-analysis and a constant 'thinking for oneself'. As a beginner, stick to the tried-and-tested methods. But later, as experience is gained, plan your own methods and do not hesitate to try something that is not completely orthodox. Remember, it is the end result that counts, and if one finds that by following a path that is slightly unorthodox but brings better results, then that is the path to take.

The following schedules are typical ones for a beginner and are well tested and proved.

Two hands snatch

Repetitions and weights are based on an assumed maximum ability of 55 kg. The repetitions are performed as follows: Make one Snatch from the starting position, recover to the concluding position and hold overhead for a second. Then lower the barbell back to the platform and assume the starting position again. Pause for a couple of deep breaths, then make another lift.

35 kg	4 reps	3 groups
40 kg	3 reps	3 groups
45 kg	2 reps	2 groups
50 kg	5 single lifts	

Rest for one or two minutes between each group and also the single lifts.

As an alternative, use the following:

30 kg	5 reps (mainly a warm-up)	1 group
45 kg	2 reps	12–15 groups

Right: three stages of a Snatch shown by Gary Langford of Australia: the initial legs drive, stretching up to get maximum height and the low squat position

About every two or three weeks, work up to a maximum weight as follows:

40 kg	3 reps	2 groups
45 kg	3 reps	1 group
50 kg	2 reps	1 group
52.5 kg	1 single lift	
55 kg	1 single lift	

Then try 57.5 kg in order to achieve a new maximum weight. If successful, all training weights should be increased by 2.5 kg. If not successful, maintain the existing training weights for a further week, then try again for an increased maximum.

Two hands clean and jerk – clean part only

Repetitions and weights are based on an assumed ability of 75 kg. Perform the repetitions in the method as described for the Snatch.

55 kg	3 reps	3 groups
60 kg	3 reps	2 groups
65 kg	2 reps	1 group
70 kg	5 single lifts	

A low position in the Clean shown by Dean Willey (Britain)

As an alternative, use the following:

55 kg	4 reps	1 group
65 kg	2 reps	8–10 groups

Jerk part only

60 kg   2 reps   5 groups
70 kg   5 single lifts

Repetitions to be made from the shoulders, with the weight taken from stands at shoulder height.

Two hands clean and jerk – complete lift

Once a week, perform the complete lift only as follows:

60 kg   2 cleans, 1 jerk   3 groups
65 kg   2 cleans, 1 jerk   2 groups
70 kg   5–6 single lifts

About every two or three weeks work up to a maximum weight as follows:

60 kg   2 cleans, 1 jerk
            1 clean, 2 jerks
65 kg   1 complete lift
67.5 kg   1 complete lift
70 kg   1 complete lift
72.5 kg   1 complete lift
75 kg   1 complete lift

Then try 77.5 kg to achieve a new maximum weight. If successful, add 2.5 kg to all training weights. If not successful, maintain the existing weights for another week or two, then try again for an increased maximum.

Assistance exercises

In addition to training on the two competitive lifts an Olympic lifter needs to practise other movements of a heavy nature as a direct method of developing great strength. The best ones are those that affect the larger muscle

Above: the 1984 Olympic champion, Rolf Milser of West Germany, just after the start of a Clean and Jerk, showing an ideal technical position

Below: preliminary dip prior to jerking the barbell overhead. The lifter is Louis Martin (Britain), four times world champion

groups and in which heavy weights can be handled. Movements such as the Squat and High Pulls are among the most popular and they are used by all the world's leading performers.

The Squat, in particular, is probably the most beneficial supplementary exercise of all and I doubt if there is one top-line lifter who does not use this in various forms. For many advanced lifters assistance exercises are practised even more than the two Olympic lifts, some of them spending considerable periods on this type of work, with occasional attention to the Snatch and Jerk in order to maintain their technical skills.

The beginner, of course, needs to concentrate mainly on the two lifts in his early training to develop his technique and lifting patterns. But the inclusion of a few assistance movements will be beneficial as an added aid to progress. Here are a few of the best.

Power clean and jerk

This is the Clean and Jerk performed without any foot movement. Start as in the regular Clean and Jerk, but instead of splitting or squatting, pull the weight into the shoulders by means of a shallow squat, just lowering the body about five or six inches to receive the weight. Keep the back as straight as possible during this movement. Recover to the jerking position. Then to make the jerk, lower the body a few inches by knees bending and with an explosive effort thrust the weight to locked arms whilst again slightly lowering the body to facilitate the arms' lock. Have a try out for a few days to ascertain your best performance

Above: Yanko Rusev (Bulgaria), former world and Olympic champion, shows a good technical Jerk. The barbell is positioned in a vertical line above the shoulders and hips, with the trunk upright

Left: correct finishing position for the Clean and Jerk demonstrated by Geoff Laws of Britain

in this manner. I will assume a limit of 60 kg. Then try the following, adjusting, of course, as necessary according to ability.

40 kg	3 reps	2 groups
45 kg	3 reps	2 groups
47.5 kg	2 reps	2 groups
50 kg	2 reps	2 groups
52.5 kg	2 reps	2 groups

Squat

Repetitions and weights are based on an assumed maximum performance of 90 kg in the squat movement to a point where the tops of the thighs are parallel with the floor.

First, warm up with one group of ten repetitions in the deep, full-squat position with 45 kg. Then use the parallel Squat as follows:

70 kg	5 repetitions
72.5 kg	4 repetitions
75 kg	3 repetitions
77.5 kg	3 repetitions
80 kg	5–6 single lifts

Half-squats (lowering until the tops of the thighs are at an angle of 45° to the floor)

90 kg	3 reps	2 groups
100 kg	3 reps	2 groups

Front Squat Hold the barbell at the shoulders instead of behind the neck, keeping the elbows well up and forwards. This is an invaluable movement for the squat-style clean. Not so much weight can be used as in the regular Squat with weight behind neck. I will assume a maximum single lift of 70 kg.

45 kg	4 reps
50 kg	3 reps
55 kg	2 reps
60 kg	5–6 single lifts

High pull (snatch grip)

Assume the starting position for the Snatch, then pull the barbell up to about the height of the lower chest (elbows pointing out sideways), stretching upwards with the whole body with locked knees and rising on the toes. Lower back to floor, resume the starting position and repeat. Repetitions and weights are based on the assumption of a 55 kg maximum Snatch.

50 kg	3 reps	2 groups
55 kg	3 reps	2 groups
60 kg	2 reps	2 groups
65 kg	2 reps	2 groups

High pull (clean grip)

A similar movement to the previous one, except that the barbell is pulled to about the height of the waist using a shoulder-width grip as for cleaning.

Repetitions and weights are based on the assumptions of a 75 kg maximum clean.

70 kg	3 reps	2 groups
75 kg	3 reps	2 groups
80 kg	2 reps	2 groups
85 kg	2 reps	2 groups

Showing the high-pull position in the Snatch, just before moving into the squat or split position with body upstretched and coming up on the toes. This is also useful as an assistance exercise with heavy weights in low repetitions. The lifter is Pavel Pervushin (USSR), former world heavyweight champion

If training normally four times a week, use these supplementary exercises on two days only, preferably on alternate training days. If training normally three times a week, then use them once a week and occasionally twice.

Other hints

Keep warm. During training it is very essential to keep warm. Cold muscles do not function at their best and as I said earlier are susceptible to strain. It is little use warming up properly, as recommended, then allowing oneself to cool down during the training period. Rests have to be taken between the groups of repetitions and this is the time that a cooling down can take place unless guarded against.

Except when the weather or the training room is exceptionally warm, I advise the wearing of a tracksuit throughout the training period. And during the rest period between groups of repetitions (which should not be too long – generally two or three minutes is ample) do not sit about too much. An occasional sit down is in order, but it is best to keep on the move, walking about slowly and perhaps doing a little deep breathing.

Grip. A strong grip is essential for an Olympic lifter, particularly on the Clean and Jerk, when the heaviest weights are handled, and if any weakness is apparent some grip-strengthening exercises should be practised. Single- and double-handed dead lifting is very good, also the picking up of barbell discs between the fingers, placing, one, two or three discs together stood on end and picking them up from the floor and holding for a few seconds. The weight of the discs can be increased gradually in order to make the work progressive.

It is important that the best grip be used for the execution of the two lifts. If one feels that the normal grip is not quite strong enough and seems to be retarding the lift, then better results will be obtained by using the 'hook' grip. In this the thumb is placed underneath the fingers, which then grip tightly and 'lock' the thumb. It may be a little painful when first tried with some lifters, but one will get used to that after a period of practice.

COMPETITION

Competition is the life-blood of any sport. Without competition and the incentives that go with it, no one can realise his full potential. One can, of course, practise Olympic weightlifting primarily for enjoyment and the physical and mental benefits, but without the opportunity of pitting oneself against the strength and skill of others, it may be difficult to maintain interest over a long period and to reach the heights of what one is capable.

A true champion is a man who revels in competing against his rivals and who produces his best under the stress of competition. And it is this driving force that often enables a man to win against opposition that, while potentially greater, fails because of a lack of the essential qualities for success.

Many weightlifters consistently leave their best performances in the training room. For some reason or another they fail to reproduce on the competition platform what they have accomplished in training. Largely this is a matter of mental attitude. For example, there is no physiological or logical reason why a man who has been snatching, say 100 kg with some degree of consistency in training, should not succeed with this weight – or even more – in competition.

I am talking now of the lifter who has some experience behind him. The beginner, obviously, cannot reasonably be expected to equal or exceed his training performances right away in competition; although some will, of course. But the experienced man should and if he finds that he doesn't, then his mental attitude needs overhauling. Consider these facts:

Training, generally, isn't conducted in the best atmosphere for maximum performances. Usually there is no incentive in the way of competition stimulus, no audience to respond to, no extreme urge to equal or exceed one's previous best. But in competition, all these factors should bring out the full current potential of the performer.

It is not uncommon for good competitors to exceed by 5 kg or 10 kg their best training Clean and Jerk when competing in a championship. Many make their recent best training performance a *starting* weight in competition – then go on to add anything up to 10 kg on top of this.

If one finds, through experience, that training performances cannot be equalled or bettered in competition, then a different mental attitude must be cultivated. One must think along more positive lines, must deliberately and determinedly set out to develop a better competitive spirit.

This is largely a mental problem and only by continually building up an urge to do better, a positive-thinking attitude to competition, can such improvement be effected. There must be no mental barrier; no weight that one sets as a definite limit.

Training can be said to be the most important part of competitive weightlifting in many respects. For what is accomplished in competition depends largely on what one does in training. Intelligent preparation for a championship or contest is the basis of efficient performance on the competitive platform.

The cultivation of good technique, the building up of more and more bodily power and fitness are all essential steps towards the climax of expression on the platform, but a competitor in any sport must be obsessed with a will-to-win spirit because he will never reach his full potential without it. Without the mental concentration on the urge to succeed, his determination to lift those weights with maximum speed, strength and ferocity, it may be difficult to exceed one's training performances to any worthwhile degree.

Temperament has some bearing on this. The phlegmatic type of individual, with a stolid and unimaginative mind, does not find it easy to cultivate this keyed-up mentality, and this type of competitor, generally, does not vary much in his training and competitive performances. On the other hand, we have the man whose mental make-up is such that he is stimulated to produce his best in competition. He is often highly-strung, with a mental attitude that is a driving force enabling him to produce a performance that is to some extent an abnormal one. His emotional state under stress of competition brings out that something extra – something that he cannot do in normal training conditions.

Choosing weights

One of the most important aspects of weightlifting competition is that of choosing the correct weights for the various attempts. With only three attempts permissible for each lift, it is essential not to make any mistakes. A wrong selection could mean that your best-registered attempt is lower than need be, or even that no success at all will result.

The first few contests for a beginner should be experimental. Essentially they must be so, because until one has actually lifted in competition it is not possible to know just how one will react to it.

Experience must be gained. It is only experience that will teach you; only experience that will enable you to know yourself and what kind of competitor you are likely to develop into.

It is a good thing to start off well: to succeed with all your attempts. You need not be too ambitious or obsessed with the desire to win in your first few competitions. You want experience. You want to learn. So plan your lifts wisely. Take weights that you are reasonably sure you can succeed with.

Normally when you enter a competition your aim will be to win if possible. By this I mean your tactics will be planned to produce a winning total if you know you have some chance of succeeding. If the opposition is such that you have no chance, then your plans will be different. Your aim will be to improve on your previous best total, so that progress can be seen. Or maybe you can aim at a second or third place.

The beginner's first competition will not, as a rule, be of any great importance. It may be a league contest, or a county championship, or just an inter-club friendly. And it should be regarded purely as a test piece.

First, let us consider your training immediately prior to the contest.

A heavy workout should be taken about a week beforehand, working up to your limit weights. This will give you a good indication of your current form. Then have two more training sessions, the last one at least two or three days before the contest. Then relax completely until the time of the event. In this way you will come to the platform rested and all ready and eager to tackle the weights. It is neither wise nor necessary to train right up to the day of the contest.

Your weights in the contest should be chosen so that your third attempt is the best you have accomplished in training. In this way it is most likely that you will succeed with all of your attempts – making a good psychological start to your weightlifting career.

As an example, let's assume your best training Snatch is 60 kg. Start in the competition with 52.5 kg. Then take 57.5 kg for your second attempt, and finally the 60 kg.

It may be that all these weights will feel light, even your final attempt. If so, then this is a good sign, an indication that you may develop into a good competitive performer. On the other hand, you may fail with some of your lifts – particularly the third attempt. Whatever happens, take a mental note of it for your future guidance.

Later, as you gain experience and improvement comes, your weights will often have to be governed by your chances in the competition. Sometimes you may have to attempt a weight that you have never succeeded with – or perhaps even attempted – before. More and more you will have to watch your chief rivals and the state of the competition.

If you have a good coach or adviser, then his help in this respect will be invaluable – as you are far more likely to do better if your mind is free to concentrate on tearing up the weights instead of also having to watch your prospects, weights and tactical moves.

Do not be afraid to take chances sometimes, or to experiment. It is all experience. But you must learn from your experience. Remember how you reacted whenever you attempted any weight that you had never lifted before. It is vitally important to have confidence whenever you do tackle personal-record weights. Any half belief in your ability, or hesitation at a vital stage of the lift, will mean failure.

Warming up

Before the contest starts you will need to warm up both physically and mentally. Physically so that when you are ready for your first attempt on the platform your muscles will be warm, your circulatory system working at an increased tempo. Mentally so that your mind will be stimulated to produce your maximum efforts.

Many individuals vary as to the extent and intensity of warming up required. Some function well in the competition with just a minimum of warming up, maybe just some free movements and a few light Snatches and Jerks. Others do better with a more intensive programme, warming up for a long period and working up to weights just below what they intend to start with.

Only experience can prove what is needed for yourself. My personal preference is to devote a period of about twenty minutes to some freestanding movements followed by light-to-moderate Snatches and Jerks, with the emphasis on speed and precision of movement, performing low repetitions and some single lifts.

The work should be timed so that you have finished your warm-up just a few minutes before taking your first competition lift. Wear a tracksuit during this warming-up period. It is essential to keep the body warm during the whole period of the competition, right from the time you weigh in to the final lift of the contest. So keep the tracksuit on between competition attemps. Also, don't sit around too much, but keep on the move most of the time between attempts.

Power of the mind

There is much more to weightlifting than employing the muscular force of the body. Of at least equal importance is the driving force of the mind. The emotional state must be such that the body is harnessed to produce maximum effort. With the mind in a normal state, not obsessed by any will-to-win, one's performance will not reach full potential. There must be determination, drive, eagerness and ambition. And this must, in many instances and to a large extent, be artificially created, depending on the individual.

Many athletes have a good measure of natural ability in this direction and, as the hour of the contest approaches, find themselves automatically building up to a mental stimulus capable of producing their absolute best on the occasion. Others find it difficult, but must constantly endeavour to develop this quality. This means mind training as well as physical training.

COMPETITION PROCEDURE AND RULES FOR OLYMPIC WEIGHTLIFTING

Here, briefly but in sufficient detail for a beginner, are the procedures and rules for competition on the two Olympic Lifts. Full, detailed rules are contained in the official BAWLA Handbook. If you join a club, the secretary will be able to obtain one for you at a moderate cost.

Three attempts are allowed on each lift, with the highest successful one counting. The weight of the barbell must be in multiples of 2.5 kg. The increase of weight between each

attempt must not be less than 5 kg, except for the last attempt, when it may be 2.5 kg. If a competitor chooses to take a 2.5 kg increase between the first and second attempt, then that will be counted as his last attempt. If three failures are made on any lift, then the competitor scores nothing for that particular lift and cannot be classified in the competition.

At the start the barbell will be loaded to the lowest weight required and must be kept rising in weight as the competition proceeds, with each lifter coming in at the weight he requires for any particular attempt.

Lifting area

A lifting area of four metres square is permitted for the lifter, and any stepping out of this area during the lift is cause for disqualification.

Adjudication

In all major championships – Olympic Games, world and continental championships, national championships and international matches – three officials are appointed to adjudicate on the lifts. A lift will be passed as valid on a majority or unanimous verdict. In this country one official may adjudicate at such minor events as county and divisional championships and in league and friendly matches.

Rules for the Snatch

From the platform the barbell shall be lifted to the full extent of the arms vertically above the head, while either bending or splitting the legs. The barbell shall pass with a continuous movement along the body, of which no part other than the feet shall touch the platform during the execution of the movement. The turning over of the wrists must not occur before the barbell has passed the top of the lifter's head.

The barbell must not be pulled from the 'hang' position; there must be no pause during the movement, no movement of the hands along the barbell during the lift, no uneven extension of the arms and no movement finishing with a 'press-out'. There must be no flexing and extension of the arms while regaining the legs position.

A press-out can occur in the following circumstances: (a) when the wrists are turned over too soon and (b) when the barbell is pulled not quite to full locked arms, stops momentarily and the movement then completed by pressing out.

The weight must be held in the final position of arms and legs extended, the feet on a line parallel with the lifter's front, until the referee gives the signal to return the barbell to the platform – placed thereon, not thrown down or dropped.

Rules for the Clean and Jerk

The Clean: From the platform the barbell shall be pulled in a single movement to the shoulders, while either bending or splitting the legs. The barbell shall not touch the chest before the final position; it shall then rest on the clavicles, on the chest or on the arms fully bent. The feet shall then be returned to the same line, with the legs straight, before the Jerk is begun. The lifter may do this in his own time.

The Jerk: The barbell shall be jerked to the full stretch of the arms vertically overhead in one movement only by bending the legs, then extend them and splitting, if the lifter so desires. The final position shall be held, with arms and legs extended, until the referee gives the signal to return the barbell to the platform – again, as in the Snatch, placed thereon, not thrown down or dropped. During the jerking movement, once the arms are locked, they must not be unlocked then locked again.

17

The Technique of Olympic Weightlifting
Al Murray

Britain's National Weightlifting Coach 1948–1972, Al Murray, has perhaps done more than anyone to popularise weight-training in all its aspects. As an Olympic coach he was accepted as one of the best in the world. Al has attended scores of international events and was British team coach at three Olympic Games, as well as many world championships, European championships and Commonwealth Games. He has lectured and taught in many countries and at one time was technical adviser to the Swiss and German weightlifting federations. It is largely because of his inquiring mind and perseverance that much of the academic background of Olympic weightlifting has been built up. Indeed, many world authorities still say that little change has been made in the basic technical points taught by Al. He was a good competitive lifter himself, undefeated Scottish lightweight champion and a British record holder. Al is now National Coaching Adviser to BAWLA and currently runs a superbly equipped gymnasium in the City of London, where he is conducting research into executive health in conjunction with the Medical and Sports Councils. He is now a world authority on cardiac prevention and rehabilitation.

Olympic weightlifting is a great sport and worthy of its place in the Olympic Games. The two double-handed tests – Snatch and Clean and Jerk – bring out some of the very best qualities in man.

To reach the top a lifter has to be fit, strong, fast and courageous, and no matter how highly developed these qualities are a great deal depends on his skill. Hence the reason why the 'greats of lifting' spend so much time perfecting their technique in each of the two lifts. The Soviet Union was among the first to produce a team who obviously performed in a manner which indicated the importance of technique.

Here in Britain the BAWLA coaching scheme, as far back as 1949, was working hard to produce a programme whereby technique would play a big part. Those of us who have seen this scheme develop are justly proud.

Champions and the great technicians, both on films and in life, have been studied from every angle and in every detail from start to finish of their Olympic movements.

Many of the intricate movements are very difficult to detect and teach, but this is not the purpose of this chapter. The purpose here is to simplify the basic movements, stage by stage, so that the beginner and experienced lifter alike can readily grasp each point, as I have explained at international conferences.

I have selected pin-man drawings to illustrate the points as I did when lecturing to the International Coaches' Conference in Paris in 1964.

The advantage of this type of drawing is that each line shows the position of the major bones of the body as they move through the lift and I believe they are better than photographs for this purpose.

Referring to positions 3 and 12 showing full extension, with top weights the legs never actually reach the vertical. But the lifter must strive to get as near as possible to this ideal position.

Figure 1. Get-set, or starting position, for the two hands snatch and clean

The get-set or starting position is extremely important, as this is where many lifts are lost, right at the start of the pull, because of an incorrect starting position.

Walk up to the centre of the barbell.

Feet. Place the insteps of both feet under the barbell, feet about hips-width apart with the toes pointing slightly outwards. Make sure that the weight of the body is evenly distributed over the whole surface of both feet.

Knees: Now bend the legs and grasp the barbell. The knees should be bent to an angle of between 90° and 100°. The barbell should touch or be very close to the shin-bones.

Back: The back and spine should be held flat or in their natural position, but care should be taken to make sure that they are not near vertical.

Shoulders: The shoulders or shoulder joints should be over or slightly in advance of the barbell.

Arms: The arms should be kept straight but not rigid (this is known as athletically straight).

Elbows: The points of both elbows should be turned slightly outwards, so that when they bend much later in the pull they will point sideways.

Hands: In the Clean for the Jerk the grip should be just about shoulder-width. This is the nearest approximate guide, but it can, of course, vary. A lifter who lacks mobility of the shoulder girdle or elbows will have to experiment with a wider grip.

Note: The hands spacing for the Snatch is wider and a good guide can be used by taking the measurements between the elbow points

when the arms are stretched out sideways. This is best done from the rear. Now mark this distance out on the centre of the barbell. The middle finger of each hand should now touch the marks made on the barbell.

Grip: In the case of heavy snatching and cleaning, use a hook grip. This is obtained by overlapping the first joint of the thumb with the first two joints of the first two fingers, and ensures a good grip.

Head: The head should be held a little nearer to the vertical than the back.

Eyes: Looking at right angles to the position of the head.

The pull

The pull refers to the lifter's attempt to raise the barbell from the floor to a point high enough to enable him to lower his body under the barbell in different positions.

Basically there are three parts to the pull:

(a) *The Lift*

From Figure 1 to Figure 2. This can be referred to as the lift.

(b) *The Swing*

From Figure 2 up to Figure 3.

(c) *Arm and Shoulder Pull*

The pull takes place as a continuation after position 3 – that is, when full extension of the legs and spine has been reached. The barbell has gained enough acceleration to ease the downwards pressure on both feet, allowing the lifter to move his feet is splitting or squatting, and enabling him to lower the body under the barbell whilst he completes the third part of the pull which, now having broken contact with the floor, is made with the arms and shoulders alone. This is the third and final part of the pull. The aim in both the split and squat styles is to arrive in the lowest possible position to receive the barbell at arm's length supported by a vertical or near-vertical trunk in the squat Snatch.

TWO HANDS SNATCH (SPLIT TECHNIQUE)

Having dealt with the starting position and the lift from the platform to the knees earlier, we can proceed from Figure 1 of the split Snatch. Note the position of the barbell and how it has moved slightly backwards on its way to the knees. The barbell is now vertically ove the mid-section of both feet, the shin bone are vertical, the shoulders are well in advanc of the barbell and the back is almost at th same angle as in the starting position.

SNATCH (split style)

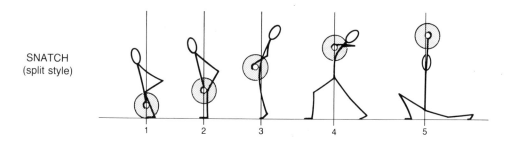

Hips thrust or second part of the pull

As the barbell passes the knees in Figure 2, drive the hips section of the body upwards and forwards towards the barbell as it travels vertically upwards. The head and shoulders should be kept in front of the barbell for as long as possible. Fight the tendency to take the head and shoulders back as the barbell passes the thighs, and delay bending the arms until the legs and body approach full extension.

When checking films of the great champions, seldom are the arms bent before the barbell passes the lowest part of the trunk.

The arms are bent vigorously just as the legs and back approach full extension. This part of the pull from the floor to Figure 3 applies to the pull for the following:

Pull for split Snatch and Clean
Pull for squat Snatch and Clean

I shall now deal with the lowering of the body under the barbell in the split style.

Having reached through a series of correct technical movements the completion of the pull, Figure 3, the mid-section of the body (hips region) should have developed a forwards and upwards momentum if carried

out correctly. As the barbell passes the level o the hip joints the arms will be bending and the elbows pointing outwards. The upward momentum applied to the barbell will relieve the downwards pressure from both feet. A this juncture take both feet off the floo precisely at the same time and continue to pul upwards strongly with the arms and shoulders The body will continue to fall downwards and a little forwards. The feet should now be moving into the split position – one foo forwards, the other to the rear. Care must be taken to ensure that the feet are kept close to the floor until they land in position Figure 4 The barbell at this stage will be passing the chest or face, depending again on the weigh being lifted.

You will find that in Figure 4 the elbows are now around shoulder level, the wrists are stil bent and the hands hanging downwards.

Receiving position (split snatch)

In order to receive the barbell in position Figure 5 the lifter must endeavour to pull the barbell upwards, push the front knee forwards from Figure 4, at the same time rotating the barbell and bringing the heels of both hands from behind to underneath the barbell. By this time the body will be half way between Figures 4 and 5.

However, the lifter will be in a much better position to press and drive upwards on the barbell as his front knee approaches position Figure 5.

The aim here is to reach Figure 5, sitting almost on the front heel with the weight slightly in advance of its starting position on the floor, with the elbows, shoulders and hip joints vertically below the barbell and under complete control of the lifter.

The recovery

Although I have not dealt with the recovery by illustration it is still extremely important. To recover to the upright and final position the barbell must be tipped slightly backwards when in position Figure 5, and as soon as the weight begins to leave the front foot use the rear leg as a prop and push vigorously upwards with the front leg. As the front knee approaches full extension, the front foot should be brought backwards a few inches and the barbell and body checked for a second. The weight should now be eased very slightly forwards, and once more when the weight leaves the rear foot bring it up in line with the front foot.

Observe the usual pause, required by the referee. Then on the signal, lower the barbell to the floor.

Despite the fact that few lifters have been using the split style for many years, I still think it is necessary to cover this style in both the Snatch and Clean.

TWO HANDS SNATCH (SQUAT TECHNIQUE)

Basically the pull for the squat Snatch is the same as described for the split Snatch. The advanced coach and lifter will realise there are subtle differences, but as this section is to deal with basic facts then we will proceed in the same vein.

At the same stage of the pull as the split snatcher splits, the squat snatcher should start squatting under the barbell. This is done by moving both feet outwards and apart, at the

SNATCH
(squat style)

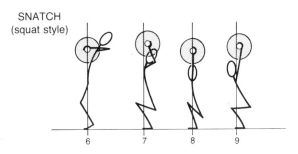

A front view of the Snatch shown by John Burns (Wales), former British champion

same time turning the knees and toes outwards. Care should be taken not to jump too wide astride – only a few inches. Endeavour to keep the hip section moving forwards and downwards whilst maintaining the trunk as near to the vertical as possible. See Figure 6. As the body approaches position Figure 7, the wrists can be turned as in the split Snatch, and as the hips approach a position as close to the heels as possible. Figure 8, the barbell can be pressed upwards strongly as the body sinks into the low squat position. The amount of upwards arm drive that can be used depends on the mobility at the hip joints. Japanese and other lifters from the East can, because of this hip mobility, keep the trunk in a similar position to Figures 7 and 8, and therefore get a tremendous upwards drive from the arms and shoulders.

The recovery

To recover from the low receiving position of the squat Snatch take care not to lose balance.

TWO HANDS JERK

Split clean

The starting position for the Clean is slightly different from that of the Snatch. The main reason for this is because of the wider grip used in the Snatch. First assume the starting position as in Figure 10, take a very wide grip, then slide the hands towards each other and note how your body position changes.

With the shoulder-width grip the shoulders are higher and there is a wider gap between the thighs and the chest than with the Snatch grip. From then on the pattern of movement is similar to the pull described for the Snatch.

The head, shoulders and hips are raised simultaneously and the back is held at the same angle from Figure 10 to Figure 11.

As the barbell reaches the knees, it has travelled ever so slightly forwards; the shin bones are vertical, but the head and shoulders are still in advance of the barbell. This part of the pull is known as the lift. From Figure 11 to Figure 12 it is known as the hips thrust or

Whilst keeping the weight under control over head, attempt to rise by first raising the hips little and allowing the head and chest to protrude slightly forwards between the arms as in Figure 9.

Once through the middle part of the recovery, the danger of losing balance almost nil. Continue to straighten both legs until the barbell is safely overhead and the trunk and legs erect. Finish the lift as in the split Snatch.

Alexander Vakhonin (USSR), former world and Olympic champion, shows the split-style Clean for the Jerk, a method seldom used nowadays

swing. Figure 12 shows the legs and trunk at the completion of the pull. This drawing is an exaggeration to encourage the lifter to swing the hips forwards and upwards as he approaches the end of the pull.

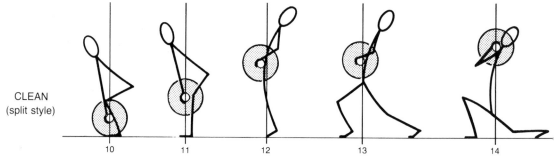

CLEAN
(split style)

10   11   12   13   14

The split and drop into the receiving position

Having reached position Figure 12, both feet should leave the floor at the same time, as fast as posible and close to the floor.

Figure 13 shows the rear foot as it lands, and the front foot about to land. Note how the chest is held high and how the hips are being forced forwards.

In Figure 14 we see the final receiving position for the split Clean. Note how the position of the trunk has been held from Figure 12 through to Figure 14; the front knee has been pushed forwards over the toes of the front foot and both elbows have been raised to secure the barbell at the chest.

The recovery from the low clean receiving position

To recover to the starting position for the Jerk, Figure 20, the same techniques as used in the split Snatch recovery is applied.

The rear leg is used as a prop, whilst the front leg is vigorously extended to raise the weight and body upwards. When the pressure is off the front foot it should be retraced a few inches.

Check and control the body before the next stage. Now transfer the weight over the front foot and as the pressure comes off the rear foot, move it up in line with the front foot ready for the jerk.

The receiving position for the squat clean

Before proceeding to describe the Jerk I will deal with the lowering of the body into the receiving position for the squat Clean.

In Figure 15 note that the body curve is not so great as that shown at the completion of the pull for the split Clean. This is because of a slight difference in the hips thrust for the squat Clean.

The hips thrust can be carried through right into the low squat position, but this is not so in the squat Clean. Note the position of the hips as the lifter jumps astride in Figure 16. They have dropped backwards slightly as they are lowered under the barbell.

This is one reason why the hips thrust in the pull for the squat Clean must be directed more upwards and less forwards than in the pull for the split Clean. Having brought out this point let us return to the completion of the pull.

The feet should then be taken apart, toes and knees turned outwards and hips forwards as they are lowered under the barbell.

Try hard to keep the position of the trunk whilst dropping from Figure 15 into Figure 17.

When jumping astride, keep the feet close to the floor and not too far apart. When the feet are too wide the knees will come inwards as you lower into the full knees-bend position; this will cause the hips to go too far back and the reaction will send the head forwards into a position which may be difficult to hold.

In the squat Snatch I pointed out that it was more important to have the knees wider apart than the feet. However, in the Clean a greater

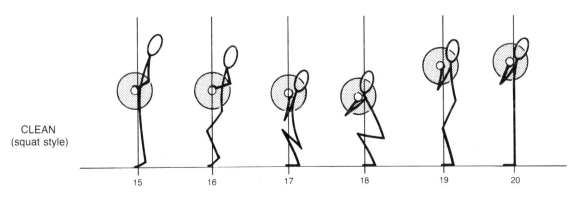

CLEAN
(squat style)

15   16   17   18   19   20

weight is being used and if the feet are turned out too far and the knees are too wide, great difficulty will be experienced during the recovery to the jerking position.

In the low receiving position shown in Figure 17 note the upper two thirds of the trunk is nearly vertical and the elbows are held forwards to secure the weight at the shoulders.

Recovery to the jerking position

As in the recovery for the squat Snatch, observe that again the hips have been raised a little from Figure 17 to Figure 18. This must be done with great care, so that the trunk is not tilted forwards too much. If the hips lift is performed correctly it enables the back to share the load with the legs.

Once the position in Figure 18 has been passed, force the hips upwards and forwards until the position in Figure 20 is reached. Hold the body erect and the weight securely at the shoulders ready for the Jerk.

The jerk

The Jerk from the shoulders and second half of the complete Clean and Jerk lift is a very exciting movement, as this decides many a championship.

I can remember many occasions where excitement charged the air with all kinds of emotions. Probably one of the greatest moments was as far back as 1948 revolving round the last attempt of Pete George (USA) to win the Olympic title against Frank Spellman, also of the USA.

Pete hovered around between the chalk-box and the barbell for some eight or nine minutes before he successfully cleaned 165 kg. Then with the weight safely at the shoulders he lingered again. You could have heard the proverbial pin drop. Eventually he made the attempt, but was unable to fix the weight at arms' length and a title was lost. Many similar occasions such as this can be remembered, so let us master the technicalities of the Jerk.

Assuming that the body, legs and arms are positioned correctly get ready to make the effort. The weight of the barbell and body should be evenly distributed over the soles of both feet. Two types of arms' position are used by the experts.

(a) Elbows fairly high.
(b) Forearms vertically under the barbell

Former world champion Rudy Plyukfelder (Soviet Union) prefers (a) and he has also pointed out in his conversation with me that he advocates that the legs drive heaves the barbell half of the upwards movement and that the arms should not be brought into play until the barbell is passing the head.

JERK

21   22   23   24

The reason for this is sound. If the elbows are forwards at the start and the arms are used as the barbell leaves the shoulders the triceps will be brought into play and the barbell may be sent forwards on its upwards path. Then the reaction on both shoulders will be to drive them backwards and down in the opposite direction from the pathway of the barbell.

When the vertical elbow position is used the triceps will not be brought into play until the barbell clears the head in any case. Experiments should be made with both techniques.

When making the initial knees bend, or dip, from Figure 20 into Figure 21, make sure that the trunk is kept in the same position as the knees are bent. Any forwards tilt of the shoulders will result in the barbell being sent forwards and out of control.

A nicely balanced Jerk shown by the 1985 world super-heavyweight champion, Antonio Krastev of Bulgaria

As both legs are extended, strive to keep the chest high, as this prevents any rounding of the upper spine which, if rounded, can also cause the barbell to go forwards. Drive the barbell vigorously upwards when the body and legs are extended and you are on the toes as in Figure 22. When the barbell has left the shoulders drive both feet apart, at exactly the same split second, and force the hips forwards under the barbell.

When the feet land as in Figure 23 the barbell will be well on its way to arms' length above the head. Press fiercely upwards with the arms and dip slightly under the barbell.

Do not get into the habit of dipping too low under the barbell as it reaches arms' length overhead. Too many lifters overthrow the barbell and when it starts to come down whilst still dipping with the legs it can, and often does, force the shoulders and elbows to unlock, and the lift is lost.

It is advisable, certainly in the early days of training, to practise driving the feet apart fore and aft, and trying to finish with an arms' drive rather than with a legs' dip.

To recover from Figure 23, follow the same method of recovery as used in the split Snatch.

Pause to show that the weight is under control once the arms, trunk and legs are vertical and the feet are in line.

Footnote: So many lifters are still fascinated by what they term the second knees-bend. In fact, it was in the 1950s that I first taught my coaches and lifters how the second knees-bend came about. What is described as the hips thrust in this chapter covers the above point. It is mainly an anatomical action which causes the so-called second knees-bend. During the pull the trunk and legs are activated by the hamstrings at the rear of the thighs and the gluteal muscles which bring the trunk to the vertical finish of the pull.

What is not generally known is that the hamstrings are attached below the knees and also when working vigorously tend to bend the knees. Also the calf muscles which raise the heels during the pull are attached above the knee joints. Therefore there is a strong tendency for the knees to bend again near the latter part of the pull, hence the great value of fiercely thrusting the hips FORWARDS and UPWARDS. This takes advantage of the so-called second knees-bend and greatly adds to the impetus to the barbell.

18
Modern Methods in Coaching
David Webster

David Webster, former chief Scottish weight-lifting coach (BAWLA), has won Scottish titles and broken Scottish records. He is qualified in a variety of sports and activities – Diploma of Physical Education. He is an excellent strand-puller and won a world title at this activity in 1954. He is the author of many books and contributes to weightlifting magazines in all parts of the world. He has appeared on various television stations teaching physical fitness, games, sports and outdoor activities. David has organised some of Scotland's biggest displays and sports exhibitions, and in 1985 played a major role in the organisation of the world junior weight-lifting championships in Edinburgh. He has filmed world and other major weightlifting championships for the IWF in Rome, Vienna, Budapest, Stockholm, Madrid and Sofia and was principal of the well-known Spartan Club in Aberdeen for many years. He has also excelled in hand-balancing and appeared with his partner at many physical-culture shows.

In weightlifting and weight-training, as in other sports, the coach plays an increasingly important part. More and more participants are realising that to get to the top they must devote their energies to the practical side of the business and if possible leave the theoretical aspects to a competent coach. It is, of course, very important that they do not come to 'lean' on the coach too heavily, and lifters, at all times, must take an intelligent interest in their training. However, the more a lifter can direct his powers to training and use his free time for relaxing and recuperation, the greater his chances of success.

This section is intended mainly for those who would like to help their fellow lifters, or perhaps some particular training companion. Even the lifter who trains himself will, I hope, find much of value in the part of this chapter which deals with such aspects as analyses of techniques.

It is my intention to cover briefly all aspects of coaching right from the beginner's stages of physical conditioning with weights to advanced coaching of world-class lifters.

In weightlifting groups of all descriptions there is a fairly high turnover of membership, and it is my belief that the biggest losses occur in the first few months of training. If potential trainees get a good start and fine results, then it is likely that they will stay in the game longer than otherwise would be the case. It is the coach's or leader's job to help them over this initial period.

During the early stages, and again in the most advanced stages, coaching can be a very time-consuming chore. The good coach must not only instruct: he must enthuse and inspire his charges. He should help create the relaxed and friendly atmosphere that makes training a pleasure and his instructions must be based on sound principles and on an extensive fund of PRACTICAL knowledge.

Let's get right down to details and see how a coach should set about the task in hand.

First of all, he must have the various exercises compiled correctly into good schedules and then he should ensure that records are kept either by himself or the trainee. I believe the trainee should be asked to get a notebook and write out the schedule, with repetitions weights, and so on, and as increases are made these are recorded. Think how valuable this is for a great many purposes. It acts as a great stimulant to further efforts when one can see at a glance just what progress is being made, and it is invaluable for reference when at a later stage one is carefully planning training.

The coach should then see the gymnasium is well laid out so that there is maximum space for working with minimum changing of equipment. I have found that rather than have lifters work on the same barbell all night and changing discs with every exercise to suit their needs, it is better to have a few barbells which always remain at certain areas with a particular job in mind.

For example, in my own club we have a special thick barbell which is always on the squat racks; it is comfortable and saves abuse of the other barbells. Furthermore, there are always two 25 kg weights on this barbell so that there is 75 kg already loaded; it doesn't take long to add a few discs to make up the required load. Similarly, for Bench Presses by the 'heavy brigade', we have an old Olympic barbell which always remains by the bench and a new Olympic barbell on the lifting platform which must be used for the two Olympic lifts only.

We find that this system of the lifters moving around and doing certain exercises in certain stations saves a lot of 'hogging' of the best barbells and instead the best ones for the job are used by everyone. As a further side-effect it also creates a more sociable atmosphere where lifters work in with other groups instead of getting in a corner (perhaps near the heater) with their own companions and never moving from there until it is time to leave the club.

When the lifting sessions actually start the coach's work also starts in earnest, too, and this is where the BAWLA coaching scheme shines, as its corps of instructors have been taught the best way to approach the subject. Obviously I cannot go into detail here on the use of the voice, qualities of leadership, assessing of pupils and so on. I will confine myself to the major points of class management and instruction.

If there are several persons in the group they must work in a formation so that they can all be seen – and also that they can see the coach for demonstrations. A semi-circle is worth considering, but do not try any formal approach with the pupils in straight lines. I would also advise the coach to use an informal manner at all times rather than a heavy 'master and pupil' technique. If the coach knows his subject well and can put it across convincingly he will earn respect without adopting a formal teaching voice and ordering folk about.

In teaching a weightlifting movement correctly there are certain facts one has to put across, and here is the approved method of incorporating all the essentials in teaching a new movement to beginners.

1. Name and purpose of the exercise. For example: 'Here is the Curl for the muscles in front of the upper arm.' As the coach says this he can indicate the biceps. Notice that in the early stages it is best not to use the names of the muscles, as although the biceps are well known one will be asking for trouble if mention of some of the lesser-known muscle groups is made. In stating the purpose it need not always be the muscles involved; the coach may wish to tell them that this is for warming up or for posture, or, if they are sportsmen, it could be to help a special aspect of their activity.

2. The coach should give a demonstration. Teaching through the eye is one of the easiest methods of teaching, so show them how the movement is done in good style. Having demonstrated this for, say, two or three repetitions without commenting on it, he can then add briefly the major points of performance so that the class avoids the most common mistakes.

3. Spoonfeed them. The coach must get them working as quickly as possible, without elaborating too much on the exercise at this stage, so now he must take the pupils step by step

through the movement. Get them to stand close to the barbell with their knees bent as they bend down. See that they keep their backs flat as they lift the weight from the floor, and so on.

4. Having given them the number of repetitions to perform, allow them to carry on with the exercise at their own speed as you *correct* and *encourage*.

This business of correcting and encouraging is where many of the qualities of a coach come into play. He should be able to spot faults very quickly and also be able to correct them without the performer having to lose face in any way. People are apt to be sensitive and sometimes resent having their mistakes pointed out to them.

Generally speaking, it is not so much being corrected they dislike, but the way they are corrected. I suggest that in class or group teaching the coach first corrects in a general way any mistakes he sees. Dealing with the major faults first, he would perhaps say such things as 'The body should be still, arms only moving', or 'Head up, backs flat'. Make the coaching positive and avoid negative teaching at all costs. If the initial comments do not have the desired effect he can give a well-directed look at the poor performer or even pause by him as he makes the correction. As they improve, compliment them briefly, without making a fuss. Little remarks like 'Well done' or 'That's better' is all that is necessary.

When they are having a breather before tackling the next movement one can recap in a few words or add a few further words of explanation. Remember, it is best to introduce just a little at a time with each movement. There should not be any time wasted between exercises; the class should be kept working at a good pace throughout their schedule. If there is a shortage of barbells and the group is working two to a barbell, then activity should be absolutely non-stop to produce a good workout for beginners.

Before leaving this sort of beginners' work here are just a few points which must be kept in mind. Avoid 'dead points' in the teaching. Some instructors, having given the preliminary details and number of repetitions, just dry up and stand still until the repetitions are completed. How awful. A class like this is boring and, of course, is not being taught correctly. One MUST COACH AND ENCOURAGE. There is no need to sound like a gramophone record, as there is a lot worth saying – and it should be said with changes of tone and even at times with a dash of humour. Move around the class, as mistakes can be seen easier from various angles, and this change of position is worth keeping in mind for demonstrations. For example, the coach could do his silent demonstration sideways to the class then turn to face them as he adds explanations to his demonstration.

Intermediate teaching

The coach should ensure that the group becomes self-sufficient as soon as possible, as it is neither possible nor desirable to devote all one's time to a single group. The class should then be broken up into small sections with two, three or four individuals of similar ability in each group. Ability should be the main factor in allocating training companions, but common sense will have to be used here so that there is no clashing of personalities.

Personal friendships outside the club, too, should be kept in mind. If an experienced member has brought along a friend it is quite likely that they will wish to train together. This is a good idea, as it would give the newcomer some extra guidance in addition to the coach's supervision.

At the intermediate level it is the coach's job to move around the club, giving hints here, encouragement there. Sometimes he should have a chat with a lifter after his workout to point out how improvements or refinements can be made in training. He should always help with the compiling of schedules and introduce new exercises by the method outlined earlier.

The intelligent leader will also prevent 'bottlenecks' from occurring by persons monopolising certain pieces of equipment, such as a bench or machine, and he should also be on the lookout for incorrect exercising technique, as these will spread rapidly. Make sure that ordinary Curls, for example, are not converted into Cheating Curls, and also ensure that when Cheating Curls are done they do exercise the arms and not put the work mainly onto the back. This is just one example, but there are many more, such as lifting the hips in bench pressing, bending forwards in Squats and pulling the knees inwards on recovery, and so on. These will quickly become accepted methods of performance unless the coach steps in at an early stage.

Advanced coaching

Reams of paper could be written about coaching at each stage, and particularly at the most advanced level, because here the lifter is competing in important competitions and needs the services of a good coach. Furthermore, in preparation for these events the performer must be completely dedicated if he is to reach the top, and quantity and quality of training are of great importance.

The coach can ensure that the quality of training is of the required standard and he can help to ensure that the quantity of training is also correct, not only by supervision but by attending to the many time-consuming details such as the planning of workouts, keeping records, keeping abreast of current developments in technique and any change of rules. By freeing the lifters from such responsibilities and keeping them informed he makes a major contribution to their performances.

The coach must, however, go much deeper into things than this. He should constantly supervise the lifting, training himself to immediately spot errors and to be able to correctly diagnose the cause of these mistakes. This is probably the hardest job of all. It is easy enough to see what happens, but not one

in a hundred can, without a great deal of experience and training, get to the root of the trouble. Even very experienced coaches cannot give an immediate diagnosis after a lift, and this is no disgrace. Far too many people will tell the lifter what went wrong immediately after a bad lift – but how often is their opinion the correct one? Very seldom.

Here are a few tips to help you to analyse performances and diagnose any faults.

Stand well back from the lifter and compare the movement of the barbell and the lifter with fixed points on the platform and the background. A Murray Cross (training cross devised by the former British National Coach, Al Murray) on the centre of the platform is a great help because as the feet land it can be seen at a glance in which direction the lifter jumped. A vertical line somewhere in the back-

Correct finishing position for the Snatch – upright, with arms and legs locked. The lifter is Tadeusz Rutkowski of Poland

ground, preferably in line with the starting position of the barbell or front line of the cross, is of considerable value. It may be a line specially painted or chalked, but a high-jump stand, height-measuring stick or even a spare 6 ft barbell can all be used. Even the edge of a door is helpful. This shows clearly whether the barbell or lifter is moving forwards or backwards and at which stage this takes place.

I am a great believer in using cine film, not only for helping to show the lifter good technique, but also for analysing the faults of club lifters. Cine analysis like this is also of tremendous value to the coach in training himself to know exactly what happens and when it happened with individual lifters. It is only since going into this business that I have realised just what a lot of nonsense has been spoken and written over the years.

In both cine analysis and club-room correction I find it suitable to consider certain key positions. Most mistakes can be traced back to these positions for simple explanations and it is easy to show movements between these key factors.

In snatching and cleaning, the key positions are:

1. As the barbell leaves the floor: not the position as he grasps the barbell but the actual position the lifter is in as the barbell begins to move upwards.
2. As the barbell passes the knees.
3. At the point of greatest body extension.
4. At the maximum height of the barbell. This is a stage which sometimes can be missed.
5. At the lowest point of the lift.

In the jerk, the key positions are:

1. Prior to the dip.
2. The lowest point of the dip.
3. At the full extension as the foot or feet breaks contact with the floor.
4. As the feet land.
5. The lowest position.

Obviously the lift happens so fast that it is difficult, even with the trained naked eye, to spot exact positions; but the key positions do provide an extremely useful guide.

In cine work these positions really come into their own and are invaluable for analysis, timing and measuring.

It is not within the scope of this chapter to give examples of analysis, but by combining the knowledge gained from perusal of the chapter on Olympic technique and the information given here the coach will not find it difficult to assess the lifts of champions and club members alike.

A useful coaching practice is to make film loops by cutting the film into lengths of about 4 to 6 ft (making sure they show complete lifts) and joining the two ends together. When projected one can watch the same lifts over and over again, each time looking for a different point, or, if studying a good lift, 'brainwashing' oneself with the points which are perfect. For such study it is essential that the film was taken with the camera on a tripod, or else camera movement may give a false impression.

Certain projectors specially made for analysis can show the film at normal speed, ultra-slow motion, or even frame-by-frame projection regardless of which speed was used when filming.

Visual aids such as films, photos, slides, models and charts are excellent for teaching on courses and in clubs provided they are not allowed to become too time-consuming or 'gimmicky'. They must only be used for a specific purpose and should always be kept in perspective.

As can be seen, the coach is expected to be a teacher, psychologist, taskmaster, bookkeeper, organiser and even something of a scientist. He should never hesitate to admit to himself shortcomings in any of these respects and for the sake of his charges he should supplement his personal knowledge by getting the assistance of others. There is one thing, however, which he *must* have if he is to succeed – a bond of sympathy and friendship with those in his care.

19

A New Concept in Olympic Weightlifting
John Lear

John Lear, who succeeded Al Murray as Britain's national weightlifting coach in 1972, has an excellent background of physical education, weightlifting experience and competitive ability. He was educated at Royal Shrewsbury School, attended the City of Cardiff College of Physical Education, earning a Diploma of Physical Education, and taught at Campions School, Boreham Wood, Herts, from 1959 to 1973. He was the British coach at the Olympic Games in 1972, 1976, 1980 and 1984, also at the Commonwealth Games in 1966, 1970, 1974, 1978, 1982 and 1986. In 1965 and 1966 he had spells as the national coach in Iran and South Korea. John has also been the IWF coach responsible for coaching clinics in Denmark, Thailand, People's Republic of China, Japan, New Zealand and America, and is a lecturer to other sporting bodies on weight-training and fitness training. As a weightlifting competitor he has represented England.

Dramatic developments in the methods of training and preparation for weightlifting have taken place in recent years. Although there have been little changes in technique the time devoted to training has increased considerably.

It is known that in some countries lifters are now training three times a day on six days a week. This is, of course, quite impossible for most lifters and needs very thorough medical supervision as well as careful coaching and early selection of those participants who are capable of following such a regime.

In the Soviet Union, Bulgaria, East Germany, Poland and Cuba the lifters now live in special training camps and schools. Many of the establishments are under the auspices of the armed forces or trade unions, but some are directly State sponsored. They do, however, provide full-time training and, in the schools, education for the young men who attend them.

To give a clear understanding of the selection and training processes I will describe the Bulgarian methods and will also discuss how such information might be adapted to the British situation and give a training programme devised by the coaching committee of the British Amateur Weight Lifters' Association (BAWLA). The description of the Bulgarian methods are based on the work of Yordan Ivanov and Ivan Abadjiev, national coaches of Bulgaria and both highly honoured in their country.

SELECTION PROCESS

One of the major problems which is becoming more important is to find, at an early age, sportsmen who possess special qualities necessary in weightlifting and which can be developed to the highest level.

Experience has shown that there is a change in the general conception for the age from which the initial and later special training in weightlifting must start. The nervous and muscular systems are highly plastic and so present the ideal opportunity for correct and fast training of motive habits.

The selection starts at the age of twelve and is carried out along the line of specialised sporting schools and sports secondary schools.

The specialised sports schools are very much the province of the club and district control. Comprehensive conditions and specialist coaches are provided and under the direction of specialist coaches many hundreds of young weightlifters are being trained.

The sports secondary schools are new and free board and general education are provided. Weightlifting is being developed in many sports schools under specialist coaches, and it is hoped that when this system is developed under specialist coaches the number of pupils will reach more than 500 and the age limits will be from twelve to eighteen. The problems encountered are to find those boys with sporting talent who indicate that they will show good future results and who have a high level of intelligence and academic ability. To this end selection is carried out in three stages: mass selection, special selection, final selection.

Mass selection

This is carried out from 15 September to 15 October in each year in schools among the twelve-year-old groups. Specialist coaches visit the physical education lessons which show the general level of physical fitness and ability. Selection is then made according to the following principles: development of bone and muscular systems, height and weight, proportional measurements (body/limbs), general coordination.

This gives a general impression of the physical qualities of the boys. Their intellectual development is considered and the coaches and teachers, physical education teachers and parents. This mass selection will result in the formation of a group of twenty-two to twenty-five boys from within the school.

Special selection

This takes place from 16 to 30 October. The selection procedure is now conducted in the sports hall where the level of the development of personal physical qualities is determined, and in the sports clinic where the health condition is checked and anthropometric data are taken.

The following tests are performed:

Physical qualities
(a) Strength: Pull strength on a dynamometer, wrist strength on a dynamometer, number of press-ups, abdominal strength (measured by leg raises to horizontal from hanging).
(b) Speed: 30- and 60-metre dashes with high and low starts.
(c) Flexibility: Spine and pelvic girdle joints, shoulder joints for flexion and hyper extension, deep squat with feet flat on floor without bending the body.
(d) Spring: High jump from standing position, long jump from standing position.
(e) Skill: Agility and coordination through a popular game, psychology of boys in competitive situation.

Medical Tests. These include general health, internal condition, possibility of infection, sight and hearing and height and weight, measurements of chest, neck, waist, thigh, shin, knee joint; width of shoulders, back/front of thorax, transversal diameter of thorax, lengths of thumb, arm and forearm, body and lower limbs; lung capacity, pulse and blood pressure before and after loading; dynamometrics of arms, shoulders, body and leg strength.

It is emphasised that the cardio-vascular system must be in excellent condition, and will deal further with this later. From these batteries of tests special selection is completed for a group of some fifteen to eighteen boys who have displayed the best physical and anatomical/physiological qualities without any health problems.

Final selection

This is carried out from 1 November to 3 December. In this period the main problem is to select those boys who show positive psychological qualities and a high ability to learn the taught material. Also of great importance is the display of activity during the training session. The sports specialists will have mind, however, that this age group is characterised by a fast rate of physical development and many psychological changes. No hasty decisions must be taken in excluding boys at this stage. Finally, a group of twelve to fourteen boys are selected and these start a special programme devised to solve the problems of this age group.

In the selection of boys certain additional problems arise:

(a) The height of the pupils. For the lighter classes it is found that the height of those selected is generally shorter than the national average at such bodyweights. Lifters of higher bodyweight categories, however, are similar in height to those athletes participating in other sports. It is established that weightlifting does not restrict height growth in the young.

(b) It is important to consult with parents as many will believe there is a possibility of damage to the growing organism because of the nature of the sport. It is explained that the training sessions in these early years are directed towards all-round development of the young organism. The special preparation for weightlifting takes up only 10 to 15 per cent of total training time and a great deal of physical training is done.

(c) These young boys will have little experience of life and will tend to accept everything, whether good or bad, without being able to distinguish. It is, therefore, most important that the coach should constantly be with the pupils, teaching, directing and organising their activities so that a firm foundation can be laid down to develop future world-class weightlifters.

ADVANCED TRAINING

Having seen the ideas behind the planning and structure of a broad-based junior development scheme, we now look at the situation that a

young lifter may find himself in having been through several years of carefully organised general and specific training.

We shall now look at the basic principles for the arrangement of the educational training process of the most outstanding Bulgarian lifters. The training of these athletes is under the direction of the coach to the Bulgarian national team, Ivan Abadjiev.

The development of Bulgarian weightlifting to its present remarkable heights has taken place over the past fifteen or so years. Prior to this the Bulgarians were unable to compete with other leading nations and, indeed, at the Tokyo and Mexico Olympic Games they were unable to place in the first six in any class. Since then, however, there have been dramatic changes in that they were able to win the world team title in Manila in 1974 from the Soviet Union. There have been big rewards for this with a multi-million pound sports complex and hotel solely for weightlifting built in Sofia.

The sports development, has, therefore, been very rapid and in many respects this has been because of the single-mindedness of Abadjiev himself. Initially he encountered problems with parents, educationalists and the medical profession. The coaches programme the training as follows:

Choice of exercises

First, the structure of the training session will depend on the selection of exercises and their number. This proper choice is essential for the effective planning of the training. Since the sport has an emphasis on the speed/strength (power) element, it is essential to select not only the type of exercise, but also the resistance.

There are different forms of strength:

(a) *Personal strength qualities* – as when there is considerable resistance to be overcome, as in weightlifting.

(b) *Speed-strength* as in discus throwing, shot-putt and so on.

(c) *Dynamic strength*.
(d) *Motivated strength*.

Although these forms of strength are basic, there are various ways of achieving them and these methods will depend on the magnitude of the resistance and the speed of the moving body. Basically in weightlifting the personal strength qualities are developed, but as during the training session the resistance varies, starting with light-to-middle, to maximum, to middle loadings, certain variations in strength development occur. The smaller the load the greater the speed. The greater the speed the smaller the strength development.

From this it follows that the magnitude of strength is inversely proportionate to the speed. Strength development at great speeds is less significant. It does not mean that because the resistance is low that energy is saved. On the contrary, at greater speeds with lighter weights considerable quantities of energy are used. It often happens that lifters wanting to make things easier avoid using very heavy weights, but although the barbell weighs less they reach conditions of great fatigue early.

It is, therefore, fair to conclude that top weights lifted at maximum speed will best develop the specific qualities of a weightlifter. One must also realise that the development of the strength abilities will also depend on the technical nature of the selected exercises. Even minimal deviation from the correct technical movements leads to the development of other muscle groups which can hamper the correct realisation of these exercises.

According to the Soviet coach Roman, technique is closely related to the effort and speed with which the weight is lifted. So it can be concluded that the lifting of fixed loaded weights in the classical techniques best develops the most specific speed-spacial characteristics (technique) and, in addition, in order to develop most effectively the speed-strength qualities, the lifter must use weights nearly as heavy as the competition ones using the classical or part-classical exercises. This

will help in the development of the m correct techniques through getting to gr with the problem under 'real' conditions. I not confuse this with the type of techni work using light weights to develop moveme pathways that we use in Britain with beg ners. Further, a good basic technical bac ground will be essential to these m advanced methods and the Bulgarians v have seen to this in their junior traini preparations.

It is also important to realise that the weig tlifting strength magnitude that can developed, and which will be displayed great speed, will depend on the lifter's absolt strength.

Bearing in mind these considerations, t following exercises are chosen:

(a) *Classical Exercises:* (1) Snatch, (2) Cle and Jerk.
(b) *Semi-classical Exercises:* (1) Squat a Clean, (2) Jerk from rack with split.
(c) *Similar to Classical Exercises:* (1) Pow Snatch, (2) Power Clean, (3) Power Jei (4) Front Squat, (5) Jerk Heave with abo 100 per cent weight, (6) Pull for Snat with about 100 per cent weight, (7) P for Jerk with about 100 per cent weigl (8) Snatch from hang start.
(d) *Exercises with isometric character:* (1) Pi for Snatch with a weight close maximum, (2) Pull for Jerk with a weig close to maximum, (4) Half Jerk with fix weights.

These exercises, which make up the m important part of the training, are chos based on the ideas of strength developme previously mentioned. In the same way t number of exercises for each day, wee month, year and multi-year cycles a established.

Exercise arrangement

We will now look at the arrangement of tl weekly selection of exercises. These a selected from the following list and include morning and afternoon training on Monday, Wednesday and Friday, and morning only on Tuesday and Saturday. The general physical training, in which ball games are included for a change and a rest, take place in the afternoon and on Thursday in the morning.

A typical daily programme for Monday, Wednesday and Friday may be as follows: *Morning*: Snatch, Power Jerk from rack, Power Clean, Front Squat, Pull for Snatch 100 per cent, Jerk Heave 100 per cent.
Afternoon: Jerk, Seated Press, Snatch from hang start, Bench Press, Pull for Jerk 100 per cent.

As we can see from the programme, the dosage of exercise is as follows: (1) Classical Exercises – three times per week; (2) Semi-classical Exercise – two times per week; (3) Similar to Classical Exercises – three times per week; (4) Exercises with isometric character – two times per week; (5) Recuperation Exercises – three times per week.

Exercises are also timed as follows: Snatch and Clean and Jerk – 35 minutes; Power Snatch, Power Clean, Power Jerk, Snatch from hang, Front Squat – 25 minutes each; Pulling movement and Jerk Heave – 20 minutes; Seated Press and Bench Press – 15 minutes.

The programme must be developed to achieve one's goals with the least wasted energy. Basically, the same programme of exercises is followed throughout the year without variation. The only changes made are: during the last twenty-five to twenty days prior to an important competition, the lifters train on a changed plan in which all exercises of an isometric nature are eliminated and sessions are every other day. During the last two weeks, training is only once a day.

Exercise arrangement

Exercise	Monday	Tuesday	Wednesday	Friday	Saturday
1 Snatch	X		X	X	
2 Clean and Jerk	X		X	X	
3 Power Snatch	X		X	X	
4 Power Clean	X		X	X	
5 Power Jerk	X		X	X	
6 Front Squat	X		X	X	
7 Back Squat		X			X
8 Jerk from rack		X			X
9 Squat Clean		X			X
10 Snatch Pull 100 per cent	X		X	X	
11 Jerk Pull 100 per cent	X		X	X	
12 Jerk Heave 100 per cent	X		X	X	
13 Snatch Pull maximum		X			X
14 Jerk Pull maximum		X			X
15 Jerk Heave maximum		X			X
16 Bench Press	X		X	X	
17 Seated Press	X		X	X	
18 Snatch hang start	X		X	X	

The adaptive process

It would appear that the lack of variety, both in loading and exercise choice for long periods of time, might result in fatigue and boredom. But Abadjiev is quick to point out that in everyday life many people are engaged in eight or more hours of often hard and boring work each day. He gives examples of coalminers, labourers and also Paganini, who played the violin for up to fourteen hours a day in practice.

The fact that there are no pathological cases of fatigue or breakdown in such work is explained by the enormous adaptive abilities of the human organism. The more frequently a movement is performed the better one should become at performing it. Arcady Vorobyev, a former world champion and now a leading Soviet doctor, states that weightlifters should be able to achieve high results at any time of the year. This will mean that all through the year the lifter should change neither the means nor the methods for training. Resulting from this the problem of deciding how much loading should be planned for each exercise, daily training and weekly, monthly and yearly cycles.

It is known that the training loads are a physiological stimulant which causes corresponding response actions in the human organism. The bigger the loadings, the stronger the response actions in the organs and systems. As a result of this, deeper physiological, morphological and psychological changes are observed. However, this does not mean that the overload can be infinitely big. This loading will depend on the training level of consequent qualification of the lifter. The more comprehensive the training, the greater will be the adaptive development, and the greater the adaptive development, so the more comprehensive will be the training methods that can be employed.

All experiments show that there are no limits to the adaptive abilities of the human organism and that by skilful arrangement of training from the earliest years the lifter can be accustomed to great loads as an endless process.

These adaptive qualities can be best developed in two ways:

(a)   *Quickly, spontaneously, for a short time.* An example of this is with the beginner, who after three or four sessions becomes accustomed to the loading (stiffness and so on starts to disappear). With the advanced lifter, quick, short-term overloading on training can lead to sharp-response adaptive reaction. These changes are called stresses. Such stress conditions are an important moment in the preparation of lifters and are placed into the weekly and monthly training programmes.

(b)   *The adaptive reactions can be very slow* in taking place over a long period of time. Such reactions ensure stable, adaptive formations in the organs and systems. However, if the stimulants remain the same their ability to influence can weaken.

The sporting qualities will remain at a level for a certain period of time, but will then gradually diminish. This may be avoided if progress is to continue. Some coaches, ourselves included, have recommended that when we see indications of the fall-off in the adaptive development of the lifter, as when he shows signs of staleness, fatigue and the like, we should reduce the loading. This will, of course, result in a further reduction of the already weakening adaptation. This has been our policy based on former Soviet research which indicated that after a period of six weeks of very hard training it would be necessary to cut back on the loading if further progress was to be made.

This policy may still be applicable to the great majority of our lifters, but if as a coach you have used these methods in programme planning for the very best lifters, then the six-week training cycle as described earlier already has built into it an excuse to limit one's efforts.

The Bulgarians do not use such a system, but plan only step-like increases in the training effort by INCREASING the loading when the adaptive process shows any signs of breakdown. Of course, this is only possible with those lifters who have high endurability based on the already achieved adaptations that have taken place over a long period throughout their youth programme.

Tonnage and intensity

The Bulgarian research has shown that the best development of the sporting competitive qualities is not greatly influenced by increasing training volume.

It is known that the training developments depend not only on the tonnage, but more importantly on the intensity of the training. Volume will depend on time, but the intensity does not, and since time is limited the volume will also be limited. The intensity, which does not depend to a large degree on the duration of the training session, can grow infinitely and in consequence the increase of intensity will lead to the increase of volume (increase in volume does not, of course, ensure an increase in intensity.)

It has always been my own belief that in order to lift heavy weights one must train with heavy weights. This theory was at one time challenged by advocates of the tonnage method of training and seems to be borne out by this approach. For example, the Bulgarians have increased the tonnage of their lifters by 1½ times since 1968, but via the increasing intensity of their training process. This intensity training is also connected with the psychological development of the lifter, creating great willpower and a fearless approach to maximum weights. Bearing this in mind, high-intensity training plays a central part in the Bulgarian plans.

Each Friday the training sessions are planned to be 'stress loaded'. The intensity training to achieve this is planned as follows:

Magnitude of weight	Sets	Reps
Over record	1	1
Record	1	1
10 kg under record	2	2
20 kg under record	2	4–5

So the intensity in our kind of sport is determined by the number of approaches and the number of lifts that need considerable efforts during one training session.

The plan can be changed according to the liabilities of the lifter during the training session (with possible advice prior to the session), but the general idea is to make the lifters used to this type of training. The lifters are coached to handle weights which are real in their demands for great effort in the condition of the competitive time-spatial characteristics. During the first repetitions the barbell must be moved with great velocity (speed training plays an important part in all their workouts) and during the last repetitions it must achieve all the characteristics of lifting top weights.

The most important aspect of their training is concerned with intensity and the following will illustrate how the tonnage will vary in the month's cycle showing three weeks of high volume followed by a week of lighter volume. Note how the volume changes for each day within the week's cycle.

Three consecutive weeks

Monday – 25 tons; Tuesday – 12 tons; Wednesday – 22 tons; Thursday – rest; Friday – 27 tons (stress training day); Saturday – 6 tons; Sunday – rest. Total – 288 tons.

One week

Monday – 15 tons; Tuesday – 7 tons; Wednesday – 15 tons; Thursday – rest; Friday – 19 tons (stress training day); Saturday – 6 tons; Sunday – rest. Total – 62 tons. Total for one month – 350 tons.

This then is a broad look at the methods currently being used in Bulgaria.

A BRITISH VIEW – SECTION 1

What does all this mean to us? It is very complex and in trying to find channels we might follow, we start off from a most disadvantageous position. As stated at the beginning, we cannot hope to equal all the material advantages, but things do improve slowly for our lifters and standards are continually rising.

It will be very difficult to help all but a few who have special abilities, from our group of senior lifters, by trying to adapt these Bulgarian programmes. However, there are certain clues to rapid progress for future lifters, and I believe that we must revise our attitude to the training of schoolboy and early junior groups.

Let us consider the very young lifter first. Without helping it, practically all his time will be spent on lifting. He will be trying to improve his strength ability and consequently the weights lifted. He will be concerned with competition, and we as coaches will encourage him in this aim. But let us be honest. The weights lifted by the very young in terms of competitions will be inconsequential and give little relevant indication of his future development.

That a boy lifts 30 kg or 40 kg at the age of fourteen does not bear any relevance to the real lifting that he should be doing between the critical years of eighteen to twenty two. The nature of the training system that he follows in trying to improve his 40 kg lift, necessitating high-intensity/low-endurance work, may really be actively preventing his future development.

We have seen that Abadjiev follows a programme in which the adaptive processes of the organism are constantly pushed. To quote from his lecture: 'Of course, this is possible only after we have in mind the normal endurability of the weightlifter which is based on the already-achieved adaptation.'

This suggests that from the earliest age of selection the young lifter is subjected to a training process that lays down a basis of physical fitness that will support the true training programmes, based on the progressive overloading of the adaptive processes, in the critical age range of eighteen to twenty two. Indeed, Abadjiev points out that the work with weightlifting takes up only 10 to 15 per cent of the training time with the youngest lifters. (Perhaps for our lifters of a similar age group it is well above 75 per cent.) Naturally this

percentage changes as the lifter grows older, so that eventually he is working on weightlifting for 80 to 90 per cent of his training time when he is a senior.

We must look at the physiology of training for a while and what its considerations mean to us. First, we need to be fit to be successful in any activity, and I suggest that weightlifting fitness means the ability to work at increasing and stressful loads and to be able to recover quickly so that the training process can continue with success.

This must be the basis of our training planning. Most of our lifters do not have the necessary type of physical fitness and consequently the levels of loading at which they are able to train must be low. There are many components of fitness, such as strength and mobility, but we are basically concerned with

The split-style Snatch – not practised much nowadays, shown by John McNiven of Scotland

the function of the heart. This organ must work very efficiently in order that the conditions of my definition of weightlifting fitness can be achieved.

We need to develop high levels of cardio-respiratory function. In all activities we need oxygen – at rest about one third of a litre and during exercise up to five litres per minute. This latter demand may necessitate an intake of up to 100 litres of air per minute. When we work this system we are said to be working aerobically, burning up oxygen and sugar. Basic fitness requires great efficiency of this system, and in order to develop its efficiency we need to train for long periods of time at a level just below anaerobic state. Work below 160 pulse beats per minute is aerobic and above anaerobic. But anaerobic work has to be done at certain stages of training. This is really cardio-vascular work and is stress training – high-intensity work such as maximums or short-burst running, necessitating a rest between attempts. Much of our weightlifting work is of this nature.

The results of these types of training are as follows: aerobic or steady-state training produces a heart with large chambers. This development results in more blood being pumped out with each beat and has a better coronary blood supply. When working at high intensity (anaerobic), the muscle of the heart is greatly strengthened, developing thick muscle walls, but the size of the chambers is not increased. This means that while the heart can work strongly, its capacity is limited. This would be typical of the heart of the weightlifter as we know him, resulting in a low endurance level and poor recovery capacity from large blocks of work.

When we move into the area of real weightlifting training, our main concern will be to develop strength. Therefore, we must work on very high-intensity levels. Unless we have done a great deal of previous training of a steady nature to build up the function of the heart, the levels at which we can work and recover quickly will be low. While one might contend

that the young lifter also has his school physical education to back him up, much of this work is also high-intensity/short-duration and not enough steady-state work is done to balance this.

It is essential to improve the heart output to accommodate future great loading in critical training programmes. Very high pulse-rate work without previous steady-state training will not permit future and progressive development of overloads. All of us expect great increases in the training loads of our charges, but as I have explained this may be difficult to achieve if previous early training has not equipped them to accept this loading. It is therefore essential that in the training of young boys a very strong basis of general fitness, that is heart capacity first, heart muscle strength second, must be laid down. We should develop this capacity early and maintain it along with the heart muscle strengthening work as produced by weightlifting. This means that at the earliest stages only a small percentage of training time is spent on weights but more running and light technical work with the weights.

This is the foundation that Bulgarian, Soviet Union and East German systems follow through their youth programmes, and that is the reason for the production of high-calibre lifters in their early twenties. In conjunction with this, of course, will have been the selection process that we considered initially.

Finally, after having considered the Bulgarian, Soviet Union and East German philosophies of training and as they are practised at the present time, we may come to the conclusion that we as coaches might also be responsible for the comparatively low standards by encouraging lifters in the belief that they are only capable of certain levels of loading. We must change this and encourage them to work harder. Much of this must be psychological persuasion. As Abadjiev pointed out: 'The body has great capacity for work and we must not be too quick to set limiting factors.'

A BRITISH VIEW – SECTION 2: BAWLA COACHING PLAN FOR THE TRAINING OF LIFTERS OF ADVANCED QUALIFICATION

As one of the principal aims of training is to show continually improving results, it is essential that those qualities of which we have already spoken should be fully developed. This will take time, possibly many years, and bearing this in mind it is essential that planning be undertaken by the coach or lifter.

Planning falls into two categories – those of a long-term nature and those of short-term. Short-term plans will be 'run-ups' to major competitions and as such are part of the long-term plan. Within the plan detailed, realistic analysis of all goals to be achieved must be considered. This involves consideration of the sports calendar, the preparation of individual sessions, organisation of the week's training, month and month-group cycles, and these together make up the final plan whether it be for a unit of six, nine or twelve months. These cycles, within the plan, will have different emphasis according to the relationship time-wise, to principal competitions, and may be selected for the development of skill and technique, powerbuilding, fitness, and so on.

Group planning can be employed, but for most advanced lifters plans are individually prepared. Such plans, however, will have the same ingredients as those for the group, but it will be likely that additional technical work, supplementary exercises and varied overload and volume will be included. Generally speaking, the advanced lifter should train all the year round, and this training can be broken down into two main cycles planned for two major competitions. There should be intermediate competitions as results in these will be used to determine the load for the forthcoming cycle. They will also help to show up weaknesses, both technical and also in the previously completed training cycle. Lifters should compete five or six times a year, with two of these being competitions in which it is

hoped to achieve the highest results, but at intermediate competitions the lifter should still aim for personal-best lifts as these will be the essential steps of progress and confidence reinforcement.

Each major competition for which we plan must have a training cycle based on the following periods: Preparatory, competitive and transitional.

Preparatory period

The length of this period will depend on the qualification of the lifter; indeed, for those in the novice category all their training may be considered under this heading. Much consideration must be given to the development of fitness, speed, coordination and endurance in the early stages. The advanced lifter spends most of his time on the assistance exercises with time devoted to the classical lifts being small. Towards the end of this period, however, more attention will be given to the Snatch and Clean and Jerk.

Competition period

During this period greater attention is paid to the classical lifts and those assistance exercises closely related to them. Maximum weights, within the range of 90 to 100 per cent, are

A side view of the squat Clean shown by David Morgan (Wales)

used more frequently and certain exercises are advanced to the 110 per cent range. During the last thirty to twenty days before competition those exercises which are slow and use maximum weights are generally reduced or excluded. The emphasis should be placed on power, so weights in the region of 90 per cent plus are best used. Only a few of the most advanced lifters apply maximums in Pulls and Squats during the last fourteen to seven days and then only with some five or six single lifts. During this period energy expenditure should not be high.

Transitional period

This period is a link between the competitive and a new preparatory period to be followed, and should provide the lifter with a period of active rest. It should be arranged so that while the volume and intensity of the load are decreased and the number of training sessions in the week's cycle is cut down, the essential high levels of physical fitness are maintained and improved. This period can last up to four weeks.

It is essential to remember that in all planning the organism cannot maintain a steady high level for a long period, and its efficiency tends to rise and fall. This must be taken into consideration when preparing all work cycles and the volume and intensity of the load must be varied to provide weeks of maximum, large, medium and light loads, and indeed within each week similar loading for each training session.

Many of those lifters who enjoy ideal training conditions are able to train twice a day, morning and afternoon. Their workload is very high and they are placed in situations of great physical stress. Such lifters have very high levels of physical fitness and recuperative powers and their tolerance to the stressful situation is well developed. Such work requires careful medical supervision at all stages.

The following is a long-term plan which has been prepared for lifters of the highest qualific-

ation in our country. It gives a build-up to two major competitions and although it is prepared on a group basis, i.e., for all lifters of the national A squad, coaches and lifters are advised to make individual changes where they consider them to be necessary.

The initial programme is aimed at producing high totals at the British Championships in the early spring and at the EEC Cup Tournament usually in April. As all the team are committed to lift in their divisional championships which have to be completed by 30 November and many will also lift in the under-23 championships in December, the programme is designed to start in the week beginning 8 December. If lifters are able to start a week or two earlier (depending on the date of the divisionals) so much the better. This gives a twelve-week build-up to the British Championships and a further few weeks build-up to the EEC Tournament. The first twelve weeks will be considered initially.

This period will be split up into three blocks, weeks 1–4, weeks 5–10 and weeks 11–12. During weeks 1–4 and 5–10 the same basic schedule will be followed, but during weeks 1–4 all exercises will be done with five sets of five reps (with the exception of hyperextensions which will be three sets of ten reps throughout). During weeks 5–10 all exercises are done with three sets of five reps, then five sets of three reps, hyperextensions included. All sets are done with a progressively heavier weight until the last set, which is a 'dropdown' set, i.e., the heaviest set is always the last but one.

A system of heavy and light weeks is used alternately, i.e., week 1 is light, week 2 heavy, week 3 light and so on. However, there is a definite progression – in week 4 the lifter should aim to get a best-ever for five reps in most lifts. Let us consider the Snatch as an example, in which we will say the lifter's record for a single is 100 kg. He should start week 1 with a top set of five reps at about 70 per cent, i.e., 70 kg. In week 2 it is up to 75 kg, week 3 down to 72½ kg, and then week

4 up to 80 kg (80 per cent) for a new best of five reps.

This progression of heavy and light weeks carries on for weeks 5–10, but the reps change, as mentioned, and three-rep bests are worked on, aiming for about 90 per cent for three reps in week 9.

It is considered that for national-calibre lifters four workouts per week are the absolute minimum for progress, and five are better. Some lifters will work six. With this in mind two separate schedules have been worked out to cater for lifters who train four times per week, or five times per week. The exercises listed are suggested and others may be put in at the discretion of the lifter and his coach. This may be to cater for individual weaknesses. Also, the order of the exercises may be changed, e.g., if a lifter is a weak jerker he may put this exercise first.

For a lifter who trains four times a week

Day 1 – Snatch, Power Clean, Clean Pull, Jerk from rack, Back Squat.

Day 2 – Snatch balance (behind neck or split), Power Snatch, Snatch Pull, Front Squat (Split Squat), Press Behind Neck, hyperextensions.

Day 3 – Snatch balance (in front or split), Power Clean, Clean Pull, Jerk from rack, Back Squat.

Day 4 – Clean, Power Snatch, Snatch Pull, Front Squat (lunge/split squat), Press Behind Neck, hyperextensions.

In a normal week on this schedule it is suggested that ideally the lifter trains on two days, rests one, trains two, rests two. However, this may not be possible for everyone.

For a lifter who trains five times a week

Day 1 – Snatch Balance (behind neck or split), Power Snatch, Snatch Pull, Front Squat (lunge), Press Behind Neck.

Day 2 – Power Clean, Clean Pull, Jerk from rack, Back Squat, hyperextensions.

Day 3 – Snatch, Clean, Snatch Pull, Clean Pull.

Day 4 – Snatch Balance (in front or split), Power Snatch, Snatch Pull, Front Squat (lunge), Press Behind Neck.

Day 5 – Power Clean, Clean Pull, Jerk from rack, Back Squat, hyperextensions.

It is suggested that a lifter trains five days in a row, or train three, rest one, train two, rest one. After this ten-week programme the last two weeks prior to the British Championships should be as follows. All exercises with the exception of Pulls should comprise three sets of three reps, then five single lifts, working up in lifts to intended starting attempts, or at least 10 kg below. Pulls should be three sets of three reps, followed by five sets of two reps. Here is the schedule.

Week 11:
Monday – Snatch, Snatch Pull, Front Squat (lunge), hyperextensions.
Tuesday – Clean and Jerk, Clean Pull, Back Squat, hyperextensions.
Thursday – Power Snatch, Power Clean, Squat Lunge.
Friday – Snatch, Clean and Jerk.

Week 12:
Monday and Tuesday – as for week 11.
Wednesday – Power Snatch three sets of three reps, plus three sets of two reps, Power Clean and Jerk with the same sets and reps as the Power Snatch.

Following the British Championships on the Saturday, there should be several days of active rest followed by light training. For the following nine weeks a programme of three-weekly cycles of light, medium and heavy work begins. The lifter will train on the original four/five days per week programme he used in weeks 1–10 prior to the British Championships, except that he will now substitute an extra Snatch and Clean exercise instead of the Power Clean and Power Snatch, i.e., he will use the Clean and Snatch twice a week and the Power Snatch and Power Clean once a week. He should Clean *and* Jerk in one of these sessions.

All Pulls should now be done with eight sets of three reps. Squats should be done with three sets of five reps followed by five sets of three reps. The breakdown of sets and reps for the light, medium and heavy weeks for all other exercises is as follows:

	Light	Medium	Heavy
Snatch and Clean and Jerk	5 sets 3 reps	2 sets 3 reps 8 sets 2 reps	2 sets 3 reps 2 sets 2 reps 8 singles
Snatch and Snatch balance	5 sets 3 reps	5 sets 3 reps	5 sets 3 reps
Press Behind Neck	3 sets 5 reps 3 sets 3 reps	3 sets 5 reps 3 sets 3 reps	3 sets 5 reps 3 sets 3 reps
Power Snatch and Power Clean	5 sets 3 reps	3 sets 3 reps 3 sets 2 reps	3 sets 3 reps 3 sets 2 reps

At the end of the ninth week, i.e., three cycles of the above, the lifter uses the same programme as he did for the two weeks prior to the British Championships.

Following the EEC Cup lifters should take a month of active rest from lifting. However, this does not mean no training. On the contrary, this time should be spent on fitness training during which the lifter will try to increase his cardio-vascular respiratory fitness. The type of work done will depend on the equipment and facilities available, but it must be of a progressive nature such as repetition 60-metre sprints, circuit training, non-body contact ball games. Workouts should be recorded in the normal way.

After this month, which may include some general weight-training towards the end, another programme similar to the British/EEC build-up will be planned with the aim of producing a total during July and at the World Championships, or English Native Championships for those who do not make the team.

Lifters should not be afraid to compete in matches during various stages of their programme, and these should be treated as gauges of progress in the production of the desired totals at the major matches.

Training records should be kept at all times in a notebook.

20

Powerlifting for Beginners
George Kirkley

In the early 1950s the BAWLA introduced the Strength Set to cater for the growing numbers who practised this form of lifting — pure strength movements that required little technique compared with the more skilful Olympic lifts. The three lifts chosen then were the Two Hands Curl, Press on Bench and the Squat. These were changed to the current set of Squat, Press on Bench and the Two Hands Dead Lift and renamed the Power Set in the 1960s.

The visual contrast is sharp between Olympic lifting and powerlifting. On the one hand we have the fast, explosive, all-action Snatch and Jerk; on the other the slower, semi-static movements of the three power lifts. However, powerlifting is *also* explosive — in the sense that maximum strength must be applied in the quickest possible time. This means that the muscles must be activated with great speed so that the power (strength x speed) is generated quickly. Of course, this explosiveness does not show in the same way as it does in Olympic lifting. Nevertheless, it is still there.

Over the years powerlifting has mushroomed in popularity to the point where it can be said that there are more powerlifters in Britain than Olympic lifters.

Another point where our powerlifters score over the Olympic men is their much greater success in international competition. Whereas British Olympic lifters have won only meagre honours in such events as world and European championships, the powerlifters have won numerous major titles and medals in the past two decades or so. A glance at the world championships results in Appendix II will give you a good idea of our successes in this sphere.

As this chapter is mainly for the guidance of the beginner I will make no attempt to delve very deeply into the subject. Once the beginner has grasped the basic principles he should (and indeed *must*) learn from his experiences as he progresses and gradually moves on to becoming an advanced lifter by applying his own intelligence and thoughts, together with those of his coach, if he is fortunate enough to acquire the services of a good one. In another chapter, John Goodbody covers advanced powerlifting, so read that carefully in conjunction with this one.

A lot of the advice I give in my chapter on Olympic lifting applies equally here, such as warming up, frequency of training, progressive training, mental attitude, competition hints, and so on, so I will not waste time by repeating everything.

Regarding the best age to start, I believe that powerlifters should be a bit older than in the case of Olympic lifters — I would say that from the age of sixteen onwards is quite early enough.

POWERLIFTING RULES AND COMPETITION PROCEDURES

Here, briefly, but in sufficient detail for a beginner, are the rules and procedures for competition. Full, detailed rules are contained in the official BAWLA Handbook.

Three attempts are allowed on each of the scheduled lifts, with the highest successful one counting towards the total. The weight of the barbell must be in multiples of 2.5 kg and (unlike Olympic lifting) the minimum increase between all attempts is 2.5 kg. If three failures are made on any lift, then the competitor scores nothing for that particular lift and cannot be classified in the competition.

At the start of the competition the barbell will be loaded to the lowest weight required and must be kept rising in weight as the competition proceeds, with each lifter coming in at the weight he requires for any particular attempt. In no case can a weight once attempted by any competitor be lowered for any other competitor.

Adjudication

In all major championships three officials are appointed to adjudicate on the lifts. A lift will be passed as valid on a majority or unanimous verdict. In this country one official may adjudicate at such minor events as county or divisional championships and in league or friendly matches.

RULES FOR THE SQUAT

The barbell shall be taken from the rack provided to rest on the back of the shoulders held not more than 3 cm below the line of the top of the deltoids. The lifter must stand upright, legs braced, to await the referee's signal to commence the lift, which will be given when the lifter is motionless with the barbell properly positioned.

After the referee's signal the lifter shall bend the knees and lower the body until the surface of the legs at the hip joint is lower than the tops of the knees. The lifter shall recover at will, without double bouncing, to the upright position, knees locked, and wait for the signal to replace the barbell on the rack, which will be given when the lifter is absolutely motionless. The barbell must have no downward movement during the recovery.

Former European super-heavyweight powerlifting champion, Andy Kerr (Britain), starting to rise with a Squat

RULES FOR THE PRESS ON BENCH

The lifter must assume the following position on the bench, which must be maintained during the lift: with head, trunk (including buttocks) extended, feet flat on the floor. The barbell must be lowered to touch the chest and remain motionless. The referee will then give the signal for the press to be made. The barbell must be raised evenly in a continuous movement to locked arms' length and held motionless to await the referee's signal for the completion of the lift. The spacing of the hands shall not exceed 81 cm (31.8 in). There must be no raising of the lifter's head, shoulder or buttocks from the bench, or movement of the feet, and there must be no heaving or bouncing of the barbell from the chest. Nor must the barbell be allowed to sink in the chest after the signal to start the press.

Top: starting position for the Press on Bench, awaiting the referee's signal

Bottom: completion of the Press on Bench, with the arms locked

RULES FOR THE DEAD LIFT

The barbell must be laid horizontally in front of the lifter's feet, gripped with an optional grip with both hands and uplifted with one continuous movement until the lifter is standing erect. The lifter must face the front of the platform.

At the completion of the lift, the knees must be locked and the shoulders thrust back. The referee will signal the completion of the lift when the barbell is held motionless in the finishing position. During the pull to the erect position the feet must not move their position and the barbell must not stop to be supported on the thighs. The barbell must not be lowered before the referee's signal to do so.

HINTS ON PERFORMANCES

Squat. Place the feet comfortably apart, toes pointing forwards or slightly out, about 18 to 20 in, but experiment to find the best position for yourself. Hold the barbell behind the shoulders in your most comfortable position – generally with the hands fairly close to the inside collars. It is, of course, important that you lower the body until the thighs are at least in a position demanded by the rules, and the lifter has to judge this for himself. So before entering any competition, practise this movement, with the aid of a training partner to advise you, until you are quite sure of performing the lift with a heavy or limit weight without being disqualified. Keep the back as straight as possible (there will inevitably be some slight curve) throughout the movement – a rounded back can put excessive strain on the lower back. It is best to lower fairly slowly and steadily, but move as fast as possible when rising. Squat on a full breath and exhale whilst rising to the erect position.

Press on Bench. Experiment to find the best width of grip to use. Generally this will be the maximum of 81 cm as allowed by the rules, but some smaller lifters especially, or those with very short arms, will find a narrower grip more suitable. Lower steadily and evenly from locked arms to the chest whilst exhaling, then inhale as the press is made. And make sure that you do not press before the referee's signal. Press as fast as possible, but concentrate on making it evenly, as if one arm lags behind the other, the lift will not be passed. One must make sure, of course, that an evenly spaced grip is taken at the start before lowering the barbell to the chest.

Dead Lift. A strong grip is essential, because with most lifters that is the first thing to 'give way'. Place the first two or three fingers over the thumb to lock the grip. Also, grip with one hand with the palm to the front and the other with the knuckles facing the front. The feet should be spaced about 18 in apart, but again one must experiment to find the best position for oneself. Some top-line lifters use what is called the 'Suma' style, with the feet placed very wide apart, but I don't advise this for the beginner. Experiments can be made later when one is more experienced, although my own opnion is that the Suma style is not the best for the great majority.

Do not raise the buttocks before the barbell leaves the floor, but raise head and buttocks simultaneously. Dig in hard with the heels and press hard as if trying to force the heels through the floor. As soon as the barbell leaves the platform try to accelerate the movement. You will not be able to, but you must TRY to. Endeavour to maintain the back as straight as possible throughout the lift.

BEGINNERS' SCHEDULES

Always have a good warm-up first before starting any schedule – a few minutes of bending and stretching movements, free squats, and so on.

Squat. I am basing the suggested weights on an assumed limit performance of 100 kg, with adjustments being made as necessary according to one's capacity.

First, warm up with one group of eight to ten repetitions using a very light weight (about half one's limit). Then:

75 kg	4 reps	3 groups
80 kg	3 reps	2 groups
85 kg	2 reps	2 groups
90 kg	5 single lifts	

Alternatively, try this fixed-weight schedule:

85–90 kg	2 reps	10–12 groups

About every three or four weeks work up to a limit performance as follows:

70 kg	3 reps	2 groups
80 kg	2 reps	2 groups
90 kg	1 single lift	
95 kg	1 single lift	
100 kg	1 single lift	

Then try 102.5 kg or 105 kg to make a new limit performance. If successful, then add 2.5 kg to all subsequent training weights. If not successful, maintain the existing training weights for another two weeks, then try again for an increased maximum.

Press on Bench. A limit of 70 kg is assumed.

50 kg	4 reps	3 groups
55 kg	3 reps	2 groups
60 kg	2 reps	2 groups
65 kg	5–6 single lifts	

Alternatively, try this fixed-weight schedule:

60 kg	2 reps	10–12 groups

About every three or four weeks work up to a limit performance as follows:

50 kg	3 reps	2 groups
55 kg	2 reps	2 groups
60 kg	1 single lift	
65 kg	1 single lift	
70 kg	1 single lift	

Then try 72.5 kg or 75 kg to make a new limit performance. If successful, then add 2.5 kg to all subsequent training weights. If not successful, maintain the existing training weights for another two weeks, then try again for an increased maximum.

Dead Lift.   A limit of 140 kg is assumed.

110 kg   4 reps   3 groups
115 kg   3 reps   2 groups
120 kg   2 reps   2 groups
130 kg   5–6 single lifts

Alternatively, try this fixed-weight schedule:
120 kg   2 reps   10–12 groups

About every three or four weeks work up
to a limit performance as follows:

110 kg   3 reps   2 groups
120 kg   2 reps   2 groups
130 kg   1 single lift
135 kg   1 single lift
140 kg   1 single lift

Then try 142.5 kg or 145 kg to make a new
limit performance. If successful, then add 5 kg
to all subsequent training weights. If not
successful, maintain the existing training
weights for another two weeks, then try again
for an increased maximum.

In all three lifts always warm up first with
a set or two using a very light weight – about
half one's limit for eight to ten repetitions.
Then proceed with the schedules as outlined.

Repetitions on the Dead Lift should be made
as follows:

Perform the first lift, finishing the lift properly in the concluding position, then lower the
barbell back to the platform, pause a few
seconds and resume the correct starting
position before making another repetition, and
so on.

ASSISTANCE EXERCISES

As in Olympic lifting, described in my earlier
chapter, assistance exercises are a very useful
addition to one's training. Good progress can,
of course, be made by just training on the three
lifts, but other suitable movements can boost
progress often to a considerable extent.

In all the following exercises use low
repetitions (fours, threes, twos and singles)
with the heaviest weights possible after suitable warming up with two or three sets of light
weights (eight to ten repetitions).

Above: Starting position for the Dead Lift – back flat
with shoulders a little way forward of the barbell,
hips not too low. The lifter is Ken McDonald
(Australia)

Right: Precious McKenzie (New Zealand), former
world powerlifting champion, half way through a
Dead Lift, just before reaching the most difficult
stage

For the Squat, use the Half-Squat (tops of
the thighs lowered to an angle of about 45° to
the platform) and the Quarter-Squat (thighs at
about a 70° angle). Very heavy weights indeed
can be used with the Quarter-Squat.

As a variation of the regular Press on Bench
with barbell, try the movement with dumbbells. Assistants will be needed to help hand
in the dumbbells for the start of the press.
Vary the movement by holding the dumbbell
rods at right angles to the body as well as
parallel. Also try, with the barbell, pressing

from various heights. Using adjustable stands, set them to a height where the barbell rests about 3 in above the chest, then press to arm's length from this point. Try other heights of about 6 in above the chest, and a height where the barbell has to be pressed about 3 in to locked arms, in which very heavy weights can be used.

For the Dead Lift, try lifting from various heights, using blocks or stands to adjust the barbell. I suggest three heights – with the bottoms of the discs about 5 in from the floor, 10 in from the floor, and finally with the barbell held just above the level of the knees. In this latter position the knees will be bent just a little for the start of the lift, and the barbell will be lifted about 4–6 in to the erect position, depending on one's physical make-up. Very heavy weights can be handled in his short movement. Handling heavier-than-normal weights in these various positions will also help to strengthen the grip, vitally important for lifting limit weights in competition.

Other useful assistance exercises are:

Shoulder shrugging: Use a heavy weight (you will have to experiment to find this, but probably about 70 per cent of maximum Dead Lift). Stand upright in the Dead Lift concluding position and rotate the shoulder girdle as follows: Pull the shoulders back, then upwards and forwards to return to the starting position, thus making a circle. Do about four or five circles, rest a while then circle the reverse way – forwards, upwards then backwards. Repeat alternately for four or five sets.

Power Clean: Use a weight that will just permit you to perform four or five repetitions and use four or five sets. Pull the weight into the shoulders, stand upright then return to the platform. Rest a few seconds then repeat. See Chapter 4 for full description.

Good Morning Exercise: This is a good one for the lower back, thus helpful for the Dead Lift. But don't use too heavy a weight in this movement. Do four or five sets of six to eight repetitions. See Chapter 4 for description.

Bent-over Rowing: Again, see Chapter 4 for description. Use as much weight as you can handle for five or six sets of six to eight repetitions.

Leg Press: Very good for both the Squat and Dead Lift, especially when using a machine, which enables you to handle really heavy weights. If no machine is available you will have to use a barbell across the soles of the feet, as described in Chapter 4, although not so much weight can be managed as with the machine. Use as much weight as possible in four or five sets of five or six repetitions. Also occasionally use six to eight single lifts with maximum weight whenever possible on a machine.

As I stated earlier, make the work progressive in all these assistance exercises by increasing the weight every few weeks (but keeping the repetitions the same) or when you feel capable of doing this.

A selection of these exercises can be done after a session on the three lifts. All of them may be too much for one training period and it might be a good plan to use only those applying to two of the three power lifts – say, the Squat and Press on Bench in one session the Squat and Dead Lift in another and the Press on Bench and Dead Lift in another, and so on.

Also, in order to build endurance, as you progress gradually cut down the rest time between the sets of assistance exercises.

An alternative plan is to use assistance exercises only on one or two days a week, rather than doing them after a session on the three lifts. This will depend largely, of course, on what time you have available for training.

One final point. As I advised in my chapter on Olympic lifting, get hold of a BAWLA Handbook, which contains all the relevant rules in detail. Before you start entering competitions, pay particular attention to your costume, etc., especially with regard to bandages, to find out what you can, or cannot, wear. Make sure you have a strong, snug-fitting costume and also invest in a sturdy belt. Good costume equipment will ensure that you can compete with confidence.

21

World Class Powerlifting
John Goodbody

Powerlifting, like most sports at international level, has benefited from the use of phases and cycles in training. After a powerlifter has acquired a high level of all-round strength and mastered the basic techniques of the three lifts he (or she) will want to start advanced training, employing the latest training methods, and concentrate on certain important competitions.

Much of the preparation in Britain for major events has been influenced by Ron Collins, who won six world titles before emigrating to New Zealand after one of the most successful careers in powerlifting history. Collins also experimented with new techniques for the Squat and Bench Press. When I interviewed him in Manchester in March 1977, he had mastered a low position for the barbell on his back during the Squat, holding the weight slightly down his back so as to improve his mechanical position and thus raise more weight. Since then the rule has been standardised with the lifter not being allowed to hold the top of the barbell more than 3 cm below the top of the anterior deltoids. Even this position does give the lifter some advantage over the orthodox one where the barbell rests on the top of the shoulders. The orthodox position is certainly safer, but less mechanically efficient.

Collins has given his name to a position he used in the Bench Press – the Collins 'Arch'. This seeks to gain maximum advantage from the action of the pectoralis major, many of whose lower fibres tend to pull the arm towards the side rather than lift the upper arm in a vertical path which is needed to drive the barbell off the chest. To use these fibres, Collins arches his body so that the sternum can be in a more vertical position and so allow these lower fibres of the pectoralis major to pull more vertically. To achieve this 'Arch' the lifter must ensure a stable basis with a strong push from the platform. The weight of his body and the barbell is primarily on his shoulders and feet. He does not rest on the hips. Instead he keeps them only just touching the bench throughout the lift. This helps a full 'arch' to be more easily completed and thus more weight to be raised.

Finishing position of the Dead Lift shown by Ron Collins, six times world powerlifting champion

Collins won his first national title in 1966 when the Dead Lift had just replaced the Curl to make up the new power set. Therefore he was one of the pioneers of training with techniques like those just described as competition became more intense with global recognition beginning with the first official world championships in 1971. Collins also standardised the preparations for competitions. After a major competition he used to take a complete lay-off and then enjoy general bodybuilding before beginning to concentrate again on the three lifts. In the last six weeks of training for a major event a typical routine he used would be as follows (the weights lifted are the maximum he employed):

Monday

Warm-up. Squats: 1 × 10 (60 kg), 1 × 10 (105 kg), 1 × 8 (150 kg), 1 × 5 (190 kg), 1 × 5 (240 kg), 1 × 3 (275 kg), 1 × 3 (305 kg), 1 × 1 (317.5 kg), 1 × 1 (325 kg), 1 × 1 (335 kg), 1 × 1 (340 kg).

Bench Press 1 × 8 (60 kg), 1 × 8 (100 kg), 1 × 5 (150 kg), 1 × 3 (180 kg), 1 × 1 (200 kg), 1 × 5 (170 kg).

Dead Lift 1 × 5 (150 kg), 1 × 5 (200 kg), 1 × 3 (240 kg), 1 × 3 (275 kg), 1 × 3 (285 kg), 1 × 1 (297.5 kg), 1 × 1 (310 kg), 1 × 1 (315 kg).

Wrist Curl: Using high repetitions with a fairly light weight.

Grip Machine: Using high repetitions and again a fairly light weight.

Wednesday

Dumbbells Press: 5 × 10 (35 kg).

Bent-over Rowing: 5 × 5 (100 kg).

Press on Bench: (narrow grip, about 18 in): 1 × 8 (60 kg), 1 × 5 (90 kg), 1 × 5 (110 kg), 1 × 5 (125 kg), 1 × 5 (140 kg).

Curl: 5 sets with a light weight.

Friday

Collins repeated his Monday session, except that he worked up to a maximum of five repetitions. The heaviest weights he used for these fives were Squat (315 kg), Press on Bench (175 kg), Dead Lift (297.5 kg).

He repeated his exercises with Wrist Curls and the Grip Machine afterwards, exactly as on Monday.

Collins used his heaviest weights about three weeks before a major competition. In the last week he would have a hard workout on Monday and then a light session on Wednesday, omitting the Dead Lift. Collins lifted well into his forties at light-heavyweight and middleweight, and his record and example proved a constant inspiration for many Britons who succeeded him.

One of these was Tony Stevens, who, like Collins, reached his peak late. Stevens became world champion in the 100 kg class at the age of thirty-five in 1984 and had only concentrated on powerlifting after his retirement from competing on the Olympic set in 1979. His training is a refinement of his predecessors. He is unable to use the Collins Arch on the Press on Bench because he has short legs in relation to his upper body. He likes to use foot blocks, but apparently not all officials permit them. These give him a secure base to push against.

Tony Stevens

In the Squat Stevens places his legs a little more than hip-width apart, with the feet slightly splayed out, the usual position. He stresses that one must keep the chest up and look up as the lift is performed. 'It is vital to go as low as one does in competition. I must find a training partner who is completely honest and tells me whether I am lifting within the rules. He should not try to please me. He must always tell me the truth.'

On the Dead Lift Stevens has a problem with his grip. Therefore he works on a squeeze grip and exercises on Wrist Curls every day if possible. His yearly routine is made up of two main phases – out-of-season and pre-competition – the latter being eight weeks building up to a major contest.

Stevens trains four times a week: Monday, Tuesday, Thursday and Friday, all the year round apart from holidays. Each session lasts about two hours and begins with a fifteen-minute warm-up. He believes this is particularly important because of some shoulder trouble. He therefore gets a partner to pull his shoulders and elbows back while he holds them in a position as if he were to start a Bench Press. He dislocates his shoulders with a towel, does wrist-stretching and hyperextensions. Then after the Bench Press he repeats the stretching.

For his legs Stevens touches his toes, does free squats and extensive hamstring exercises. On Monday and Thursday he does legs and back work, whilst on Tuesday and Friday he works his arms and shoulders.

The sessions are built up as follows:

Monday/Thursday

Squat: 5 sets building up to 5 × 4 (200 kg)
Leg Extension: 5 × 8
Rowing: 5 × 8
Calf Raises: 5 × 8
Thigh Curls: 5 × 8

These last four exercises are carried out with moderate weights, allowing Stevens enough resistance to complete the sets with difficulty.

Tuesday/Friday

Bench Press: 4 sets (increasing the weight) building up to 5 × 8 (150 kg)
Standing Press: 5 × 8
Curl: 5 × 8
Triceps Extension: 5 × 8
Bent-over Lateral Raise: 3 × 8

Again, these last four exercises are carried out with moderate weights.

This gives Stevens the basis for his intensive training in the pre-competition phase. During 1985, when the European Championships were in May, the World Games in July and the world championships in November, he spent most of this period using the following schedule:

On Monday he did his main heavy Squats and Dead Lift session and on Tuesday his main Press on Bench workout. On Thursday, when he bench pressed, and Friday, when he did Squats and Dead Lifts, he used weights of about 80 per cent of those employed earlier in the week. This only applied to the classic exercises. For all assistance exercises, except one, the weights remained the same for both sessions – no definite weight was used for these assistance exercises, the resistance being just enough to work the muscles strongly. The exception was the Dead Lift assistance exercise as Steven does not use the ordinary Dead Lift in training. Instead he stands on two-inch (20 kg) discs and does Dead Lifts from there. This is to put extra stress on the start of the lift as he is comparatively weak off the floor. ('Any weight I can pull to my knees I can lift successfully.')

Here is his routine on the Monday for the first session of the eight-week period:

Squat: 2 × 5 (65 kg), 1 × 3 (115 kg), 1 × 3 (155 kg), 1 × 2 (185 kg), 1 × 2 (205 kg), 1 × 2 (245 kg), 1 × 2 (265 kg), 3 × 2 (285 kg).
Dead Lift Assistance: 1 × 3 (165 kg), 1 × 2 (205 kg), 3 × 2 (245 kg).
Leg Extension: 5 × 5
Thigh Curl: 5 × 5

Bent-over Rowing: 3 × 5 (90 kg)
Sit-ups and Leg Raises

On Tuesday, Stevens concentrates on the Press on Bench.

Press on Bench: 2 × 8 (65 kg), 1 × 6 (105 kg), 1 × 5 (135 kg), 3 × 5 (155 kg).
Close-grip Press on Bench: 4 × 5 (155 kg)

Triceps Extension: 3 × 8
Standing Press: 3 × 8 (80 kg)
Curl: 3 × 8
Bent-over Lateral Raise: 3 × 8

From this basis of the first week he increases every week as follows. The build-up is the same and the weights lifted below are the 'working' weights, his final sets in the classic exercises:

	Squat	Press on Bench	Dead Lift
Week two	3 × 2 (305 kg)	4 × 5 (165 kg)	4 × 3 (265 kg)
Week three	2 × 2 (320 kg)	3 × 5 (175 kg)	3 × 2 (285 kg)
Week four	2 × 2 (330 kg)	2 × 3 (185 kg)	2 × 2 (305 kg)
Week five	2 × 1 (345 kg)	2 × 5 (195 kg)	2 × 1 (320 kg)
Week six	1 × 1 (365 kg)	2 × 2 (210 kg)	1 × 1 (340 kg)
Week seven	1 × 1 (375 kg)	1 × 1 (225 kg)	1 × 1 (345 kg)
Week eight	1 × 1 (320 kg)	1 × 1 (205 kg)	no lift

In the final week he just does the Press on Bench and Squat and no assistance exercises at all. If the competition is on a Saturday he will have a very light session on Thursday just on the Press on Bench. From week six he bench presses with a pause at the chest, as in a competition. 'I try to increase my 'working' weight each week. I know when I cannot and so do not try such a big increase. This type of routine should not be copied by everyone. But it is what appears to suit me.'

Top-class powerlifting demands concentration on the three lifts. It requires weights close to one's maximum and therefore low repetitions, because this is what is required in the actual competition, and what has been proved to be the best method of increasing one's strength.

World Weightlifting Championships and Olympic Games Results 1960–1985

(all results shown in kilos)

OLYMPIC GAMES 1960 – Rome, Italy

Bantamweight

1.	C. Vinci (USA)	345
2.	Y. Miyake (Japan)	337.5
3.	E. Elmkah (Iran)	330

Featherweight

1.	E. Minaev (USSR)	372.5
2.	I. Berger (USA)	362.5
3.	S. Mannironi (Italy)	352.5
	A. Robinson (Britain) was eighteenth with 292.5.	

Lightweight

1.	V. Bushuev (USSR)	397.5
2.	Tan Howe Liang (Singapore)	380
3.	A. Abdul (Iraq)	380
	B. Helfgott (Britain) was eighteenth with 337.5.	

Middleweight

1.	A. Kurinov (USSR)	437.5
2.	T. Kono (USA)	427.5
3.	G. Veres (Hungary)	405
	B. Blenman (Britain) failed to make a total.	

Light-heavyweight

1.	I. Palinski (Poland)	442.5
2.	J. George (USA)	430
3.	J. Bochenek (Poland)	420
	P. Caira (Britain) was fifteenth with 385.	
	S. Blackman (Britain) failed to make a total.	

Mid-heavyweight

1.	A. Vorobyev (USSR)	472.5
2.	T. Lomakin (USSR)	457.5
3.	L. Martin (Britain)	445

Heavyweight

1.	Y. Vlasov (USSR)	537.5
2.	J. Bradford (USA)	512.5
3.	N. Schemansky (USA)	500

WORLD CHAMPIONSHIPS 1961 – Vienna, Austria

Bantamweight

1.	V. Stogov (USSR)	345
2.	I. Foldi (Hungary)	345
3.	Y. Miyake (Japan)	337.5

Featherweight

1.	I. Berger (USA)	367.5
2.	E. Minaev (USSR)	357.5
3.	S. Mannironi (Italy)	357.5
	K. Chung (Britain) was eleventh with 320.	

Lightweight

1.	W. Baszanowski (Poland)	402.5
2.	S. Lopatin (USSR)	400
3.	M. Zielinski (Poland)	395
	C. Goring (Britain) was eleventh with 342.5.	

Middleweight

1.	A. Kurinov (USSR)	435
2.	G. Veres (Hungary)	420
3.	M. Paterni (France)	405
	B. Blenman (Britain) was tenth with 370.	

Light-heavyweight

1. R. Plyukfelder (USSR)	450
2. G. Toth (Hungary)	432.5
3. T. Kono (USA)	430

S. Blackman (Britain) was sixth
with 417.5.

Mid-heavyweight

1. I. Palinski (Poland)	475
2. L. Martin (Britain)	462.5
3. A. Vorobyev (USSR)	457.5

Heavyweight

1. Y. Vlasov (USSR)	525
2. R. Zirk (USA)	475
3. E. Makinen (Finland)	462.5

D. Hillman (Britain) was tenth
with 392.5.

WORLD CHAMPIONSHIPS 1962 – Budapest, Hungary

Bantamweight

1. Y. Miyake (Japan)	352.5
2. I. Foldi (Hungary)	337.5
3. V. Stogov (USSR)	330

Featherweight

1. E. Minaev (USSR)	362.5
2. J. Katsura (USSR)	357.5
3. R. Koslowski (Poland)	352.5

Lightweight

1. V. Kaplunov (USSR)	415
2. W. Baszanowski (Poland)	412.5
3. M. Zielinski (Poland)	405

Middleweight

1. A. Kurinov (USSR)	422.5
2. M. Huszka (Hungary)	415
3. M. Teherani (Iran)	412.5

M. Pearman (Britain) was
fourteenth with 365.

Light-Heavyweight

1. G. Veres (Hungary)	460
2. T. Kono (USA)	455
3. G. Toth (Hungary)	442.5

G. Manners (Britain) was ninth
with 397.5

Mid-heavyweight

1. L. Martin (Britain)	480
2. I. Palinski (Poland)	470
3. W. March (USA)	460

Heavyweight

1. Y. Vlasov (USSR)	540
2. N. Schemansky (USA)	537.5
3. G. Gubner (USA)	497.5

D. Prowse (Britain) failed to
make a total.

WORLD CHAMPIONSHIPS 1963 – Stockholm, Sweden

Bantamweight

1. A. Vakhonin (USSR)	345
2. H. Fukuda (Japan)	340
3. S. Ichinoseki (Japan)	330

Featherweight

1. Y. Miyake (Japan)	375
2. I. Berger (USA)	367.5
3. I. Foldi (Hungary)	365

G. Newton (Britain) was eighth
with 317.5.

Lightweight

1. M. Zielinski (Poland)	417.5
2. W. Baszanowski (Poland)	410
3. V. Kaplunov (USSR)	410

C. Goring (Britain) was fifteenth
with 350.

Middleweight

1. A. Kurinov (USSR)	437.5
2. M. Huszka (Hungary)	437.5
3. H. Zdrazila (Czech)	422.5

M. Pearman (Britain) was sixteenth
with 370.

A. Wotherspoon (Britain) was nineteenth
with 350.

Light-heavyweight

1. G. Veres (Hungary)	477.5
2. R. Plyukfelder (USSR)	467.5
3. G. Toth (Hungary)	450

S. Blackman (Britain) was eighth
with 407.5.

Mid-heavyweight

1. L. Martin (Britain)   480
2. I. Palinski (Poland)   475
3. E. Brovko (USSR)   470

Heavyweight

1. Y. Vlasov (USSR)   557.5
2. N. Schemansky (USA)   537.5
3, L. Zhabotinsky (USSR)   482.5

OLYMPIC GAMES 1964 – Tokyo, Japan

Bantamweight

1. A. Vakhonin (USSR)   357.5
2. I. Foldi (Hungary)   355
3. S. Ichinoseki (Japan)   347.5

Featherweight

1. Y. Miyake (Japan)   397.5
2. I. Berger (USA)   382.5
3. M. Nowak (Poland)   377.5
   K. Chung (Britain) was tenth
   with 335.

Lightweight

1. W. Baszanowski (Poland)   432.5
2. V. Kaplunov (USSR)   432.5
3. M. Zielinski (Poland)   420

Middleweight

1. H. Zdrazila (Czech)   445
2. V. Kurentsov (USSR)   440
3. M. Ohuchi (Japan)   437.5
   M. Pearman (Britain) was
   fourteenth with 387.5.

Light-heavyweight

1. R. Plyukfelder (USSR)   475
2. G. Toth (Hungary)   467.5
3. G. Veres (Hungary)   467.5
   S. Blackman (Britain) was tenth
   with 427.5.
   G. Manners (Britain) was fifteenth
   with 410.

Mid-heavyweight

1. M. Golovanov (USSR)   487.5
2. L. Martin (Britain)   475
3. I. Palinski (Poland)   467.5

Heavyweight

1. L. Zhabotinsky (USSR)   572.5
2. Y. Vlasov (USSR)   570
3. N. Schemansky (USA)   537.5

WORLD CHAMPIONSHIPS 1965 – Teheran, Iran

Bantamweight

1. I. Foldi (Hungary)   360
2. S. Ichinoseki (Japan)   355
3. Yoshiyuki Miyake (Japan)   345

Featherweight

1. Yoshinobu Miyake (Japan)   385
2. M. Nowak (Poland)   375
3. R. Kozlowski (Poland)   360
   K. Chung (Britain) was fifth
   with 327.5.

Lightweight

1. W. Baszanowski (Poland)   427.5
2. M. Zielinski (Poland)   425
3. V. Kaplunov (USSR)   412.5

Middleweight

1. V. Kurentsov (USSR)   437.5
2. W. Dittrich (E. Germany)   437.5
3. A. Kurinov (USSR)   432.5

Light-heavyweight

1. N. Ozimek (Poland)   472.5
2. A. Kidyaev (USSR)   460
3. J. Kaczkowski (Poland)   445
   S. Blackman (Britain) was fifth
   with 420.

Mid-heavyweight

1. L. Martin (Britain)   487.5
2. V. Golovanov (USSR)   480
3. G. Toth (Hungary)   457.5

Heavyweight

1. L. Zhabotinsky (USSR)   552.5
2. G. Gubner (USA)   545
3. K. Ecser (Hungary)   522.5

WORLD CHAMPIONSHIPS 1966 – East Berlin, Germany

Bantamweight

1. A. Vakhonin (USSR)   362.5
2. I. Foldi (Hungary)   360
3. M. Nassiri (Iran)   350

Featherweight

1. Yoshinobu Miyake (Japan) 387.5
2. M. Nowak (Poland)   382.5
3. Yoshiyuki Miyake (Japan) 370

Lightweight

1. E. Katsura (USSR)   437.5
2. M. Zielinski (Poland)   410
3. P. Jalayer (Iran)   405

Middleweight

1. V. Kurentsov (USSR)   450
2. W. Baszanowski (Poland)   447.5
3. W. Dittrich (E. Germany) 442.5

Light-heavyweight

1. V. Belyaev (USSR)   485
2. G. Veres (Hungary)   485
3. H. Zdrazila (Czech)   465

Mid-heavyweight

1. G. Toth (Hungary)   487.5
2. I. Palinski (Poland)   477.5
3. M. Golab (Poland)   475
    L. Martin (Britain) failed to make a total.

Heavyweight

1. L. Zhabotinsky (USSR)   567.5
2. R. Bednarski (USA)   537.5
3. S. Batishev (USSR)   530

NO WORLD CHAMPIONSHIPS IN 1967

OLYMPIC GAMES 1968 – Mexico City, Mexico

Bantamweight

1. M. Nassiri (Iran)   367.5
2. I. Foldi (Hungary)   367.5
3. H. Trebicki (Poland)   357.5
    P. McKenzie (Britain) was ninth with 330.

Featherweight

1. Yoshinobu Miyake (Japan) 392.5
2. D. Shanidze (USSR)   387.5
3. Yoshiyuki Miyake (Japan) 385
    G. Perrin (Britain) failed to make a total.

Lightweight

1. W. Baszanowski (Poland)   437.5
2. P. Jalayer (Iran)   422.5
3. M. Zielinski (Poland)   420

Middleweight

1. V. Kurentsov (USSR)   475
2. M. Ohuchi (Japan)   455
3. K. Bakos (Hungary)   440

Light-heavyweight

1. B. Selitsky (USSR)   485
2. V. Belyaev (USSR)   485
3. N. Ozimek (Poland)   472.5
    M. Pearman (Britain) was fourteenth with 425.
    P. Arthur (Britain) was eighteenth with 415.

Mid-heavyweight

1. Kaarlo Kangasniemi (Finland) 517.5
2. J. Talts (USSR)   507.5
3. M. Golab (Poland)   495
    L. Martin (Britain) failed to make a total.

Heavyweight

1. L. Zhabozinsky (USSR)   572.5
2. S. Reding (Belgium)   555
3. J. Dube (USA)   555
    T. Perdue (Britain) was tenth with 487.5

WORLD CHAMPIONSHIPS 1969 – Warsaw, Poland

(Two additional classes were added this year – Flyweight and Super-heavyweight)

Flyweight

1. V. Krishishin (USSR)   337.5
2. V. Smietanin (USSR)   337.5
3. W. Szoltyzek (Poland)   335

Bantamweight

1. M. Nassiri (Iran)   360
2. A. Kirov (Bulgaria)   347.5
3. H. Ono (Japan)   342.5
   P. McKenzie (Britain) was sixth with 315.
   J. McNiven (Britain) was eleventh with 282.5.

Featherweight

1. Yoshiyuki Miyake (Japan)   385
2. M. Kuchev (Bulgaria)   385
3. D. Shanidze (USSR)   380

Lightweight

1. W. Baszanowski (Poland)   445
2. J. Bacos (Hungary)   430
3. Z. Kaczmarek (Poland)   425

Middleweight

1. V. Kurentsov (USSR)   467.5
2. G. Szarvas (Hungary)   440
3. J. Mursu (Finland)   437.5
   A. Ford (Britain) was thirteenth with 377.5.

Light-heavyweight

1. M. Ohuchi (Japan)   487.5
2. K. Bakos (Hungary)   487.5
3. B. Selitsky (USSR)   482.5
   P. Arthur (Britain) retired injured.

Mid-heavyweight

1. Kaarlo Kangasniemi (Finland) 515
2. B. Johansson (Sweden)   500
3. G. Toth (Hungary)   495

Heavyweight

1. R. Bednarski (USA)   547.5
2. J. Talts (USSR)   547.5
3. Kauko Kangasniemi (Finland)   507.5
   D. Hancock (Britain) was seventeenth with 422.5.

Super-heavyweight

1. J. Dube (USA)   577.5
2. S. Reding (Belgium)   570
3. S. Batishev (USSR)   570
   T. Perdue (Britain) was eighth with 485.

WORLD CHAMPIONSHIPS 1970 – Columbus, USA

Flyweight

1. S. Del Rosario (Philippines) 322.5
2. Z. Smalcerz (Poland)   317.5
3. C. Depthios (Indonesia)   307.5

Bantamweight

1. M. Nassiri (Iran)   362.5
2. K. Ando (Japan)   352.5
3. F. Baez (Puerto Rico)   335
   P. McKenzie (Britain) was sixth with 325.
   J. McNiven (Britain) was eleventh with 267.5.

Featherwweight

1. J. Benedek (Hungary)   382.5
2. M. Kuchev (Bulgaria)   380
3. P. Tanti (Italy)   372.5
   K. Chung (Britain) was fourth with 340.

Lightweight

1. Z. Kaczmarek (Poland)   440
2. W. Baszanowski (Poland)   437.5
3. M. Dehnavi (Iran)   420
   G. Newton (Britain) was tenth with 360.
   I. Owen (Britain) was eleventh with 347.5.

Middleweight

1. V. Kurentsov (USSR)	462.5
2. L. Jensen (Norway)	455
3. G. Szarvas (Hungary)	445

Light-heavyweight

1. G. Ivanchenko (USSR)	505
2. N. Ozimek (Poland)	482.5
3. D. Rigert (USSR)	482.5

Mid-heavyweight

1. V. Kolotov (USSR)	537.5
2. P. Grippaldi (USA)	490
3. G. Toth (Hungary)	490

Heavyweight

1. J. Talts (USSR)	565
2. A. Kraichev (Bulgaria)	535
3. R. Bednarski (USA)	530

D. Hancock (Britain) was eleventh with 480.

Super-heavyweight

1. V. Alexeev (USSR)	612.5
2. S. Reding (Belgium)	590
3. K. Lahdenranta (Finland)	577.5

WORLD CHAMPIONSHIPS 1971 – Lima, Peru

Flyweight

1. Z. Smalcerz (Poland)	340
2. S. Holczreiter (Hungary)	335
3. M. Ueki (Japan)	307.5

Bantamweight

1. G. Chetin (USSR)	370
2. H. Trebicki (Poland)	367.5
3. M. Nassiri (Iran)	360

Featherweight

1. Yoshiyuki Miyake (Japan)	387.5
2. K. Ando (Japan)	382.5
3. N. Nurikyan (Bulgaria)	377.5

Lightweight

1. Z. Kaczmarek (Poland)	440
2. W. Baszanowski (Poland)	435
3. M. Kirzhinov (USSR)	430

Middleweight

1. V. Kanygin (USSR)	477.5
2. L. Jensen (Norway)	467.5
3. A. Silvino (Italy)	465

Light-heavyweight

1. B. Pavlov (USSR)	495
2. Kaarlo Kangasniemi (Finland)	490
3. G. Horvath (Hungary)	480

Mid-heavyweight

1. D. Rigert (USSR)	542.5
2. V. Kolotov (USSR)	537.5
3. B. Johansson (Sweden)	522.5

K. Price (Britain) failed to make a total.

Heavyweight

1. Y. Kozin (USSR)	552.5
2. S. Grutzner (E. Germany)	547.5
3. A. Kraichev (Bulgaria)	545

B. Strange (Britain) was twelfth with 447.5.

D. Hancock (Britain) failed to make a total.

Super-heavyweight

1. V. Alexeev (USSR)	635
2. K. Patera (USA)	592.5
3. I. Atanasov (Bulgaria)	532.5.

OLYMPIC GAMES 1972 – Munich, West Germany

Flyweight

1. Z. Smalcerz (Poland)	337.5
2. L. Szucs (Hungary)	330
3. S. Holczreiter (Hungary)	327.5

Bantamweight

1. I. Foldi (Hungary)   377.5
2. M. Nassiri (Iran)   370
3. G. Chetin (USSR)   367.5
   P. McKenzie (Britain) was ninth with 342.5.

Featherweight

1. N. Nurikyan (Bulgaria)   402.5
2. D. Shanidze (USSR)   400
3. J. Benedek (Hungary)   390

Lightweight

1. M. Kirzhinov (USSR)   460
2. M. Kuchev (Bulgaria)   450
3. Z. Kaczmarek (Poland)   437.5
   G. Newton (Britain) was fifteenth with 395.
   I. Owen (Britain) was eighteenth with 375.

Middleweight

1. Y. Bikov (Bulgaria)   485
2. M. Trabulsi (Lebanon)   472.5
3. A. Silvino (Italy)   470

Light-heavyweight

1. L. Jensen (Norway)   507.5
2. N. Ozimek (Poland)   497.5
3. G. Horvath (Hungary)   495
   M. Pearman (Britain) was eleventh with 435.
   A. Ford (Britain) was thirteenth with 435.

Mid-heavyweight

1. A. Nikolov (Bulgaria)   525
2. A. Shopov (Bulgaria)   517.5
3. H. Bettembourg (Sweden) 512.5
   P. Arthur (Britain) was fifteenth with 455.

Heavyweight

1. J. Talts (USSR)   580
2. A. Kraichev (Bulgaria)   562.5
3. S. Grutzner (E. Germany) 555
   D. Hancock (Britain) was thirteenth with 510.
   K. Price (Britain) was eighteenth with 480.

Super-heavyweight

1. V. Alexeev (USSR)   640
2. R. Mang (W. Germany)   610
3. G. Bonk (E. Germany)   572.5
   T Perdue (Britain) was tenth with 512.5.

WORLD CHAMPIONSHIPS 1973 – Havana, Cuba

From 1973 onwards only two lifts comprised the championship set – Snatch and Jerk

Flyweight

1. M. Nassiri (Iran)   240
2. L. Szucs (Hungary)   230
3. Z. Smalcerz (Poland)   227.5
   P. McKenzie (Britain) was eleventh with 207.5.

Bantamweight

1. A. Kirov (Bulgaria)   257.5
2. G. Todorov (Bulgaria)   255
3. K. Miki (Japan)   252.5

Featherweight

1. D. Shanidze (USSR)   272.5
2. N. Nurikyan (Bulgaria)   267.5
3. J. Wojnowski (Poland)   257.5

Lightweight

1. M. Kirzhinov (USSR)   305
2. M. Kuchev (Bulgaria)   302.5
3. P. Yanev (Bulgaria)   292.5
   G. Newton (Britain) was fifteenth with 257.5.

Middleweight

1. N. Kolev (Bulgaria)	337.5
2. P. Wenzel (E. Germany)	317.5
3. A. Stark (Hungary)	312.5

T. Bennett (Britain) was fourteenth with 265.

Light-heavyweight

1. V. Rizhenkov (USSR)	350
2. F. Zielecke (E. Germany)	347.5
3. S. Sochanski (Poland)	332.5

M. Pearman (Britain) was thirteenth with 290.

Mid-heavyweight

1. D. Rigert (USSR)	365
2. V. Kolotov (USSR)	360
3. P. Petzold (E. Germany)	357.5

J. Burns (Britain) was fourteenth with 310.

Heavyweight

1. P. Pervushin (USSR)	385
2. H. Losch (E. Germany)	370
3. J. Gonzalez (Cuba)	362.5

Super-heavyweight

1. V. Alexeev (USSR)	402.5
2. R. Mang (W. Germany)	400
3. S. Batishev (USSR)	392.5

T. Perdue (Britain) was ninth with 327.5

A. Kerr (Britain) was tenth with 325.

WORLD CHAMPIONSHIPS 1974 – Manila, Philippines

Flyweight

1. M. Nassiri (Iran)	232.5
2. G. Koszegi (Hungary)	230
3. T. Horikoshi (Japan)	227.5

Bantamweight

1. A. Kirov (Bulgaria)	255
2. L. Skorupa (Poland)	250
3. J. Hosotani (Japan)	245

P. McKenzie (Britain) was eleventh with 232.5.

Featherweight

1. G. Todorov (Bulgaria)	280
2. N. Kolesnikov (USSR)	277.5
3. N. Nurikyan (Bulgaria)	277.5

Lightweight

1. P. Korol (USSR)	305
2. Z. Kaczmarek (Poland)	302.5
3. N. Dehnavi (Iran)	295

A. Winterbourne (Britain) was thirteenth with 247.5.

K. Welch (Britain) was fourteenth with 240.

Middleweight

1. N. Kolev (Bulgaria)	335
2. R Rusev (Bulgaria)	332.5
3. P. Wenzel (E. Germany)	322.5

Light-heavyweight

1. T. Stoichev (Bulgaria)	350
2. L. Jensen (Norway)	350
3. R. Milser (W. Germany)	347.5

M. Pearman (Britain) was tenth with 287.5.

G. Langford (Britain) was thirteenth with 232.5.

Mid-heavyweight

1. D. Rigert (USSR)	387.5
2. S. Poltoratsky (USSR)	367.5
3. P. Petzold (E. Germany)	365

Heavyweight

1. V. Ustyuzhin (USSR)	380
2. L. Ciezki (E. Germany)	377.5
3. Y. Zaitsev (USSR)	367.5

J. Burns (Britain) was ninth with 330.

Super-heavyweight

1. V. Alexeev (USSR)	425
2. S. Reding (Belgium)	390
3. J. Heuser (E. Germany)	382.5

A. Kerr (Britain) was eighth with 340.

WORLD CHAMPIONSHIPS 1975 – Moscow, USSR

Flyweight

1. Z. Smalcerz (Poland)	237.5
2. A. Voronin (USSR)	232.5
3. L. Szucs (Hungary)	230

Bantamweight

1. A. Kirov (Bulgaria)	255
2. W. Korcz (Poland)	252.5
3. K. Prohl (Czech)	250

Featherweight

1. G. Todorov (Bulgaria)	285
2. N. Kolesnikov (USSR)	277.5
3. A. Pawlak (Poland)	275

Lightweight

1. P. Korol (USSR)	312.5
2. Z. Kaczmarek (Poland)	312.5
3. M. Kuchev (Bulgaria)	302.5

K. Welch (Britain) was twenty-sixth with 255.

Middleweight

1. P. Wenzel (E. Germany)	335
2. Y. Mitkov (Bulgaria)	332.5
3. N. Kolev (Bulgaria)	325

Light-heavyweight

1. V. Shary (USSR)	357.5
2. T. Stoichev (Bulgaria)	357.5
3. J. Avellan (Finland)	350

Mid-heavyweight

1. D. Rigert (USSR)	377.5
2. S. Poltorasky (USSR)	372.5
3. P. Petzold (E. Germany)	362.5

Heavyweight

1. V. Khristov (Bulgaria)	417.5
2. V. Mozhiekov (USSR)	390
3. J. Ciezki (E. Germany)	390

Super-heavyweight

1. V. Alexeev (USSR)	427.5
2. G. Bonk (E. Germany)	422.5
3. K. Plachkov (Bulgaria)	420

A. Kerr (Britain) was ninth with 347.5.

OLYMPIC GAMES 1976 – Montreal, Canada

Flyweight

1. A. Voronin (USSR)	242.5
2. G. Koszegi (Hungary)	237.5
3. M. Nassiri (Iran)	235

P. McKenzie (Britain) was thirteenth with 200.

Bantamweight

1. N. Nurikyan (Bulgaria)	262.5
2. G. Cziura (Poland)	252.5
3. K. Ando (Japan)	250

Featherweight

1. N. Kolesnikov (USSR)	285
2. G. Todorov (Bulgaria)	280
3. K. Hirai (Japan)	275

V. Daniels (Britain) was thirteenth with 227.5.

Lightweight

1. P. Korol (USSR)	305
2. D. Senet (France)	300
3. K. Czarnecki (Poland)	295

K. Welch (Britain) was ninth with 282.5

A. Winterbourne (Britain) was fifteenth with 267.5.

Z. Kaczmarek (Poland) finished first with 307.5, but was later disqualified after a positive test for anabolic steroids.

Middleweight

1. Y. Mitkov (Bulgaria)	335
2. V. Militosian (USSR)	330
3. P. Wenzel (E. Germany)	327.5

Light-heavyweight
1. V. Shary (USSR)   365
2. T. Stoichev (Bulgaria)   360
3. P. Baczako (Hungary)   345
   B. Blagoev (Bulgaria) finished second with 362.5, but was later disqualified after a positive test for anabolic steroids.

Mid-heavyweight
1. D. Rigert (USSR)   382.5
2. L. James (USA)   362.5
3. A. Shopov (Bulgaria)   360
   G. Langford (Britain) was tenth with 327.5.
   K. Price (Britain) was fourteenth with 307.5.

Heavyweight
1. Y. Zaitsev (USSR)   385
2. K. Semerdjiev (Bulgaria) 385
3. T. Rutkowski (Poland)   377.5
   J. Burns (Britain) was fourteenth with 347.5.
   V. Khristov (Bulgaria) finished first with 400, but was later disqualified after a positive test for anabolic steroids.

Super-heavyweight
1. V. Alexeev (USSR)   440
2. G. Bonk (E. Germany)   405
3. H. Losch (E. Germany)   387.5

WORLD CHAMPIONSHIPS 1977 – Stuttgart, West Germany

Flyweight
1. A. Voronin (USSR)   247.5
2. G. Koszegi (Hungary)   235
3. F. Casamayor (Cuba)   230

Bantamweight
1. J. Hosotani (Japan)   252.5
2. G. Todorov (Bulgaria)   247.5
3. Chen Man-lin (China)   245

Featherweight
1. N. Kolesnikov (USSR)   280
2. Y. Rusev (Bulgaria)   277.5
3. G. Cziura (Poland)   270
   V. Daniels (Britain) was thirteenth with 230.

Lightweight
1. R. Urrutia (Cuba)   315
2. S. Pevzner (USSR)   302.5
3. Z. Kaczmarek (Poland)   297.5
   A. Winterbourne and K. Welch (Britain) both failed to make a total.

Middleweight
1. Y. Vardanyan (USSR)   345
2. P. Wenzel (E. Germany)   337.5
3. G. Schliwka (E. Germany) 330

Light-heavyweight
1. G. Bessonov (USSR)   352.5
2. P. Baczako (Hungary)   345
3. P. Rabczewski (Poland)   337.5

Mid-heavyweight
1. S. Poltoraski (USSR)   375
2. R. Milser (W. Germany)   370
3. A. Blanco (Cuba)   355
   G. Langford (Britain) failed to make a total.

100 kg class (introduced this year)
1. A. Kozlov (USSR)   367.5
2. H. Losch (E. Germany)   367.5
3. M. Broillet (Switzerland) 365
   J. Burns (Britain) was thirteenth with 330.

Heavyweight
1. V. Khristov (Bulgaria)   405
2. Y. Zaitsev (USSR)   395
3. J. Ciezki (E. Germany)   390
   A. Drzewiecki (Britain) was tenth with 342.5.

Super-heavyweight

1. V. Alexeev (USSR)   430
2. E. Enaldiev (USSR)   422.5
3. J. Heuser (E. Germany)   420

WORLD CHAMPIONSHIPS 1978 – Gettysburg, USA

Flyweight

1. K. Osmonaliev (USSR)   240
2. T. Golik (Poland)   237.5
3. F. Casamayor (Cuba)   230
   C. Revolta (Britain) was seventeenth with 185.

Bantamweight

1. D. Nunez (Cuba)   260
2. M. Seweryn (Poland)   252.5
3. K. Ando (Japan)   252.5

Featherweight

1. N. Kolesnikov (USSR)   270
2. T. Saito (Japan)   267.5
3. V. Todorov (Bulgaria)   267.5

Lightweight

1. Y. Rusev (Bulgaria)   310
2. Z. Kaczmarek (Poland)   302.5
3. G. Ambrass (E. Germany)   300

Middleweight

1. R. Urrutia (Cuba)   347.5
2. V. Militosian (USSR)   337.5
3. P. Wenzel (E. Germany)   335

Light heavyweight

1. Y. Vardanyan (USSR)   377.5
2. P. Baczako (Hungary)   352.5
3. P. Rabczewski (Poland)   345
   M. Keelan (Britain) was fourteenth with 295.

Mid-heavyweight

1. R. Milser (W. Germany)   377.5
2. G. Bessonov (USSR)   375
3. F. Antalovics (Hungary)   367.5
   G. Langford (Britain) was twelfth with 322.5.

100 kg class

1. D. Rigert (USSR)   390
2. S. Arakelov (USSR)   390
3. M. Funke (E. Germany)   367.5
   J. Burns (Britain) was thirteenth with 325

Heavyweight

1. Y. Zaitsev (USSR)   402.5
2. J. Ciezki (E. Germany)   385
3. L. Nilsson (Sweden)   385
   A. Drzewiecki (Britain) was ninth with 325.

Super-heavyweight

1. J. Heuser (E. Germany)   417.5
2. S. Rakhmanov (USSR)   417.5
3. G. Bonk (E. Germany)   410

WORLD CHAMPIONSHIPS 1979 – Saloniki, Greece

Flyweight

1. K. Osmonaliev (USSR)   242.5
2. F. Hornyak (Hungary)   242.5
3. A. Voronin (USSR)   242.5

Bantamweight

1. A. Kodjabashev (Bulgaria)   267.5
2. A. Veretennikov (USSR)   262.5
3. T. Dembonczyk (Poland)   260
   D. Willey (Britain) was fifteenth with 205.

Featherweight

1. M. Seweryn (Poland)   282.5
2. G. Todorov (Bulgaria)   275
3. S. Goto (Japan)   270
   G. Laws (Britain) failed to make a total.

Lightweight

1. Y. Rusev (Bulgaria)   332.5
2. J. Kunz (E. Germany)   325
3. D. Senet (France)   312.5
   L. Isaac (Britain) was tenth with 280.

Middleweight	
1. R. Urrutia (Cuba)	345
2. N. Kolev (Bulgaria)	342.5
3. P. Wenzel (E. Germany)	337.5

N. Burrowes (Britain) failed to make a total.

Light-heavyweight	
1. Y. Yardanyan (USSR)	370
2. B. Blagoev (Bulgaria)	362.5
3. D. Poliacik (Czech)	350

S. Pinsent (Britain) was twelfth with 305.

M. Keelan (Britain) retired injured.

Mid-heavyweight	
1. G. Bessonov (USSR)	380
2. R. Milser (W. Germany)	377.5
3. W. Walo (Poland)	362.5

G. Langford (Britain) failed to make a total.

100 kg class	
1. P. Sirchin (USSR)	385
2. J. Solyomvari (Hungary)	385
3. A. Blanco (Cuba)	372.5

Heavyweight	
1. S. Arakelov (USSR)	410
2. V. Khristov (Bulgaria)	402.5
3. L. Taranenko (USSR)	402.5

Super-heavyweight	
1. S. Rakhmanov (USSR)	430
2. J. Heuser (E. Germany)	420
3. G. Bonk (USSR)	412.5

OLYMPIC GAMES 1980 – Moscow, USSR

Flyweight	
1. K. Osmonaliev (USSR)	245
2. Bong Chol Hoe (Korea)	245
3. Gyong Si Han (Korea)	245

Bantamweight	
1. D. Nunez (Cuba)	275
2. Y. Sarkisian (USSR)	270
3. T. Dembonczyk (Poland)	265

Featherweight	
1. V. Mazin (USSR)	290
2. S. Dimitrov (Bulgaria)	287.5
3. M. Seweryn (Poland)	282.5

G. Laws (Britain) was twelfth with 245.

J. Bryce (Britain) failed to make a total.

Lightweight	
1. Y. Rusev (Bulgaria)	342.5
2. J. Kunz (E. Germany)	335
3. M. Pachov (USSR)	325

A. Winterbourne (Britain) was eighteenth with 267.5.

Middleweight	
1. A. Zlatev (USSR)	360
2. A. Pervy (USSR)	357.5
3. N. Kolev (Bulgaria)	345

N. Burrowes (Britain) was eighth with 302.5.

K. Kennedy (Britain) was eleventh with 295.

Light-heavyweight	
1. Y. Vardanyan (USSR)	400
2. B. Blagoev (Bulgaria)	372.5
3. D. Poliacik (Czech)	367.5

S. Pinsent (Britain) was thirteenth with 305.

Mid-heavyweight	
1. P. Baczako (Hungary)	377.5
2. B. Alexandrov (Bulgaria)	375
3. F. Mantek (E. Germany)	370

G. Langford (Britain) was ninth with 330.

100 kg class	
1. O. Zaremba (Czech)	395
2. I. Nikitin (USSR)	392.5
3. A. Blanco (Cuba)	385

J. Burns (Britain) was eleventh with 337.5.

Heavyweight

1. L. Taranenko (USSR)   422.5
2. V. Khristov (Bulgaria)   405
3. G. Szalai (Hungary)   390
   A. Drzewiecki (Britain) was tenth
   with 320.

Super-heavyweight

1. S. Rakhmanov (USSR)   440
2. J. Heuser (E. Germany)   410
3. T. Rutkowski (Poland)   407.5

WORLD CHAMPIONSHIPS 1981 – Lille, France

Flyweight

1. K. Osmonaliev (USSR)   247.5
2. J. Gutowski (Poland)   240
3. K. Manabe (Japan)   240

Bantamweight

1. A. Kodjabashev (Bulgaria)   272.5
2. A. Letz (E. Germany)   272.5
3. N. Zacharov (USSR)   265

Featherweight

1. B. Manolov (Bulgaria)   302.5
2. D. Nunez (Cuba)   302.5
3. S. Sarkisian (USSR)   295
   G. Laws (Britain) was sixteenth
   with 250.

Lightweight

1. J. Kunz (E. Germany)   340
2. M. Pachov (USSR)   330
3. D. Senet (France)   320
   A. Winterbourne (Britain) was
   tenth with 267.5.

Middleweight

1. Y. Rusev (Bulgaria)   360
2. A. Pervy (USSR)   357.5
3. J. Echenique (Cuba)   340
   S. Pinsent (Britain) was thirteenth
   with 307.5.

Light-heavyweight

1. Y. Vardanyan (USSR)   392.5
2. A. Zlatev (Bulgaria)   372.5
3. D. Poliacik (Czech)   367.5
   N. Burrowes (Britain) was
   sixteenth with 300.
   M. Keelan (Britain) was seventeenth
   with 300.

Mid-heavyweight

1. B. Blagoev (Bulgaria)   405
2. Y. Zakharevich (USSR)   397.5
3. L. Usherov (Bulgaria)   380

100 kg class

1. V. Sots (USSR)   407.5
2. B. Matkiewicz (Czech)   392.5
3. V. Osikovski (Bulgaria)   387.5
   G. Langford (Britain) was eighth
   with 355.

Heavyweight

1. V. Kravchuk (USSR)   415
2. V. Klokov (USSR)   410
3. O. Asparahukov (Bulgaria)   405

Super-heavyweight

1. A. Pisarenko (USSR)   425
2. S. Salzwedel (E. Germany)   417.5
3. T. Rutkowski (Poland)   415

WORLD CHAMPIONSHIPS 1982 – Ljubljana, Yugoslavia

Flyweight

1. S. Leletko (Poland)   250
2. Y. Sarandaliev (Bulgaria)   245
3. J. Gutowski (Poland)   245

Bantamweight

1. A. Kodjabashov (Bulgaria)   280
2. O. Mirzoian (USSR)   272.5
3. Wu Shude (China)   270

Featherweight

1. Y. Sarkisian (USSR)   302.5
2. A. Behm (E. Germany)   300
3. D. Nunez (Cuba)   295

Lightweight

1.	P. Mandra (Poland)	325
2.	V. Dociu (Rumania)	310
3.	Xinming Zhao (China)	305

Middleweight

1.	Y. Rusev (Bulgaria)	365
2.	M. Pachov (USSR)	357.5
3.	V. Mikhalev (USSR)	345

M. Ball (Britain) was twenty-first with 280.

Light-heavyweight

1.	A. Zlatev (Bulgaria)	400
2.	A. Pervi (USSR)	392.5
3.	B. Mandzak (Hungary)	350

K. Boxell (Britain) was nineteenth with 292.5.

G. Lambert (Britain) was twenty-first with 282.5.

Mid-heavyweight

1.	B. Blagoev (Bulgaria)	415
2.	Y. Vardanyan (USSR)	395
3.	F. Mantek (E. Germany)	377.5

100 kg class

1.	V. Sots (USSR)	422.5
2.	Y. Zakharevich (USSR)	420
3.	B. Matykiewicz (Czech)	397.5

Heavyweight

1.	S. Arekelov (USSR)	427.5
2.	V. Klokov (USSR)	427.5
3.	A. Baraniak (Czech)	405

A. Drzewiecki (Britain) was eighteenth with 302.5.

Super-heavyweight

1.	A. Pisarenko (USSR)	445
2.	A. Krastev (Bulgaria)	442.5
3.	B. Braum (Czech)	420

WORLD CHAMPIONSHIPS 1983 – Moscow, USSR

Flyweight

1.	N. Terziiski (Bulgaria)	260
2.	J. Gutowski (Poland)	250
3.	S. Leletko (Poland)	247.5

Bantamweight

1.	O. Mirzoian (USSR)	292.5
2.	N. Suleimanov (Bulgaria)	290
3.	A. Letz (E. Germany)	280

Featherweight

1.	Y. Sarkisian (USSR)	312.5
2.	S. Topurov (Bulgaria)	312.5
3.	G. Radu (Rumania)	292.5

G. Laws (Britain) was thirteenth with 255.

Lightweight

1.	J. Kunz (E. Germany)	340
2.	Y. Rusev (Bulgaria)	337.5
3.	A. Behm (E. Germany)	337.5

D. Willey (Britain) failed to make a total.

Middleweight

1.	A. Varbanov (Bulgaria)	370
2.	V. Kuznetsov (USSR)	370
3.	Z. Stoichkov (Bulgaria)	362.5

S. Pinsent (Britain) was ninth with 317.5.

D. Morgan (Britain) was tenth with 315.

Light-heavyweight

1.	Y. Vardanyan (USSR)	392.5
2.	A. Zlatev (Bulgaria)	390
3.	L. Barsi (Hungary)	370

N. Burrowes (Britain) was thirteenth with 330.

K. Boxell (Britain) was fifteenth with 320.

Mid-heavyweight

1. B. Blagoev (Bulgaria) — 417.5
2. V. Solodov (USSR) — 410
3. A. Piotrowski (Poland) — 382.5
   D. Mercer (Britain) was fifteenth with 325.
   D. Coates (Britain) was nineteenth with 300.

100 kg class

1. P. Kuznietsov (USSR) — 422.5
2. A. Popov (USSR) — 422.5
3. A. Komar (Poland) — 407.5
   P. Pinsent (Britain) was eighth with 360.

Heavyweight

1. V. Klokov (USSR) — 440
2. J. Jacso (Hungary) — 410
3. A. Baraniak (Czech) — 400

Super-heavyweight

1. A. Pisarenko (USSR) — 450
2. A. Kurlovich (USSR) — 450
3. A. Krastev (Bulgaria) — 427.5

OLYMPIC GAMES 1984 – Los Angeles, USA

Flyweight

1. G. Zeng (China) — 235
2. P. Zhou (China) — 235
3. K. Manabe (Japan) — 232.5

Bantamweight

1. Wu Shude (China) — 267.5
2. R. Lai (China) — 265
3. M. Kotaka (Japan) — 252.5

Featherweight

1. W. Chen (China) — 282.5
2. G. Radu (Rumania) — 280
3. Wen-Yee Tsai (Chinese Taipei) — 272.5
   G. Laws (Britain) was twelfth with 245.

Lightweight

1. J. G. Yao (China) — 320
2. A. Socaci (Rumania) — 312.5
3. J. Gronman (Finland) — 312.5
   D. Willey (Britain) was fourth with 310.

Middleweight

1. K. H. Radschinsky (W. Germany) — 340
2. J. Demers (Canada) — 335
3. D. Cioroslan (Rumania) — 332.5
   D. Morgan (Britain) was fourth with 330.

Light-heavyweight

1. F. Becheru (Rumania) — 355
2. R. Kabbas (Australia) — 342.5
3. R. Isaoka (Japan) — 340
   N. Burrowes (Britain) was fourth with 327.5.

Mid-heavyweight

1. N. Vlad (Rumania) — 392.5
2. D. Petre (Rumania) — 360
3. D. Mercer (Britain) — 352.5
   K. Boxell (Britain) was tenth with 342.5.

100 kg class

1. R. Milser (W. Germany) — 385
2. V. Gropa (Rumania) — 382.5
3. P. Niemi (Finland) — 367.5
   P. Pinsent (Britain) failed to make a total.

Heavyweight

1, N. Oberburger (Italy) — 390
2. S. Tasnadi (Rumania) — 380
3. G. Carlton (USA) — 377.5
   G. Taylor (Britain) failed to make a total.

Super-heavyweight

1. D. Lukin (Australia)   412.5
2. M. Martinez (USA)   410
3. M. Herlinger (W. Germany)   397.5

WORLD CHAMPIONSHIPS 1985 – Sondertalje, Sweden

Flyweight

1. S. Marinov (Bulgaria)   252.5
2. G. Zeng (China)   242.5
3. B. Piekorz (Poland)   237.5

Bantamweight

1. N. Terziiski (Bulgaria)   280
2. O. Mirzoian (USSR)   280
3. Y. He (China)   270

Featherweight

1. N. Shalamanov (Bulgaria)   322.5
2. Y. Sarkisian (USSR)   307.5
3. A. Letz (E. Germany)   292.5
   G. Laws (Britain) was fourteenth
   with 242.5

Lightweight

1. M. Petrov (Bulgaria)   335
2. V. Galabarov (Bulgaria)   330
3. J. Yao (China)   315
   D. Willey (Britain) was seventh
   with 295.

Middleweight

1. A. Varbanov (Bulgaria)   370
2. M. Pachov (Bulgaria)   357.5
3. O. Sacaci (Rumania)   355
   D. Morgan (Britain) was tenth
   with 315.

Light-heavyweight

1. Y. Vardanyan (USSR)   397.5
2. A. Zlatev (Bulgaria)   392.5
3. L. Kiraly (Hungary)   375.

Mid-heavyweight

1. A. Khrapaty (USSR)   395
2. V. Solodov (USSR)   395
3. P. Krukowski (Poland)   385
   K. Boxell (Britain) was ninth
   with 347.5.
   D. Mercer (Britain) was fourteenth
   with 330.

100 kg class

1. A. Szanyi (Hungary)   415
2. P. Kuznietsov (USSR)   407.5
3. N. Vlad (Rumania)   405
   M. Groombridge (Britain) was
   twentieth with 330.

Heavyweight

1. Y. Zakharevich (USSR)   422.5
2. M. Ciernik (Czech)   397.5
3. M. Oberburger (Italy)   397.5

Super-heavyweight

1. A. Krastev (Bulgaria)   437.5
2. A. Gunyashev (USSR)   432.5
3. M. Nerlinger (W. Germany)   422.5

Appendix II
World Powerlifting Championships
Results 1971–1985

(all results shown in kilos)

World Championships 1971–York, USA

Bantamweight

1. P. McKenzie (Britain)   531
2. D. Moyer (USA)   506
3. J. Redding (USA)   483

Featherweight

1. McKinney (USA)   567.5
2. E. Hernandez (USA)   562.5
3. L. Mabie (USA)   551

Lightweight

1. M. Shaw (Britain)   624
2. J. Welch (USA)   620
3. J. Keammerer (USA   599
    M. McHugh (Britain) failed to make a total

Middleweight

1. G. Crawford (USA)   685
2. J. Pyra (USA)   592.5
    R. Collins (Britain) failed to make a total

Light-heavyweight

1. J. Barnes (USA)   742
2. G. Clark (USA)   719
3. F. Gomes (USA)   697

Mid-heavyweight

1. L. Pacifico (USA)   817
2. J. Kanter (USA)   817
3. V. Anello (USA)   779

Heavyweight

1. C. Snitkin (USA)   805
2. J. Weinstein (USA)   776

Super-heavyweight

1. H. Cassidy (USA)   980
2. J. Williams (USA)   980
3. J. Kuc (USA)   955

World Championships 1972–Harrisburg, USA

Bantamweight

1. P. McKenzie (Britain)   549
2. M. Cross (USA)   499
3. J. Redding (USA)   499

Featherweight

1. F. Riley (USA)   574
2. L. Mabie (USA)   540
3. A Lord (USA   535
    D. Ambler (Britain) was sixth with 490
    P. Weiss (Britain) was seventh with 486

Lightweight

1. J. Keammerer (USA)   631
2. M. Shaw (Britain)   622
3. J. Welch (USA)   619

Middleweight

1. R. Collins (Britain)   715
2. H. Moreau (Canada)   656
3. M. Lettieri (USA)   645
    R. Bonner (Britain) was fifth with 592.5

Light-heavyweight

1. V. Anello (USA)   742.5
2. V. Peterson (USA)   701
3. N. Newcomer (USA)   685

Mid-heavyweight

1. J. Jones (USA)   820
2. A. Fratto (USA)   795
3. J. Barnes (USA)   792
   J. Pegler (Britain) was fifth with 751
   B. O'Brien (Britain) was sixth with 748.5

Heavyweight

1. L. Pacifico (USA)   897.5
2. M. Hennessey (USA)   880
3. N. Pitceathly (Britain)   821

Super-heavyweight

1. J. Kuc (USA)   1066.5
2. J. Williams (USA)   1009
3. D. Reinhoudt (USA   975

World Championships 1973–Harrisburg, USA

Bantamweight

1. P. McKenzie (Britain)   535
2. L. Gant (USA)   485.5
3. V. Bowser (USA)   460.5
   C. Thomas (Britain) was fourth
      with 447

Featherweight

1. A. Lord (USA)   560.5
2. L. Ramos (Puerto Rico)   515
3. E. Hernandez (USA)   508

Lightweight

1. L. D. Blue (USA)   640
2. J. Keammerer (USA)   608
3. M. McHugh (Britain)   603.5

Middleweight

1. R. Collins (Britain)   726
2. G. Crawford (USA)   715
3. W. Thomas (USA)   685

Light-heavyweight

1. R. McKee (USA)   762.5
2. R. Memery (Britain)   735
3. V. Anello (USA)   723.5
   J. Pegler (Britain) failed to make a total

Mid-heavyweight

1. A. Fratto (USA)   801
2. J. Jones (USA)   787.5
3. T. Farchione (USA)   753.5
   B. O'Brien (Britain) was fourth with 731

100 kg class

1. W. Seno (USA)   835
2. J. Taylor (USA)   707.5

Heavyweight

1. L. Pacifico (USA)   910
2. T. Scott (USA)   862
3. A. Fitton (Britain)   823.5

Super-heavyweight

1. D. Reinhoudt (USA)   1035

World Championships 1974–York, USA

Flyweight

1. H. Inaba (Japan)   520
2. K. McDowell (USA)   430
3. F. Baez (Puerto Rico)   425

Bantamweight

1. J. Boyazi (USA)   472.5
2. V. Bowser (USA)   467.5

Featherweight

1. L. A. Lord (USA)   532.5
2. S. Hoxworth (USA)   515
3. G. Wandell (USA)   512.5
   K. Thrush (Britain) was fourth with 505
   P. Weiss (Britain) was fifth with 505

Lightweight

1. D. Blue (USA)   637.5
2. J. Keammerer (USA)   617.5
3. M. McHugh (Britain)   600

Middleweight

1. R. Collins (Britain)   732.5
2. W. Thomas (USA)   727.5
3. G. Crawford (USA)   717.5

Light-heavyweight

1. E. Frantz (USA)   765
2. F. Barefield (USA)   740
3. D. Wright (USA)   740
3. E. Toal (Britain) was fourth with 717.5

Mid-heavyweight

1. P. Woods (USA)   805
2. B. Ravenscroft (USA)   805
3. A. Fratto (USA)   775

100 kg class

1. L. Pacifico (USA)   885
2. M. Phillips (USA)   827.5
3. M. McDonald (USA)   802.5
   C. Lewis (Britain) was fifth with 702.5

Heavyweight

1. J. Kuc (USA)   932.5
2. W. Seno (USA)   837.5
3. W. Horwitz (USA)   837.5
   A. Fitton (Britain) failed to make a total

Super-heavyweight

1. D. Reinhoudt (USA)   1042.5
2. D. Kenady (USA)   950
3. J. White (USA)   930
   B. Saunders (Britain) was fifth with 795

World Championships
1975–Birmingham, England

Flyweight

1. H. Inaba (Japan)   527.5
2. H. Watabe (Japan)   432.5
3. J. Niemi (Finland)   430
   N. Bhairo (Britain) was fourth with 422.5

Bantamweight

1. L. Gant (USA)   507.5
2. V. Issacakainen (Finland) 475
3. K. Thrush (Britain)   452.5
   P. McKenzie (Britain) failed to make a total

Featherweight

1. E. Hernandez (USA)   550
2. J. Ambler (Britain)   520
3. Y. Haatanen (Finland)   517.5

Lightweight

1. J. Welch (USA)   640
2. J. Moir (Canada)   595
3. R. Valineva (Finland)   557.5
3. M. Shaw (Britain) failed to make
   a total

Middleweight

1. W. Thomas (USA)   717.5
2. P. Fiore (Zambia)   647.5
3. S. Oskarsson (Iceland)   612.5

Light-heavyweight

1. R. Collins (Britain)   800
2. D. Wright (USA)   742.5
3. U. Honkonen (Finland)   677.5

Mid-heavyweight

1. E. Ravenscroft (USA)   792.5
2. B. O'Brien (Jamaica)   755
3. E. Toal (Britain)   752.5

100 kg class

1. L. Pacifico (USA)   865
2. M. Phillips (USA)   810
3. R. Halvorsen (Finland)   717.5

Heavyweight

1. D. Young (USA)   875
2. D. Carter (Britain)   840
3. H. Saarelainen (Finland)   837.5

Super-heavyweight

1. D. Reinhoudt (USA)   1032.5
2. J. Phillip (Tonga)   837.5
3. J. Alderson (Britain)   827.5

World Championships 1976–Harrisburg, USA

Flyweight

1. H. Inaba (Japan)   530
2. J. Redding (USA)   477.5
3. J. Niemi (Finland)   465
   N. Bhairo (Britain) was fourth with 460

Bantamweight

1. L. Gant (USA)   552.5
2. Y. Haatanen (Finland)   495
3. V. Issakainen (Finland)   485

Featherweight

1. E. Pengelly (Britain)   545
2. Y. Tominanga (Japan)   522.5
3. L. Ramos (Puerto Rico)   502.5

Lightweight

1. M. Pasquale (Canada)   630
2. D. Pal (Britain)   605
3. D. Attland (Sweden)   587.5
   T. Kirton (Britain) was fourth with 580

Middleweight

1. W. West (Britain)   677.5
2. T. Carpino (USA)   677.5
3. L. Backlund (Sweden)   672.5

Light-heavyweight

1. R. Collins (Britain)   817.5
2. W. Thomas (USA)   782.5
3. T. Campbell (Canada)   767.5

Mid-heavyweight

1. L. Pacifico (USA)   817.5
2. E. Toal (Britain)   795
3. R. Yvander (Sweden)   745

100 kg class

1. P. Jordan (Britain)   860
2. V. Anello (USA)   822.5
3. A. Fitton (Britain)   812.5

Heavyweight

1. D. Young (USA)   932.5
2. H. Saarelainen (Finland)   860
3. M. Phillips (USA)   857.5
   D. Carter (Britain) was fourth with 830

Super-heavyweight

1. D. Reinhoudt (USA)   1020
2. T. Haara (Finland)   925
3. J. Philip (Tonga)   867.5

World Championships 1977–Perth, Australia

Flyweight

1. H. Inaba (Japan)   525
2. N. Bhairo (Britain)   485
3. A. Tuomisto (Finland)   455

Bantamweight

1. L. Gant (USA)   567.5
2. P. McKenzie (New Zealand)   552.5
3. Y. Haatanen (Finland)   527.5

Featherweight

1. E. Pengelly (Britain)   580
2. P. Trujillo (USA)   565
3. M. Johansson (Sweden)   547.5

Lightweight

1. R. Gaughler (USA)   675
2. J. Moir (Canada)   652.5
3. R. Wilton (Australia)   642.5
   T. Kirton (Britain) was fourth with 642.5

Middleweight

1. J. Rhodes (USA)   705
2. P. Fiore (Britain)   702.5
3. L. Backlund (Sweden)   690

Light-heavyweight

1. R. Collins (Britain)   795
2. W. West (Britain)   722.5
3. L. Bjorck (Sweden)   722.5

Mid-heavyweight

1. V. Anello (USA)   865
2. E. Toal (Britain)   805
3. U. Honkonen (Finland)   777.5

100 kg class

1. L. Pacifico (USA)   935
2. U. Morin (Sweden)   805
3. R. Kiviranta (Finland)   752.5
   P. Jordan (Britain) retired injured

Heavyweight

1. D. Young (USA)   887.5
2. C. Patterson (USA)   867.5
3. H. Saarelainen (Finland)   852.5
   A. Fitton (Britain) was fourth with 830

Super-heavyweight

1. T. Haara (Finland)   935
2. K. Keppainen (Finland)   895
3. J. Philip (Tonga)   887.5
   E. Kershaw (Britain) was fourth with 880

World Championships 1978–Turku, Finland

1. H. Inaba (Japan)   552.5
2. N. Bhairo (Britain)   490
3. P. Stringer (Britain)   470

Bantamweight

1. P. McKenzie (New Zealand)   590
2. Y. Haatanen (Finland)   525
3. T. Zappia (Australia)   500

Featherweight

1. L. Gant (USA)   640
2. E. Pengelly (Britain)   615
3. A. Koykka (Finland)   552.5

Lightweight

1. M. Bridges (USA)   730
2. M. Pasquale (Canada)   675
3. D. Garner (Britain)   670
   D. Pal (Britain) was fifth with 657.5

Middleweight

1. P. Fiore (Britain)   732.5
2. S. Oskarsson (Iceland)   722.5
3. J. Nyssonen (Finland)   720

Light-heavyweight

1. W. Thomas (USA)   817.5
2. W. West (Britain)   765
3. K. Mattsson (Sweden)   752.5

Mid-heavyweight

1. V. Anello (USA)   865
2. U. Honkonen (Finland)   805
3. S. Miller (USA)   795
   E. Toal (Britain) was fourth with 787.5

100 kg class

1. L. Pacifico (SA)   912.5
2. R. Nobile (Britain)   875
3. R. Kiviranta (Finland)   850

Heavyweight

1. T. McCormick (USA)   917.5
2. H. Saarelainen (Finland)   907.5
3. U. Morin (Sweden)   882.5

Super-heavyweight

1. D. Kenady (USA)   1027.5
2. T. Haara (Finland)   940
3. S. Zetolofsky (Britain)   870

World Championships 1979 – Dayton, USA

1. H. Inaba (Japan)   565
2. C. Dunbar (USA)   520
3. N. Bhairo (Britain)   500

Bantamweight

1. L. Gant (USA)   610
2. P. McKenzie (New Zealand)   610
3. J. Niemi (Finland)   545
   P. Stringer (Britain) was fifth with 515

Featherweight

1. E. Pengelly (Britain)   607.5
2. A. Koykka (Finland)   590
3. K. Lampela (Finland)   560

Lightweight

1. J. Moir (Canada)   695
2. H. Salih (Britain)   675
3. D. Garner (Britain)   655

Middleweight

1. M. Bridges (USA)   830
2. M. Pasquale (Canada)   750
3. L. Backlund (Sweden)   740
   P. Fiore (Britain) failed to make a total

Light-heavyweight

1. R. Collins (Britain)   815
2. W. Thomas (USA)   812.5
3. K. Mattsson (Sweden)   775

Mid-heavyweight

1. T. Campbell (Canada)   870
2. R. Estep (USA)   842.5
3. V. Anello (USA)   825

100 kg class

1. L. Pacifico (USA)   905
2. L. Yvander (Sweden)   877.5
3. R. Kiviranta (Finland)   877.5
   R. Nobile (Britain) was fourth with 875

Heavyweight

1. J. Kuc (USA)   965
2. H. Saarelainen (Finland)   887.5
3. A. White (Britain)   855

Super-heavyweight

1. W. Kazamier (USA)   1040
2. P. Wrenn (USA)   995
3. L. Hedlund (Sweden)   962.5
   S. Zetolofsky (Britain) was fourth with 887.5

World Championships 1980 – Arlington, Texas, USA

Flyweight

1. H. Inaba (Japan)   567.5
2. C. Dunbar (USA)   540
3. N. Bhairo (Britain)   527.5

Bantamweight

1. P. McKenzie (New Zealand)   587.5
2. J. Niemi (Finland)   565
3. H. Isagawa (Japan)   552.5
   D. Mannering (Britain) was eighth with 505

Featherweight

1. L. Gant (USA)   705
2. K. Lampela (Finland)   590
3. R. Verdonck (USA)   590
   A. Galvez (Britain) was fourth with 582.5

Lightweight

1. R. Crain (USA)   730
2. J. Moir (Canada)   727.5
3. T. Sjostrom (Sweden)   660
   E. Pengelly (Britain) failed to make a total

Middleweight

1. R. Gaugler (USA)   787.5
2. M. Pasquale (Canada)   765
3. L. Backlund (Sweden)   765

Light-heavyweight

1. W. West (Britain)   777.5
2. P. Fiore (Britain)   775
3. J. Tahtinen (Finland)   770

Mid-heavyweight

1. V. Anello (USA)   867.5
2. C. Nilsson (Sweden)   865
3. J. Jones (USA)   850

100 kg class

1. M. Dimiduk (USA)   922.5
2. A. Stevens (Britain)   885
3. R. Kiviranta (Finland)   880

Heavyweight

1. J. Kuc (USA)   1000
2. H. Saarelainen (Finland)   930
3. A. White (Britain)   885

Super-heavyweight

1. D. Kenady (USA)   1000
2. A. Kerr (Britain)   922.5
3. J. Heinonen (Finland)   882.5

World Championships 1981–Calcutta, India

Flyweight

1. H. Inaba (Japan)   560
2. C. Dunbar (USA)   522.5
3. A. Tuomisto (Finland)   515
   P. Stringer (Britain) was fourth with 515

Bantamweight

1. H. Isagawa (Japan)   577.5
2. N. Bhairo (Britain)   562.5
3. Y. Haatanen (Finland)   550

Featherweight

1. L. Gant (USA)   625
2. A. Galvez (Britain)   605
3. K. Lampela (Finland)   550

Lightweight

1. J. Bradley (USA)   732.5
2. E. Pengelly (Britain)   705
3. S. Nentis (Sweden)   695

Middleweight

1. S. Alexander (Britain)   752.5
2. L. Backlund (Sweden)   732.5
3. S. Oskarsson (Iceland)   700

Light-heavyweight

1. M. Stamm (W. Germany)   780
2. V. Kumpaniemi (Finland)   750
3. N. Byssonen (Finland)   750
   R. Collins (Britain) failed to make a total

Mid-heavyweight

1. W. Thomas (USA)   930
2. K. Mattsson (Sweden)   867.5
3. W. West (Britain)   832.5

100 kg class

1. J. Cash (USA)   922.5
2. C. Nilsson (Sweden)   892.5
3. A. Stevens (Britain)   865

Heavyweight

1. R. Kiviranta (Finland)   920
2. H. Saarelainen (Finland)   920
3. A. White (Britain)   855

125 kg class (introduced this year)

1. E. Hackett (USA)   962.5
2. T. Magee (Canada)   927.5
3. J. Sigmarsson (Iceland)   912.5

Super-heavyweight

1. P. Wrenn (USA)   1027.5
2. A. Kapica (Australia)   875
3. R. Rigby (Australia)   830
   A. Kerr (Britain) failed to make a total

World Championships 1982–Munich, West Germany

Flyweight

1. H. Inaba (Japan)   552.5
2. C. Dunbar (USA)   550
3. P. Stringer (Britain)   512.5

Bantamweight

1. L. Gant (USA)   590
2. Y. Haatanen (Finland)   560
3. N. Bhairo (Britain)   547.5

Featherweight

1. K. Lampela (Finland)   582.5
2. G. Henrysson (Sweden)   580
3. E. Van Wemmel (Belgium)   565
   D. Mannering (Britain) was fourth with 562.5

Lightweight

1. S. Nentis (Sweden)   697.5
2. E. Pengelly (Britain)   667.5
3. G. Wasckiel (Australia)   640

Middleweight

1. R. Crain (USA)   772.5
2. M. Personen (Finland)   702.5
3. M. Martina (Holland)   695
   S. Alexander (Britain) failed to make a
   total

Light-heavyweight

1. M. Bridges (USA)   845
2. M. Duffy (Britain)   775
3. M. Stamm (W. Germany)   760

Mid-heavyweight

1. W. Thomas (USA)   857.5
2. W. West (Britain)   805
3. S. Kierivaara (Finland)   805
   J. Neighbour (Britain) was seventh with
   780

100 kg class

1. K. Mattsson (Sweden)   880
2. J. Cash (USA)   852.5
3. A. Stevens (Britain)   850

Heavyweight

1. H. Saarelainen (Finland)   887.5
2. S. Wulfse (Holland)   880
3. R. Darnell (Canada)   877.5

125 kg class

1. J. Gamble (USA)   907.5
2. R. Ekstrom (Sweden)   857.5
3. A. Wolters (Holland)   842.5

Super-heavyweight

1. T. Magee (Canada)   942.5
2. W. Bouvier (USA)   942.5
3. A. Kerr (Britain)   917.5

World Championships
1983–Gothenburg, Sweden

Flyweight

1. H. Inaba (Japan)   565
2. R. Lehtonen (Finland)   495
3. M. Wilkar (Canada)   492.5
   J. Maxwell (Britain) was fifth with 455

Bantamweight

1. L. Gant (USA)   575
2. N. Bhairo (Britain)   542.5
3. H. Isagawa (Japan)   540

Featherweight

1. G. Henrysson (Sweden)   605
2. L. De Faria (France)   580
3. E. Van Wemmel (Belgium)   547.5
   P. Stringer (Britain) was fourth with 542.5

Lightweight

1. B. Wahl (USA)   705
2. S. Nentis (Sweden)   670
3. E. Pengelly (Britain)   670

Middleweight

1. R. Crain (USA)   762.5
2. S. Alexander (Britain)   752.5
3. J. Virtanen (Finland)   750

Light-heavyweight

1. M. Bridges (USA)   807.5
2. L. Augustsson (Sweden)   767.5
3. J. Tathinen (Finland)   750

Mid-heavyweight

1. K. Mattsson (Sweden)   872.5
2. D. Caldwell (Britain)   817.5
3. O. Eriksson (Sweden)   807.5
   E. Toal (Britain) was fifth with 765

100 kg class

1. F. Hatfield (USA)   920
2. J. Laidner (USA)   920
3. C. Nilsson (Sweden)   870
   A. Stevens (Britain) failed to make a total

Heavyweight

1. S. Kivi (Sweden)   910
2. S. Wilson (USA)   910
3. A. Wolders (Holland)   880
    M. Savage (Britain) was fifth with 860

125 kg class

1. J. Gamble (USA)   967.5
2. L. Noren (Sweden)   890
3. T. McGowan (Australia)   805

Super-heavyweight

1. W. Kazamier (USA)   975
2. A. Kerr (Britain)   950
3. R. Rigby (Australia)   900

World Championships 1984–Dallas, USA

Flyweight

1. C. Dunbar (USA)   532.5
2. H. Inaba (Japan)   527.5
3. J. Madsen (New Zealand)   490

Bantamweight

1. L. Gant (USA)   580
2. H. Isagawa (Japan)   580
3. P. Joseph (India)   552.5
    P. Stringer (Britain) was fourth with 530

Featherweight

1. G. Henrysson (Sweden)   600
2. H. Van Wemmel (Belgium)   592.5
3. K. Lampela (Finland)   587.5
    C. Lewis (Britain) was fourth with 567.5

Lightweight

1. D. Austin (USA)   722.5
2. E. Pengelly (Britain)   685
3. S. Nantis (Sweden)   650

Middleweight

1. G. Bell (USA)   762.5
2. G. Waszkiel (Australia)   740
3. E. Coppin (Belgium)   725

Light-heavyweight

1. E. Coan (USA)   875
2. J. Virtanen (Finland)   812.5
3. S. Alexander (Britain)   802.5

Mid-heavyweight

1. D. Wright (USA)   840
2. T. Maeda (Japan)   817.5
3. D. Caldwell (Britain)   815
    E. Toal (Britain) was fourth with 782.5

100 kg class

1. A. Stevens (Britain)   915
2. M. Szafranski (Greece)   870
3. D. Toci (Algeria)   842.5
3. J. Cash (USA) finished first with 917.5, but was later disqualified after a positive drug test

Heavyweight

1. D. Jacoby (USA)   935
2. M. Savage (Britain)   877.5
3. H. Saarelainen (Finland)   877.5

125 kg class

1. A. Wolders (Holland)   945
2. M. Chaillet (USA)   905
3. J. Brulois (France)   875

Super-heavyweight

1. L. Moran (USA)   977.5
2. A. Kerr (Britain)   930
3. R. Rigby (Australia)   927.5

World Championships 1985–Espoo, Finland

Flyweight

1. H. Inaba (Japan)   562.5
2. J. Maxwell (Britain)   487.5
3. P. Yesodhara (India)   482.5

Bantamweight

1. H. Isagawa (Japan)   562.5
2. Y. Haatanen (Finland)   527.5
3. B. Singh (India)   525

Featherweight

1. C. Hanson (USA)   620
2. G. Henrysson (Sweden)   605
3. K. Lampela (Finland)   590

Lightweight

1. E. Pengelly (Britain)   667.5
2. K. Elison (Iceland)   660
3. J. Theys (Belgium)   647.5

Middleweight

1. E. Coppin (Belgium)   765
2. G. Bell (USA)   765
3. G. Waskiel (Australia)   740
   A. Rose (Britain) was fourth with 697.5

Light-heavyweight

1. J. Virtanen (Finland)   842.5
2. K. Johansen (Norway)   762.5
3. D. Gay (USA)   745
   M. Duffy (Britain) failed to make a total

Mid-heavyweight

1. E. Coan (USA)   890
2. D. Caldwell (Britain)   832.5
3. M. Tokiharu (Japan)   817.5

100 kg class

1. T. Pharr (USA)   927.5
2. A. Stevens (Britain)   907.5
3. C. Nilsson (Sweden)   827.5

Heavyweight

1. D. Jacoby (USA)   907.5
2. M. Savage (Britain)   890
3. J. Neighbour (Britain)   887.5

125 kg class

1. T. Henderson (USA)   935
2. S. Spillane (Britain)   890
3. A. Nevanpaa (Finland)   880

Super-heavyweight

1. C. De Vreugd (Holland)   972.5
2. G. Hetcher (USA)   947.5
3. A. Kerr (Britain)   895

Appendix III
Major Bodybuilding Results
1960–1985

IFBB Mr Olympia

1965 Larry Scott (US)
1966 Larry Scott (US)
1967 Sergio Oliva (US)
1968 Sergio Oliva (US)
1969 Sergio Oliva (US)
1970 Arnold Schwarzenegger (Austria)
1971 Arnold Schwarzenegger (Austria)
1972 Arnold Schwarzenegger (Austria)
1973 Arnold Schwarzenegger (Austria)
1974 Arnold Schwarzenegger (Austria)
1975 Arnold Schwarzenegger (Austria)
1976 Franco Columbu (US)
1977 Frank Zane (US)
1978 Frank Zane (US)
1979 Frank Zane (US)
1980 Arnold Schwarzenegger (Austria)
1981 Franco Columbu (US)
1982 Chris Dickerson (US)
1983 Samir Bannout (US
1984 Lee Haney (US)
1985 Lee Haney (US)

NABBA Mr Universe (A: denotes amateur; P: denotes professional)

1960 A. Henry Downs (GB)
     P. Paul Wynter (GB)
1961 A. Ray Routledge (US)
     P. Bill Pearl (US)
1962 A. Joe Abbenda (US)
     P. Len Sell (GB)
1963 A. Tom Sansone (US)
     P. Joe Abbenda (US)
1964 A. John Hewlett (GB)
     P. Earl Maynard (GB)
1965 A. Elmo Santiago (US)
     P. Reg Park (GB)

1966 A. Chester Yorton (US)
     P. Paul Wynter (GB)
1967 A. Arnold Schwarzenegger (Austria)
     P. Bill Pearl (US)
1968 A. Dennis Tinerino (US)
     P. Arnold Schwarzenegger (Austria)
1969 A. Boyer Coe (US)
     P. Arnold Schwarzenegger (Austria)
1970 A. Frank Zane (US)
     P. Arnold Schwarzenegger (Austria)
1971 A. Ken Waller (US)
     P. Bill Pearl (US)
1972 A. Elias Petsas (South Africa)
     P. Frank Zane (US)
1973 A. Chris Dickerson (US)
     P. Boyer Coe (US)
1974 A. Roy Duval (GB)
     P. Chris Dickerson (US)
1975 A. Ian Lawrence (GB)
     P. Boyer Coe (US)
1976 A. Shigeru Sugita (Japan)
     P. Serge Nubret (France)
1977 A. Bertil Fox (GB)
     P. Tony Emmot (GB)
1978 A. Dave Johns (US)
     P. Bertil Fox (GB)
1979 A. Ahmet Enunlu (Turkey)
     P. Bertil Fox (GB)
1980 A. Bill Richardson (GB)
     P. Tony Pearson (US)
1981 A. John Brown (US)
     P. Robbie Robinson (US)
1982 A. John Brown (US)
     P. Eduard Kawak (France)
1983 A. Jeff King (US)
     P. Eduard Kawak (France)
1984 A. Brian Buchanan (GB)
     P. Eduard Kawak (France)

1985 A. Tim Belknap (US)
      P. Eduard Kawak (France)

IFBB Mr Universe/World Championships

1961 Chuck Sipes (US)
1962 George Eifferman
1963 Harold Poole (US)
1964 Larry Scott (US)
1965 Earl Maynard (GB)
1966 Dave Draper (US)
1967 Sergio Oliva (US)
1968 Frank Zane (US)
1969 Arnold Schwarzenegger (Austria)
1970 Arnold Schwarzenegger (Austria)
1971 Al Beckles (GB)
1972 Ed Corney (US)
1973 Lou Ferrigno (US)
1974 Lou Ferrigno (US)
1975 Ken Waller (US)
1976 Light: Mohamed Makkaway (Egypt)
      Middle: Robby Robinson (US)
      Heavy: Roger Walker (Australia)
1977 Light: Dan Padilla (US)
      Middle: Roy Callendar (Barbados)
      Heavy: Kalman Szalak (US)
1978 Light: Carlos Rodriguez (US)
      Middle: Tom Platz (US)
      Heavy: Mike Mentzer (US)
1979 Light: Renato Bertagna (Italy)
      Middle: Roy Duval (GB)
      Light-heavy: Samir Bannout (Lebanon)
      Heavy: Jusup Wilcosz (W. Germany)
1980 Light: Heinz Sallmoyer (Austria)
      Middle: Jorme Raty (Finland)
      Light-heavy: John Fuller (GB)
      Heavy: Hubert Metz (W. Germany)
1981 Light: Ken Passarello (US)
      Middle: Gerard Buinoud (France)
      Light-heavy: Jacques Neuville (France)
      Heavy: Lance Dreher (US)
1982 Light: James Gaubert (US)
      Middle: Dale Rulinger (US)
      Light-heavy: Ahmet Enulu (Turkey)
      Heavy: Lee Haney (US)

1983 Light: Ken Passarello (US)
      Middle: Gerard Buinoud (France)
      Light-heavy: Jacques Neuville (France)
      Heavy: Lance Docher (US)
1984 Light: Wilf Sylvester (GB)
      Middle: John Haatyschak (US)
      Light-heavy: Richard Gaspari (US)
      Heavy: Mike Christian (US)
1985 Light: Herman Hoffend (W. Germany)
      Middle: Lee Labrada (US)
      Light-heavy: Peter Hensel (W. Germany)
      Heavy: Josef Gromulus (Germany)

NABBA Mr Britain

1960 Adrian Heryet
1961 Dave Stroud
1962 Ted Gutteridge
1963 Paul Nash
1964 Terry Parkinson
1965 John Citrone
1966 John Citrone
1967 Wilf Sylvester
1968 Brian Eastman
1969 Frank Richard
1970 Al Beckles
1971 Al Beckles
1972 Paul Grant
1973 Roy Duval
1974 Eddie McDonough
1975 Ian Lawrence
1976 Bertil Fox
1977 Eddie McDonough
1978 Bill Richardson
1979 Terry Phillips
1980 Graham Ogden
1981 Eddie Miller
1982 Ian Dowe
1983 Brian Buchanan
1984 Eugene Laviscount
1985 Linki Wilson
1986 Owen Neil

The Editors are grateful for the assistance of David Webster, Oscar Heidenstam and Chris Lund in preparing this appendix.

Appendix IV
Conversion Table
Kilos to pounds

Kg	Lb								
		110	242.5	410	903.25	710	1565
		120	264.5	420	925.75	720	1587.25
1	2.2046	130	286.5	430	947.75	730	1609.25
1.5	3.3	140	308.5	440	970	740	1631.25
2	4.4	150	330.5	450	992	750	1653.25
2.5	5.5	160	352.5	460	1014	760	1675.25
3	6.6	170	374.75	470	1036	770	1697.5
3.5	7.7	180	396.75	480	1057.75	780	1719.5
4	8.8	190	418.75	490	1079.75	790	1741.5
4.5	9.9	200	440.75	500	1102.25	800	1763.5
5	11	210	462.75	510	1124.25	810	1785.5
5.5	12.1	220	484.75	520	1146.25	820	1807.5
6	13.2	230	506.75	530	1168.25	830	1829.75
6.5	14.3	240	529	540	1190.25	840	1851.75
7	15.4	250	551	550	1212.25	850	1873.75
7.5	16.5	260	573	560	1234.5	860	1895.75
8	17.6	270	595	570	1256.5	870	1917.75
8.5	18.7	280	617	580	1278.5	880	1939.75
9	19.8	290	639	590	1300.75	890	1962
9.5	20.9	300	661.25	600	1322.75	900	1984
10	22	310	683.25	610	1344.75	910	2006
20	44	320	705.25	620	1366.75	920	2028
30	66	330	727.25	630	1388.75	930	2050
40	88	340	749.25	640	1410.75	940	2072
50	110	350	771.25	650	1432.75	950	2094.25
60	132.25	360	793.25	660	1455	960	2116.25
70	154.25	370	815.25	670	1477	970	2138.25
80	176.25	380	837.25	680	1499	980	2160.25
90	198.25	390	859.25	690	1521	990	2182.25
100	220.25	400	881.5	700	1543	1000	2204.5

References

CHAPTER THREE

1. Astrand and Rodah, *Textbook of Work Physiology*, 1970.
2. Bosco and Gustafson, *Measurement and Evaluation in Physical Education Fitness and Sport*, 1983.
3. Berger, Various papers on varied effects of weight training programs, 1962–1965, and *The Important Components of Physical Fitness*, 1964.
4. DeLorme and Watkins, *Techniques of Progressive Resistance Exercise*, 1978.
5. Darden, *Strength Training Principles*, 1977.
6. Donnelly, *Living Anatomy*, 1982.
7. Fox, *Sports Physiology*, 1979.
8. Gestman-Ward and Hagan, *Strength and Endurance through Circuit Weight Training*, 1982.
9. Gray, *Gray's Anatomy*, Reprinted 1977.
10. Hettinger, *Physiology of Strength*, 1961.
11. Klafs and Lyon, *The Female Athlete*, 1978.
12. Manz and Carnes, *Manual for Omni-Kinetic Training*, 1983.
13. Pollock/Wilmore and Fox, *Health and Fitness through Physical Activity*, 1978.
14. Rasch, *Weight Training*, 1979.
15. Rasch and Burke, *Kinesiology and Applied Anatomy*, 1978.
16. Rickards and Price, *Super Fit for Business*, 1983.
17. Rickards, *Manual of Health and Fitness*, 1977.
18. Tancred and Tancred, *Weight Training for Sport*, 1984.
19. Westcott, *Strength Fitness*, 1982.
20. Wirhed, *Athletic Ability and the Anatomy of Motion*, 1984.
21. National Coaching Foundation, Coaching-Introductory Study Packs, 1984.